R

LG
free

GALE DIRECTORY OF PUBLICATIONS AND BROADCAST MEDIA
Update

DISCARDED

For Reference

Not to be taken from this room

133rd Edition

GALE DIRECTORY OF PUBLICATIONS AND BROADCAST MEDIA

Update

An Interedition Service Providing New Listings
and Updates to Listings in the Main Volume
See Introduction for Details

Amy L. Rance, Editor

GALE GROUP

Detroit
New York
San Francisco
London
Boston
Woodbridge, CT

Amy L. Rance, *Editor*
Kristin B. Mallegg, Bill Richards, and Jeff Sumner, *Contributors*

Mary Alampi, *Managing Editor*

Theresa A. Rocklin, *Manager, Technical Support Services*
Venus Little, *Programmer/Analyst*

NeKita McKee, *Buyer*
Cindy Baldwin, *Product Design Manager*

ISBN 0-7876-2401-2 (Update)
ISBN 0-7876-2397-0 (Complete set with Update)

ISSN 1048-7972

Contents

UNITED STATES

CANADA

Introduction

This *Update* to the *Gale Directory of Publications and Broadcast Media*, (*GDPBM*) presents the latest industry information, including:

- *Over 950 new entries*

- *Additional E-mail and URL information*

Preparation, Content, and Arrangement

Published midway between editions of GDPBM, this *Update* is sent free to all subscribers. Information presented is obtained from questionaire responses, brochures, catalogs, faxes, and phone calls.

Entries for newly established or newly identified media outlets are listed. All entries contain full text as in the main volume.

More detail regarding the scope and coverage of GDPBM listings is contained in the Sample Entries following this introduction.

Available in Electronic Formats

Diskette/Magnetic Tape. *Gale Directory of Publications and Broadcast Media* is available for licensing on magnetic tape or diskette in a fielded format. The database is available for internal data processing and nonpublishing purposes only. For more information, call 800-877-GALE.

Online. *GDPBM* (along with *Directories in Print* and *Newsletters in Print*) is accessible as File 469 through the Dialog Corporation's DIALOG service. For more information, contact The Dialog Corporation, 2440 El Camino Real, Mountain View, CA 94040; phone: (415) 254-7000; toll-free: 800-3-DIALOG.

GaleNet. *GDPBM* (along with *Directories in Print* and *Newsletters in Print*) is available as the *Gale Database of Publications and Broadcast Media* on a subscription basis through GaleNet, Gale's online information resource that features an easy-to-use end-user interface, powerful search capabilities, and ease of access through the World-Wide Web. For more information, call 800-877-GALE. *GDPBM* is also accessible as part of *Gale's Ready Reference Shelf* on GaleNet.

CD-ROM. *GDPBM* is available on CD-ROM as part of *Gale's Ready Reference Shelf* CD-ROM.

Acknowledgments

The editors are grateful to the many media professionals who generously responded to our requests for information, provided additional data by telephone or fax, and helped in the shaping of this Update with their comments and suggestions throughout the year. Special thanks also go to Hilary Weber for her contributions.

Comments and Suggestions Welcome

We invite comments and suggestions for improvement and ask the users of this book to send us possible sources of additional listings. Please contact:

Editor
Gale Directory of Publications and Broadcast Media
27500 Drake Rd.
Farmington Hills, MI 48331-3535

Phone: (248)699-4253
Toll free: (800)877-GALE
Fax: (248)699-8069

Sample Entries

The samples that follow are fabricated entries in which each numbered section designates information that might appear in a listing. The numbered items are explained in the descriptive paragraphs following each sample.

SAMPLE PUBLICATION LISTING

① **222** ② **American Computer Review**
③ Black Cat Publishing Company, Inc.
④ 199 E. 49th St. ⑤ Phone: (518)555-9966
  PO Box 724866 ⑥ Fax: (518)555-1028
  Salem, NY 10528-5555 ⑦ Free: 800-555-0212
⑧ **Publication E-mail:** acr@bcpci.com
⑨ **Publisher E-mail:** bcpci@bcpci.com
⑩ Magazine for users of Super Software Plus products. ⑪ **Subtitle:** The Programmer's Friend. ⑫ **Founded:** June 1979. ⑬ **Freq:** Monthly (combined issue July/Aug.). ⑭ **Print Method:** Offset. ⑮ **Trim Size:** 8/12 x 11. ⑯ **Cols./Page:** 3. ⑰ **Col. Width:** 24 nonpareils. ⑱ **Col. Depth:** 294 agate lines. ⑲ **Key Personnel:** Dan Carne, Editor, phone (518)555-1010, fax (518)555-0710, dcarne@jdpci.com; Ryan Boyce, Publisher; Lingl Mungo Jr., Advertising Mgr. ⑳ **ISSN:** 5555-6226. ㉑ **Subscription Rates:** $25; $30 Canada; $2.50 single issue. ㉒ **Remarks:** Color advertising not accepted. ㉓ **Online:** Lexis-Nexis **URL:** http://www.acrmagazine.com. ㉔ **Alternate Format(s):** Braille; CD-ROM; Microform. ㉕ **Variant Name(s):** Formerly: Computer Software Review (Dec. 13, 1986). ㉖ **Feature Editors:** Kit Mungo, *Consumer Affairs, Editorials,* phone (518)555-2306, fax (518)555-2307, km@jdpci.com. ㉗ **Additional Contact Information: Advertising:** 123 Main St., New York, NY 10016, (201)555-0417, fax: (201)555-6812.
㉘ **Ad Rates:** BW: $850 ㉙ **Circulation:** 25,000
    PCI: $.75

---

① **Symbol/Entry Number.** Each publication entry number is preceded by a symbol (a magazine or newspaper) representing the publishing industry. Entries are numbered sequentially. Entry numbers, rather than page numbers, are used in the index to refer to listings.

② **Publication Title.** Publication names are listed *as they appear on the masthead or title page*, as provided by respondents.

③ **Publishing Company.** The name of the commercial publishing organization, association, or academic institution, as provided by respondents.

④ **Address.** Full mailing address information is provided wherever possible. This may include: street address; post office box; city; state or province; and ZIP or postal code. ZIP plus-four numbers are provided when known.

⑤ **Phone.** Phone numbers listed in this section are usually the respondent's switchboard number.

⑥ **Fax.** Facsimile numbers are listed when provided.

⑦ **Free.** Toll-free numbers are listed when provided.

⑧ **Publication E-mail.** Electronic mail addresses for the publication are included as provided by the listee.

⑨ **Publisher E-mail:** Electronic mail addresses for the publishing company are included as provided by the listee.

⑩ **Description.** Includes the type of publication (i.e., newspaper, magazine) as well as a brief statement of purpose, intended audience, or other relevant remarks.

⑪ **Subtitle.** Included as provided by the listee.

⑫ **Founded.** Date the periodical was first published.

⑬ **Frequency.** Indicates how often the publication is issued--daily, weekly, monthly, quarterly, etc. Explanatory remarks sometimes accompany this information (e.g., for weekly titles, the day of issuance; for collegiate titles, whether publication is limited to the academic year; whether certain issues are combined.)

⑭ **Print Method.** Though offset is most common, other methods are listed as provided.

⑮ **Trim Size.** Presented in inches unless otherwise noted.

⑯ **Number of Columns Per Page.** Usually one figure, but some publications list two or more, indicating a variation in style.

⑰ **Column Width.** Column sizes are given exactly as supplied, whether measure in inches, picas (6 picas to an inch), nonpareils (each 6 points, 72 points to an inch), or agate lines (14 to an inch).

⑱ **Column Depth.** Column sizes are given exactly as supplied, whether measure in inches, picas (6 picas to an inch), nonpareils (each 6 points, 72 points to an inch), or agate lines (14 to an inch).

⑲ **Key Personnel.** Presents the names and titles of contacts at each publication. May include phone, fax, and e-mail addresses if different than those for the publication and company.

⑳ **International Standard Serial Number (ISSN).** Included when provided. Occasionally, United States Publications Serial (USPS) numbers are reported rather than ISSNs.

㉑ **Subscription Rates.** Unless otherwise stated, prices shown in this section are the individual annual subscription rate. Other rates are listed when known, including multiyear rates, prices outside the United States, discount rates, library/institution rates, and single copy prices.

㉒ **Remarks.** Information listed in this section further explains the Ad Rates (see ㉘ below).

㉓ **Online.** If a publication is accessible online via computer, that information is listed here. If the publication is available online but the details of the URL (universal resource locator) or vendor are not known, the notation '**Available Online.**' will be listed.

㉔ **Alternate Format(s).** Lists additional mediums in which a publication may be available (other than online), including CD-ROM and microform.

㉕ **Variant Name(s).** Lists former or variant names of the publication, including the year the change took place, when known.

㉖ **Feature Editors.** Lists the names and beats of any feature editors employed by the publication.

㉗ **Additional Contact Information.** Includes mailing, advertising, news, and subscription addresses and phone numbers when different from the editorial/publisher address and phone numbers.

㉘ **Ad Rates.** Respondents may provide non-contract (open) rates in any of six categories:

> GLR = general line rate
> BW = one-time black & white page rate
> 4C = one-time four-color page rate
> SAU = standard advertising unit rate
> CNU = Canadian newspaper advertising unit rate
> PCI = per column inch rate

Occasionally, explanatory information about other types of advertising appears in the Remarks section of the entry (see ㉒ above.)

㉙ **Circulation.** Figures represent various circulation numbers; the figures are accompanied by a symbol (except for sworn and estimated figures). Following are explanations of the eight circulation classifications used by *GDPBM*, the corresponding symbols, if any, are listed at the bottom of each right hand page. All circulation figures *except* publisher's reports and estimated figures appear in boldface type.

These audit bureaus are independent, nonprofit organizations (with the exception of VAC, which is for-profit) that verify circulation rates. Interested users may contact the association for more information.

ABC: Audit Bureau of Circulations, 900 N. Meacham Rd., Schaumburg, IL 60173; (847)605-0909
CAC: Certified Audit of Circulations, Inc., 155 Willowbrook Blvd., 4th Fl., Wayne, NJ 07470-7036; (201)785-3000
CCAB: Canadian Circulations Audit Board, 188 Eglinton Ave. E, Ste. 304, Toronto, ON Canada M4P 2X7; (416)487-2418
VAC: Verified Audit Circulation, 319 Miller Ave., Mill Valley, CA 90292; (415)383-3623
Post Office Statement: These figures were verified from a U.S. Post Office form.
Publisher's Statement: These figures were accompanied by the signature of the editor, publisher, or other officer.
Sworn Statement: These figures, which appear in **boldface** without a symbol, were accompanied by the notarized signature of the editor, publisher, or other officer of the publication.
Estimated Figures: These figures, which are shown in lightface without a symbol, are the unverified report of the listee.

The footer on every odd-numbered page contains a key to circulation and entry type symbols, as well as advertising abbreviations.

SAMPLE BROADCAST LISTING

① **111** ② **WDOG-AM - 1530**
③ 34 N South St.
  PO Box 09876
  Sahko, NY 10789-0198
④ Phone: (518)678-9288
⑤ Fax: (518)412-3456
⑥ Free: 800-724-5678
⑦ **E-mail:** wdog@wdog.com
⑧ **Format:** Classical. ⑨ **Simulcasts:** WDOG-FM. ⑩ **Network(s):** Westwood One Radio; ABC. ⑪ **Owner:** Sheltie Communications, Inc., at above address. ⑫ **Founded:** 1990. ⑬ **Variant Name(s):** Formerly: WCHA-AM (1992). ⑭ **Operating Hours:** Continuous; 85% local, 15% network. ⑮ **ADI:** Elmira, NY. ⑯ **Key Personnel:** Michael Vainio, General Mgr., phone (518)556-1020, fax (518)556-1010, mvainio@wdog.com; Josh Butland, Program Dir. ⑰ **Cities Served:** Salem, NY. ⑱ **Postal Areas Served:** 10528; 10529. ⑲ **Local Programs:** Who's Beethoven? Richard Jim, Contact, (518)556-1031, fax (518)556-1032. ⑳ **Wattage:** 3000. ㉑ **Ad Rates:** Underwriting available. $20-25 for 30 seconds; $50-55 for 60 seconds. Combined advertising rates available with WPAN-FM. ㉒ **Additional Contact Information:** Mailing address: PO Box 661, Elmira, NY, 10529.
㉓ **URL:** http://www.wdog.com.

---

① **Entry Number.** Each broadcast or cable entry is preceded by a symbol (a microphone) representing the broadcasting industry. Entries are numbered sequentially. Entry numbers (rather than page numbers) are used in the index to refer to listings.

② **Call Letters and Frequency/Channel** or **Cable Company Name.**

③ **Address.** Location and studio addresses appear as supplied by the respondent. If provided, alternate addresses are listed in the Additional Contact Information section of the entries (see ㉒ below).

④ **Phone.** Telephone numbers are listed as provided.

⑤ **Fax.** Facsimile numbers are listed when provided.

⑥ **Free.** Toll-free numbers are listed when provided.

⑦ **E-mail.** Electronic mail addresses are included as provided by the listee.

⑧ **Format.** For television station entries, this subheading indicates whether the station is commercial or public. Radio station entries contain industry-defined (and, in some cases, station-defined) formats as indicated by the listee.

⑨ **Simulcasts.** Lists stations that provide simulcasting.

⑩ **Network(s).** Notes national and regional networks with which a station is affiliated. The term 'independent' is used if indicated by the listee.

⑪ **Owner.** Lists the name of an individual or company, supplemented by the address and telephone number, when provided by the listee. If the address is the same as that of the station or company, the notation 'at above address' is used, referring to the station or cable company address.

⑫ **Founded.** In most cases, the year the station/company began operating, regardless of changes in call letters/names and ownership.

⑬ **Variant Name(s).** For radio and television stations, former call letters and the years in which they were changes are presented as provided by the listee. Former cable company names and the years in which they were changed are also noted when available.

⑭ **Operating Hours.** Lists on-air hours and often includes percentages of network and local programming.

⑮ **ADI (Area of Dominant Influence).** The Area of Dominant Influence is a standard market region defined by the Arbitron Ratings Company for U.S. television stations. Some respondents also list radio stations as having ADIs.

⑯ **Key Personnel.** Presents the names and titles of contacts at each station or cable company.

⑰ **Cities Served.** This heading is primarily found in cable system entries and provides information on channels and the number of subscribers.

⑱ **Postal Areas Served.** This heading is primarily found in cable system entries and provides information on the postal (zip) codes served by the system.

⑲ **Local Programs.** Lists names, air times, and contact personnel of locally-produced television and radio shows.

⑳ **Wattage.** Applicable to radio stations, the wattage may differ for day and night in the case of AM stations. Occasionally a station's ERP (effective radiated power) is given in addition to, or instead of, actual licensed wattage.

㉑ **Ad Rates.** Includes rates for 10, 15, 30, and 60 seconds as provided by respondents. Some stations price advertisement spots "per unit" regardless of length; these units vary.

㉒ **Additional Contact Information.** Includes mailing, advertising, news, and studio addresses and phone numbers when different from the station, owner, or company address and phone numbers.

㉓ **URL.** If a radio station or cable company is accessible online via computer, that information is listed here. If the station or company is available online but the details of the URL (universal resource locator) or vendor are not known, the notation **'Available Online.'** will be listed.

Entry information appearing in the Sample Entries portion of this directory has been fabricated. The entries named here do not, to the best of our knowledge, exist.

Index Notes

Following the main body of the *Update* is the Master Name and Keyword Index. Citations in this index are listed alphabetically regardless of media type.

Publication citations include the following:

- titles
- important keywords within titles
- former titles
- foreign language titles
- alternate titles

Broadcast media citations include the following:

- station call letters
- cable company names
- former station call letters
- former cable company names

Indexing is word-by-word rather than letter-by-letter. For example, "New York" is listed before "News". Current listings in the Index include geographic information and entry number.

INDEXING SAMPLE

① Administration in Mental Health ② (New York, NY) 575

① Allied Cable Systems ② (Lancaster, NH) 476

③ Mental Health; Administration in (New York, NY) ④575

⑤ Metro Tattler (Chicago, IL) *Ceased*

⑥ Administration in Mental and Physical Health 575*

⑦ WMDC-TV (Detroit, MI) *Unable to Locate*

---

① The full name (i.e. publication title, station call letters, or cable company name) of each entry is cited as it appears in the main body.

② Citations include in parentheses the city and state (or province and country for Canadian entries) in which the entry is located.

③ Publications are also indexed by subject keywords and other important words within titles.

④ References are to entry numbers rather than page numbers.

⑤ Notices of cessations are included.

⑥ Former names and call letters indicated by an * and do not include a geographic designation.

⑦ Notices are included in cases where the editors have not been able to verify the location or continued existence of a publication, broadcast station, or cable company.

Abbreviations, Symbols, and Codes

Miscellaneous Abbreviations

& .... And
4C .... One-Time Four Color Page Rate

ABC .... Audit Bureau of Circulations
Acad. .... Academy
Act. .... Acting
Adm. .... Administrative, Administration
Admin. .... Administrator
AFB .... Air Force Base
AM .... Amplitude Modulation
Amer. .... American
APO .... Army Post Office
Apt. .... Apartment
Assn. .... Association
Assoc. .... Associate
Asst. .... Assistant
Ave. .... Avenue

Bldg. .... Building
Blvd. .... Boulevard
boul. .... boulevard
BPA .... Business Publications Audit of Circulations
BTA .... Best Time Available
BW .... One-time Black & White Page Rate

C .... Central
CAC .... Certified Audit of Circulations
CCAB .... Canadian Circulations Audit Board
CEO .... Chief Executive Officer
Chm. .... Chairman
Chwm. .... Chairwoman
CNU .... Canadian Newspaper Advertising Unit Rate
c/o .... Care of
Col. .... Column
Coll. .... College
Comm. ....Committee
Co. .... Company
COO .... Chief Operating Officer
Coord. .... Coordinator
Corp. .... Corporation
Coun. .... Council
CP .... case postale
Ct. .... Court

Dept. .... Department
Dir. .... Director
Div. .... Division
Dr. .... Doctor, Drive

E. .... East
EC .... East Central

ENE .... East Northeast
ERP .... Effective Radiated Power
ESE .... East Southeast
Eve. .... Evening
Exec. .... Executive
Expy. .... Expressway

Fed. .... Federation
Fl. .... Floor
FM .... Frequency Modulation
FPO .... Fleet Post Office
Fri. .... Friday
Fwy. .... Freeway

Gen. .... General
GLR .... General Line Rate

Hd. .... Head
Hwy. .... Highway

Inc. .... Incorporated
Info. .... Information
Inst. .... Institute
Intl. .... International
ISSN .... International Standard Serial Number

Jr. .... Junior

Libn. .... Librarian
Ln. .... Lane
Ltd. .... Limited

Mgr. .... Manager
mi. .... miles
Mktg. .... Marketing
Mng. .... Managing
Mon. .... Monday
Morn. .... Morning

N. .... North
NAS .... Naval Air Station
Natl. .... National
NC .... North Central
NE .... Northeast
NNE .... North Northeast
NNW .... North Northwest
No. .... Number
NW .... Northwest

Orgn. .... Organization

PCI	Per Column Inch Rate
Pkwy.	Parkway
Pl.	Place
PO	Post Office
Pres.	President
Prof.	Professor
Rd.	Road
RFD	Rural Free Delivery
Rm.	Room
ROS	Run of Schedule
RR	Rural Route
Rte.	Route
S.	South
Sat.	Saturday
SAU	Standard Advertising Unit Rate
SC	South Central
SE	Southeast
Sec.	Secretary
Soc.	Society
Sq.	Square
Sr.	Senior
SSE	South Southeast
SSW	South Southwest
St.	Saint, Street
Sta.	Station
Ste.	Sainte, Suite
Sun.	Sunday
Supt.	Superintendent
SW	Southwest
Terr.	Terrace
Thurs.	Thursday
Tpke.	Turnpike
Treas.	Treasurer
Tues.	Tuesday
Univ.	University
USPS	United States Publications Serial
VAC	Verified Audit Circulation
VP	Vice President
W.	West
WC	West Central
Wed.	Wednesday
WNW	West Northwest
WSW	West Southwest
x/month	Times per Month
x/week	Times per Week
x/year	Times per Year

U.S. State and Territory Postal Codes

AK	Alaska	MT	Montana
AL	Alabama	NC	North Carolina
AR	Arkansas	ND	North Dakota
AZ	Arizona	NE	Nebraska
CA	California	NH	New Hampshire
CO	Colorado	NJ	New Jersey
CT	Connecticut	NM	New Mexico
DC	District of Columbia	NV	Nevada
DE	Delaware	NY	New York
FL	Florida	OH	Ohio
GA	Georgia	OK	Oklahoma
HI	Hawaii	OR	Oregon
IA	Iowa	PA	Pennsylvania
ID	Idaho	PR	Puerto Rico
IL	Illinois	RI	Rhode Island
IN	Indiana	SC	South Carolina
KS	Kansas	SD	South Dakota
KY	Kentucky	TN	Tennessee
LA	Louisiana	TX	Texas
MA	Massachusetts	UT	Utah
MD	Maryland	VA	Virginia
ME	Maine	VT	Vermont
MI	Michigan	WA	Washington
MN	Minnesota	WI	Wisconsin
MO	Missouri	WV	West Virginia
MS	Mississippi	WY	Wyoming

Canadian Province and Territory Postal Codes

AB .... Alberta
BC .... British Columbia
MB .... Manitoba
NB .... New Brunswick
NF .... Newfoundland
NS .... Nova Scotia

NT .... Northwest Territories
ON .... Ontario
PE .... Prince Edward Island
PQ .... Quebec
SK .... Saskatchewan
YT .... Yukon Territory

ALABAMA

ATHENS

🎤 1 WUMP-AM - 730
PO Box 389
Athens, AL 35612

Phone: (256)830-8300
Fax: (256)232-6842

Format: Sports; Talk. **Key Personnel:** Bill West, Sales Mgr., phone (256)216-0124. **URL:** http://www.730ump.com.

BIRMINGHAM

📖 2 Southern Living Garden Guide
Southern Progress
2100 Lakeshore Dr.
Birmingham, AL 35209-6721

Phone: (205)877-6000
Fax: (205)877-6600
Free: (888)737-3529

Consumer magazine covering gardening. **Freq:** Semiannual. **Key Personnel:** Linda C. Askey, Editor; Jon Thompson, Art Dir.; Pat Vander Meer, VP, Circ.; Kevin Lynch, Publisher. **Subscription Rates:** $3.99 single issue.

📖 3 Southern Living Home for the Holidays
Southern Progress
2100 Lakeshore Dr.
Birmingham, AL 35209-6721

Phone: (205)877-6000
Fax: (205)877-6600
Free: (888)737-3529

Consumer magazine covering holiday home decoration. **Freq:** Annual. **Key Personnel:** Jackie Mills, Editor; Jon Thompson, Art Dir.; Pat Vander Meer, VP, Circ.; Kevin Lynch, Publisher. **Subscription Rates:** $4 single issue. **Remarks:** Accepts advertising.

Circ: (Not Reported)

📖 4 Southern Living Summertime
Southern Progress
2100 Lakeshore Dr.
Birmingham, AL 35209-6721

Phone: (205)877-6000
Fax: (205)877-6600
Free: (888)737-3529

Consumer magazine covering regional interest. **Freq:** Annual. **Key Personnel:** Andria Scott Hurst, Editor; Gae Watson, Art Dir.; Pat Vander Meer, VP, Circ.; Kevin Lynch, Publisher. **Subscription Rates:** $3.99 single issue. **Remarks:** Accepts advertising.

Circ: (Not Reported)

🎤 5 WBHM-FM - 90.3
650 11th St. S.
Birmingham, AL 35294
E-mail: info@wbhm.org

Phone: (205)934-2606
Fax: (205)934-5075

Format: Public Radio. **Operating Hours:** Continuous. **Key Personnel:** Mike Morgan, General Mgr.; Patrick Dorriety, Operations Mgr.; Michael Krall, Program Dir. **Ad Rates:** Noncommercial. **URL:** http://www.wbhm.org.

🎤 6 WODL-FM - 106.9
301 Beacon Pkwy. W., Ste. 200
Birmingham, AL 35209

Phone: (205)916-1100
Fax: (205)916-1145

Format: Oldies. **URL:** http://www.wodl.com.

LANETT

📖 7 The Valley Times-News
Valley Newspapers, Inc.
220 N. 12th St.
PO Box 850
Lanett, AL 36863
Publication E-mail: advertising@valleytimes-news.com

General newspaper. **Freq:** Daily. **Key Personnel:** Cy Wood, Editor and Publisher; Bridge Turner, Advertising Mgr. **Subscription Rates:** $68 individuals. **Remarks:** Advertising accepted; rates available upon request. **URL:** http://www.valleytimes-news.com.

Circ: (Not Reported)

MOBILE

🎤 8 WRKH-FM - 96.1
555 Broadcast Dr., 3rd Fl.
Mobile, AL 36606

Phone: (334)770-9600
Fax: (334)479-3418
Free: (800)666-9696

E-mail: leeallen@ccmobile.com

Format: Classic Rock. **Operating Hours:** Continuous. **Key Personnel:** Bill Roth, Sales Mgr.

NORMAL

🎤 9 WJAB-FM - 90.9
Alabama A&M University
Telecommunications Center
PO Box 174
Normal, AL 35762

Format: Jazz; Blues. **Operating Hours:** Continuous. **Key Personnel:** Lois Watkins, Producer/Editor, lwatkins@asnaam.aamu.edu; Michael Burns, Production Mgr., mburns@asnaam.aamu.edu; Samuel E. Mathews, Station Mgr., smathews@asnaam.aamu.edu; Ellen C. Washington, Program Mgr./Music Dir., aamemw01@asnaam.aamu.edu. **Ad Rates:** Noncommercial. **URL:** http://www.aamu.edu/wjab/.

OXFORD

📖 10 The Oxford Independent
John A. Childs
PO Box 7188
Oxford, AL 36203

Community newspaper. **Freq:** Weekly (Fri.). **Key Personnel:** John A. Childs, Publisher. **URL:** http://www.oxfordi.com.

TUSCALOOSA

📖 11 Rent Smart!
Randall Publishing Co.
3200 Rice Mine Rd. N.E.
Tuscaloosa, AL 35406

Phone: (205)349-2990
Fax: (205)752-0930

Professional magazine covering building and construction. **Subtitle:** Solutions

---

Ad Rates: GLR = general line rate; BW = one-time black & white page rate; 4C = one-time four color page rate; SAU = standard advertising unit rate; CNU = Canadian newspaper advertising unit rate; PCI = per column inch rate.
Circulation: ★ = ABC; △ = BPA; ◆ = CAC; ● = CCAB; ❑ = VAC; ⊕ = PO Statement; ‡ = Publisher's Report; Boldface figures = sworn; Light figures = estimated.
Entry type: 📖 = Print; 🎤 = Broadcast.

for the Construction Professional. **Founded:** 1997. **Freq:** Monthly. **Print Method:** Web offset. **Trim Size:** 8 1/8 x 10 7/8. **Cols./Page:** 3. **Col. Width:** 2 1/8 inches. **Col. Depth:** 9 7/8 inches. **Key Personnel:** Terry Killgore, Group Publisher, tkillgore@randallpub.com; Jim Longton, Publisher, jlongton@randallpub.com; Steve Lillybeck, Senior Editor, slillybeck@randallpub.com; Marcia Gruver, Editorial Dir., mgruver@randallpub.com; Rebecca Todd Bushery, Managing Editor, rbushery@randallpub.com. **Subscription Rates:** $60.45 individuals; $10 single issue. **Remarks:** Accepts advertising. **URL:** http://www.rentsmartonline.com.

| Ad Rates: | BW: $4610 | Circ: Controlled ‡50,876 |
| | 4C: $5970 | |

12 Trucking Co.
Randall Publishing Co.
3200 Rice Mine Rd. N.E.
Tuscaloosa, AL 35406   Phone: (205)349-2990
                              Fax: (205)752-0930
Publication E-mail: editors@truckingco.com

Trade magazine covering trucking for truckers. **Founded:** 1998. **Freq:** Monthly. **Print Method:** Web offset. **Trim Size:** 8 1/8 x 10 7/8. **Cols./Page:** 2. **Col. Width:** 6 7/8 inches. **Col. Depth:** 9 1/8 inches. **Key Personnel:** Mark Kessler, Publisher, mkessler@truckingco.com; Avery Vise, Editor; Johnna Pitts, Managing Editor; Barry Tice, Assoc. Editor. **ISSN:** 0030-7394. **Subscription Rates:** $48 individuals; $3.95 single issue. **Remarks:** Accepts advertising. **URL:** http://www.truckingco.com.

Ad Rates:	BW: $4412	Circ: Controlled ‡40,000
	4C: $5152	
	PCI: $175	

ALASKA

ANCHOR POINT

13 The Bush Blade
PO Box 168
Anchor Point, AK 99556
Publication E-mail: theblade@arctic.net

Phone: (907)566-8406
Fax: (888)776-6789

Community newspaper. **Freq:** Monthly. **Print Method:** Web offset. **Cols./Page:** 4. **Key Personnel:** Ingrid Peterson, Editor-in-Chief; Leif Peterson, Circulation Mgr.; Lars Peterson, Advertising Mgr. **Subscription Rates:** $7.50 individuals. **Remarks:** Accepts advertising.
Ad Rates: BW: $600
4C: $2,000
PCI: $10

Circ: Controlled 3,000

KODIAK

14 Kodiak Daily Mirror
1419 Selig St.
Kodiak, AK 99615

Phone: (907)486-3227
Fax: (907)486-3088

General newspaper. **Founded:** 1940. **Freq:** Daily. **Key Personnel:** Duane Freeman, Owner; Nancy Freeman, Owner. **Subscription Rates:** $85 individuals; $109 by mail; $169 out of state. **Remarks:** Accepts advertising. **URL:** http://www.ptialaska.net/~kdmnews/.
Ad Rates: PCI: $6.94

Circ: Combined 4,000

Ad Rates: GLR = general line rate; BW = one-time black & white page rate; 4C = one-time four color page rate; SAU = standard advertising unit rate; CNU = Canadian newspaper advertising unit rate; PCI = per column inch rate.
Circulation: ★ = ABC; △ = BPA; ✦ = CAC; • = CCAB; ❑ = VAC; ⊕ = PO Statement; ‡ = Publisher's Report; Boldface figures = sworn; Light figures = estimated.
Entry type: = Print; = Broadcast.

3

ARIZONA

BULLHEAD CITY

15 Booster Advertiser
News West Publishing Co.
PO Box 21209
Bullhead City, AZ 86439   Phone: (520)763-2505

Shopping guide. **Freq:** Weekly. **Subscription Rates:** Free.
Circ: Combined **14,751**

16 Colorado River Weekender
News West Publishing Co.
PO Box 21209
Bullhead City, AZ 86439   Phone: (520)763-2505

Community newspaper. **Freq:** Weekly (Thurs.). **Subscription Rates:** Free.
Circ: Combined **29,146**

17 Laughlin Nevada Entertainer
News West Publishing Co.
PO Box 21209
Bullhead City, AZ 86439   Phone: (520)763-2505

Community newspaper. **Freq:** Weekly (Wed.). **Subscription Rates:** Free.
Circ: Combined **47,853**

CASA GRANDE

18 K47FW-TV - 47
PO Box 15001   Phone: (520)876-4080
Casa Grande, AZ 85230   Fax: (520)876-4085
E-mail: frogmont@yahoo.com

Format: Commercial TV. **Owner:** Central Arizona Broadcasting, L.L.C., at above address. **Founded:** Apr. 1, 1999. **Operating Hours:** Continuous. **Key Personnel:** John W. McEvoy, CEO, phone (520)836-7483, jwmcevoy@mahoneygroup.com; Brett F. Eisele, President, phone (520)560-2555, frogmont@yahoo.com; Bea Lueck, Sales Mgr., frogmont@yahoo.com. **Wattage:** 1,000. **Ad Rates:** $10 for 30 seconds. **URL:** http://tv47.casagrande.com.

CAVE CREEK

19 Sonoran News
6812 Cave Creek Rd.   Phone: (480)488-2021
Cave Creek, AZ 85331   Fax: (480)488-6216
Publication E-mail: sonnews@aol.com

Community newspaper. **Freq:** Weekly (Wed.). **Key Personnel:** Don Sorchych, Editor and Publisher; Jo Marocco, Assoc. Editor/Manager; Linda Olson, Advertising Sales. **Subscription Rates:** Free; $71.40 by mail. **Remarks:** Accepts advertising. **URL:** http://www.sonorannews.com.
Ad Rates: PCI: $15.88   **Circ:** Combined **24,500**

FLAGSTAFF

20 International Journal of Humanities and Peace
Vasant V. Merchant
1436 Evergreen Dr.
Flagstaff, AZ 86001   Phone: (520)774-4793

Scholarly, multidisciplinary journal covering humanities, the arts, and peace. **Founded:** 1983. **Freq:** Annual. **Cols./Page:** 3. **Key Personnel:** Dr. V. V. Merchant, Editor; Dr. Mark Siegmund, Assoc. Editor, siegmund@thegrid.net. **ISSN:** 1042-4032. **Subscription Rates:** $22 U.S. and Canada; $28 elsewhere. **Remarks:** Advertising not accepted. **Former name:** AZ Humanities Association Journal (1989).
Circ: Paid **2000**

PARKER

21 The Sun Times
PO Box 5054
Parker, AZ 85344
Publication E-mail: suntimes@suntimesaz.com

Community newspaper. **Freq:** Weekly (Thurs.). **URL:** http://www.suntimesaz.com.

PHOENIX

22 Arizona Pet Guide Magazine
Arizona Pet Guide Magazine, Inc.
8433 N. Black Canyon Hwy., No. 100   Phone: (602)995-5000
Phoenix, AZ 85021   Fax: (602)995-8040

Consumer magazine covering pets for pet owners, breeders, and pet show exhibitors. **Founded:** May 1989. **Freq:** Monthly. **Print Method:** Offset. **Trim Size:** 8 1/4 x 10 3/4. **Cols./Page:** 2. **Col. Width:** 3 1/2 inches. **Key Personnel:** Mal Freedman, Publisher; Corinne Barrett, Marketing Dir. **Subscription Rates:** $16.95 individuals. **Remarks:** Accepts advertising.
Ad Rates: BW: $665   **Circ:** Combined ‡**15,000**
              4C: $950

23 The Business Journal of Phoenix
American City Business Journals
3030 N. Central Ave., Fl. 15   Phone: (602)230-8400
Phoenix, AZ 85012-2707   Fax: (602)230-0955
Publication E-mail: phoenix@amcity.com
Publisher E-mail: info@amcity.com

Local business newspaper. **Freq:** Weekly. **Key Personnel:** Don Henninger, Editor, dhenninger@amcity.com; Cathy Luebke, cluebke@amcity.com; Ilana Ruber, Managing Editor, iruber@amcity.com; Nancy Best, Adv. Sales Dir., nbest@amcity.com. **Remarks:** Advertising accepted; rates available upon request. **URL:** http://www.amcity.com/phoenix/.
Circ: Combined **13,806**

SEDONA

24 Cottonwood Journal Extra
Sedona Red Rock News
PO Box 619
Sedona, AZ 86339

Phone: (520)282-7795
Fax: (520)282-6011

Community newspaper. **Freq:** Weekly (Wed.). **Subscription Rates:** Free.
Circ: Combined **7013**

SIERRA VISTA

25 Bisbee Daily Review
Sierra Vista Herald
102 Fab Ave.
Sierra Vista, AZ 85635
Publisher E-mail: svhnews@c2i2.com

Phone: (520)458-9440
Fax: (520)459-0120

Daily newspaper. **Freq:** Daily and Sunday. **Subscription Rates:** $105.60
individuals.

TOMBSTONE

26 Tombstone Tumbleweed
Tombstone Publishing, Inc.
PO Box 1025
Tombstone, AZ 85638

Phone: (520)457-3008
Fax: (520)457-2378

Community newspaper. **Founded:** 1882. **Freq:** Weekly (Thurs.). **Key
Personnel:** Pat Koester, Publisher; Robert Candland, Publisher. **Subscription
Rates:** $25 individuals; $28 out of area; $30 out of state; $40 out of country.
Remarks: Advertising accepted; rates available upon request. **URL:** http://
www.theriver.com/tombstonenews/.

Circ: (Not Reported)

TUCSON

27 Studies in Latin American Popular Culture
University of Arizona
Modern Languages Bldg., Rm. 345
PO Box 210067
Tucson, AZ 85721-0067

Phone: (520)621-9294
Fax: (520)621-5594

Scholarly journal covering Latin American popular culture studies. **Freq:**
Annual. **Key Personnel:** Harold E. Hinds, Jr., Senior Editor; Charles M.
Tatum, Senior Editor, ctatum@uarizona.edu. **Subscription Rates:** $25
individuals; $55 institutions. **URL:** http://www.humnet.ucla.edu/spanport/
slapc/.

28 The Weekly Observer
Bob Ellis
PO Box 50733
Tucson, AZ 85703

Phone: (520)622-7176

Community newspaper for a gay and lesbian audience. **Freq:** Weekly (Wed.).
Key Personnel: Bob Wllis, Editor and Publisher. **URL:** http://
www.bonzo.com/observer.

ARKANSAS

ARKADELPHIA

🎙 **29 KSWH-FM - 91.9**
PO Box 7872
Arkadelphia, AR 71923

Format: Alternative/New Music/Progressive. **Owner:** Henderson State College Board of Trustees, 1100 Henderson St., Arkadelphia, AR 71999. **Founded:** 1968. **Operating Hours:** 7 a.m.-12 a.m. **Key Personnel:** Dustin Lawhorn, General Mgr., phone (870)230-5218. **Wattage:** 1,000.

DARDANELLE

📖 **30 The Courier**
Russellville Newspapers
107 Harrison St.
PO Box 270
Dardanelle, AR 72834-0270

Phone: (501)229-2250
Fax: (501)229-1159

General newspaper. **Freq:** Daily (morn.) (except Mon.). **Subscription Rates:** $111 individuals; $107.40 by mail. **Remarks:** Accepts advertising. **URL:** http://www.couriernews.com.
Ad Rates: PCI: $11.90   **Circ:** (Not Reported)

HARRISON

🎙 **31 KHOZ-FM - 102.9**
One Radio Ave.
PO Box 430
Harrison, AR 72601
E-mail: khoz@cswnet.com

Phone: (870)741-2301
Fax: (870)741-3299
Free: (800)553-6103

Format: Country. **Networks:** CBS. **Owner:** Harrison Broadcasting Corp., at above address. **Founded:** 1963. **Formerly:** KWNQ-FM (1990). **Operating Hours:** Continuous. **ADI:** Springfield, MO. **Key Personnel:** Jamie Holt, General Mgr., juholt@cswnet.com; Dave Fransen, Sales Mgr.; Jim Fitzgerald, Operations Dir., jfitz@cswnet.com; Jerry Bowman, Music Dir., jbowman@cswnet.com; Bill Wilcox, Chief Engineer, wbwilcox@cswnet.com. **Wattage:** 100,000. **Ad Rates:** $16.50-17.50 for 30 seconds; $24.75-26.25 for 60 seconds. **URL:** http://www.khoz.com.

LITTLE ROCK

📖 **32 Little Rock Family**
Arkansas Business Publishing Group
201 E. Markham
PO Box 3686
Little Rock, AR 72203

Phone: (501)372-1443
Fax: (501)375-0933

Consumer magazine covering local parenting and families. **Freq:** Monthly. **Subscription Rates:** Free.
Circ: Combined **19,809**

NEWPORT

📖 **33 Newport Daily Independent**
Liberty Group Publishing
2408 Hwy. 367 N.
Newport, AR 72112

Community newspaper. **Freq:** Daily. **Key Personnel:** Minnie Sanders, Publisher; Elle Jones, General Mgr.; Holly Latimer, Editor; Summer Welsh, Office Mgr.; Susan Harris, Production Mgr. **URL:** http://www.newportindependent.com.

PARAGOULD

📖 **34 Paragould Daily Press**
1401 W. Hunt St.
Paragould, AR 72450
Publication E-mail: delivery@paragoulddailypress.com

Community newspaper. **Freq:** Daily. **Key Personnel:** Dina Mason, Publisher, dmaso@paragoulddailypress.com; Richard Brummett, Editor, scoop@paragoulddailypress.com; Donna Estes, Advertising Dir., destes@cswnet.com; Mike Rogers, Circulation Mgr. **URL:** http://www.paragoulddailypress.com.

📖 **35 Paragould Tribune**
Corning Publishing
1 Stout Spur Shopping Center
Paragould, AR 72450

Phone: (501)239-5000
Fax: (501)239-3403

Community newspaper. **Founded:** 1989. **Freq:** Weekly (Wed.). **Key Personnel:** Owen Lusk, Publisher. **Subscription Rates:** Free.
Circ: Combined ◆**22,450**

SEARCY

📖 **36 White County Heritage**
White County Historical Society
501 Live Oak Dr.
Searcy, AR 72143

Journal covering local history and genealogy. **Founded:** 1963. **Freq:** Annual. **Trim Size:** 8 1/2 x 11. **Subscription Rates:** $12 individuals. **Remarks:** Advertising not accepted.
Circ: (Not Reported)

CALIFORNIA

ANAHEIM

📖 **37 World of Pageantry**
Harvey Berish
PO Box 2961
Anaheim, CA 92804   Phone: (714)952-2263

Newspaper for marching bands, drill teams, cheerleaders and related groups. **Subtitle:** Band & Drill Team News. **Freq:** Monthly. **Key Personnel:** Harvey Berish, Editor and Publisher. **Subscription Rates:** $12 individuals; $20 two years. **URL:** http://www.worldofpageantry.com.

ATWATER

🎙 **38 KLOQ-FM - 98.7**
514 E. Bellevue Rd.   Phone: (209)358-9723
Atwater, CA 95301   Fax: (209)358-9796

Format: Hispanic. **Owner:** Randolph Holder, at above address. **Founded:** 1956. **Former name:** KFMK-FM. **Operating Hours:** Sunrise-sunset; 100% local. **Key Personnel:** Joan Rios, Office Mgr.; Yolanda Navarro, Program Dir.; Javier Fuentes, Sales. **Wattage:** 6,000.

AZUSA

📖 **39 Cactus and Succulent Journal**
Cactus and Succulent Society of America, Inc.
c/o Myron Kimnach
5508 N. Astell Ave.   Phone: (818)334-7349
Azusa, CA 91702   Fax: (818)334-0658
Publisher E-mail: grarad@eclipse.net

Trade journal covering cactus and succulents. **Founded:** 1929. **Freq:** Bimonthly. **Key Personnel:** Myron Kimnach, Editor, mkimnach@aol.com. **Remarks:** Accepts advertising.

Circ: Paid 4000

BIG PINE

🎙 **40 KWTY-FM - 102.9**
PO Box 773
Big Pine, CA 93513   Phone: (760)764-1111
E-mail: admin@kwty.com

Format: Classic Rock. **Networks:** Westwood One Radio. **Operating Hours:** Continuous. **Key Personnel:** M. Miller, General Mgr.; Dan Owen, Account Mgr., phone (760)872-3102, sales@kwty.com. **Wattage:** 2,000. **Ad Rates:** $9 for 30 seconds.

BRISBANE

📖 **41 The Net**
Imagine Media
150 N. Hill Dr.   Phone: (415)468-4684
Brisbane, CA 94005   Fax: (415)468-4686
Publication E-mail: talktous@thenet-usa.com

Trade magazine covering Internet content. **Freq:** Monthly. **Key Personnel:** Jon Zilber, Editor-in-Chief, jzilber@thenet-usa.com; Alicia Eckley, Managing Editor, aeckley@thenet-usa.com; Karen Tarrant, Publisher, hop@thenet-usa.com. **Subscription Rates:** $25 individuals. **URL:** http://www.thenet-usa.com.

📖 **42 Next Generation**
Imagine Media
150 N. Hill Dr.   Phone: (415)468-4684
Brisbane, CA 94005   Fax: (415)468-4686

Consumer magazine covering personal computer and console games. **Freq:** Monthly. **Subscription Rates:** $12 individuals; $26 Canada; $36 elsewhere. **URL:** http://www.imaginemedia.com/mag_ nextgeneration.html.

📖 **43 PC Accelerator**
Imagine Media
150 N. Hill Dr.   Phone: (415)468-4684
Brisbane, CA 94005   Fax: (415)468-4686
Publication E-mail: custserv@pcxl.com

Consumer magazine covering personal computer gaming. **Freq:** Monthly. **Key Personnel:** Mike Salmon, Editor-in-Chief, mike@pcxl.com; Rob Smith, Exec. Editor, rob@pcxl.com; Philip Mayard, Managing Editor, philip@pcxl.com. **Subscription Rates:** $12 individuals; $26 Canada; $36 elsewhere. **URL:** http://www.imaginemedia.com/mag_ pcaccelator.html.

📖 **44 PC Gamer**
Imagine Media
150 N. Hill Dr.   Phone: (415)468-4684
Brisbane, CA 94005   Fax: (415)468-4686

Consumer magazine covering computer games. **Freq:** Monthly. **Trim Size:** 10 3/4 x 16. **Key Personnel:** Caroline Simpson-Bint, Publisher, csimpson-bint@imaginemedia.com; Karen Quilantang, kquilan-tang@imaginemedia.com; Matt Firme, VP/Editorial Dir., mfirm@imaginemedia.com. **Subscription Rates:** $29.95 individuals; $43.95 Canada; $67 elsewhere. **Remarks:** Accepts advertising. **URL:** http://www.imaginemedia.com/mag_ pcgamer.html. **Alt. Formats:** CD-ROM.
Ad Rates: BW: $13,125   **Circ:** (Not Reported)

📖 **45 PSM**
Imagine Media
150 N. Hill Dr.   Phone: (415)468-4684
Brisbane, CA 94005   Fax: (415)468-4686
Publication E-mail: psm@imagemedia.com

Consumer magazine covering Sony PlayStation games. **Subtitle:** 100% Independent PlayStation Magazine. **Freq:** Monthly. **Key Personnel:** Chris Slate, Editor-in-Chief; Bill Donohue, Managing Editor. **Subscription Rates:** $12 individuals; $28.75 Canada; $38.95 elsewhere. **Remarks:** Accepts advertising. **URL:** http://www.psmonline.com.
Ad Rates: BW: $9,250   **Circ:** (Not Reported)

BURBANK

📖 **46 Inside Kung-Fu**
C.F.W. Enterprises, Inc.
4201 Vanowen Pl.   Phone: (818)845-2656
Burbank, CA 91505-1139   Fax: (818)845-7761
Publication E-mail: ikf@cfwenterprises.com

Ad Rates: GLR = general line rate; BW = one-time black & white page rate; 4C = one-time four color page rate; SAU = standard advertising unit rate; CNU = Canadian newspaper advertising unit rate; PCI = per column inch rate.
Circulation: ★ = ABC; △ = BPA; ♦ = CAC; • = CCAB; ❏ = VAC; ⊕ = PO Statement; ‡ = Publisher's Report; Boldface figures = sworn; Light figures = estimated.
Entry type: 📖 = Print; 🎙 = Broadcast.

9

Consumer magazine covering martial arts. **Freq:** Monthly. **Subscription Rates:** $29 individuals. **URL:** http://www.cfwenterprises.com/ikf/ikfcontact.html.

📖 **47 Martial Arts Illustrated**
C.F.W. Enterprises, Inc.
4201 Vanowen Pl.   Phone: (818)845-2656
Burbank, CA 91505-1139   Fax: (818)845-7761
Publication E-mail: mai@cfwenterprises.com

Consumer magazine covering martial arts. **Freq:** Monthly. **Subscription Rates:** $29 individuals. **URL:** http://www.cfwenterprises.com/mai/mai-home.html.

CALIFORNIA CITY

🎤 **48 KCEL-FM - 106.9**
8401 California Blvd., No. 9   Phone: (760)373-1069
California City, CA 93505   Fax: (760)373-3333

Format: Eclectic; Country. **Owner:** Kathryn J. Efford, at above address. **Founded:** May 22, 1999. **Operating Hours:** Continuous. **Key Personnel:** Kathryn J. Efford, General Mgr., phone (760)373-4552, kathy@kcel.com; James W. Reeder, Chief Operator, phone (760)373-2550, jim@kcel.com. **Wattage:** 2,435. **Ad Rates:** $12-17 for 30 seconds; $15-20 for 60 seconds. **URL:** http://www.kcel.com.

CAMARILLO

🎤 **49 KGZO-FM - 90.9**
2310 Ponderosa Dr., Ste. 28   Fax: (805)388-5202
Camarillo, CA 93010   Free: (888)209-2775
E-mail: kmro@vvcnet.com

Format: Religious; Ethnic. **Simulcasts:** KMRO-FM. **Owner:** The Association for Community Education, Inc., at above address. **Founded:** 1996. **Operating Hours:** 6 a.m.-12 a.m. **Key Personnel:** Mary Guthrie, General Mgr. **Ad Rates:** Noncommercial.

🎤 **50 KMRO-FM - 90.3**
2310 Ponderosa Dr., Ste. 28   Fax: (805)388-5202
Camarillo, CA 93010   Free: (888)209-2775
E-mail: kmro@vcnet.com

Format: Religious; Ethnic. **Simulcasts:** KGZO-FM. **Owner:** The Association for Community Education, Inc., at above address. **Founded:** 1987. **Operating Hours:** 6 a.m.-12 a.m. **Key Personnel:** Mary Guthrie, General Mgr. **Wattage:** 44,300. **Ad Rates:** Noncommercial.

CANOGA PARK

📖 **51 Air Classics**
Challenge Publications, Inc.
7950 Deering Ave.   Phone: (818)887-0550
Canoga Park, CA 91304-5063   Fax: (818)884-1343
Publication E-mail: office@challengeweb.com
Publisher E-mail: mail@challengeweb.com

Consumer magazine covering aviation for pilots and others. **Freq:** Monthly. **Subscription Rates:** $27.95 individuals; $41.95 two years; $51.95 out of country individual.

📖 **52 Car Toy Collectibles**
Challenge Publications, Inc.
7950 Deering Ave.   Phone: (818)887-0550
Canoga Park, CA 91304-5063   Fax: (818)884-1343
Publication E-mail: office@challengeweb.com
Publisher E-mail: mail@challengeweb.com

Consumer magazine covering toy and model cars. **Freq:** Bimonthly. **Subscription Rates:** $18.95 individuals; $30.95 two years; $30.95 out of country individual.

📖 **53 Kart Racer**
Challenge Publications, Inc.
7950 Deering Ave.   Phone: (818)887-0550
Canoga Park, CA 91304-5063   Fax: (818)884-1343
Publication E-mail: office@challengeweb.com

Publisher E-mail: mail@challengeweb.com

Consumer magazine covering go-kart racing. **Freq:** Bimonthly. **Subscription Rates:** $18.95 individuals; $30.95 two years; $30.95 out of country individual.

📖 **54 Scale Ship Modeler**
Challenge Publications, Inc.
7950 Deering Ave.   Phone: (818)887-0550
Canoga Park, CA 91304-5063   Fax: (818)884-1343
Publication E-mail: office@challengeweb.com
Publisher E-mail: mail@challengeweb.com

Consumer magazine covering model shipbuilding. **Freq:** Bimonthly. **Subscription Rates:** $18.95 individuals; $30.95 two years; $30.95 out of country individual.

📖 **55 Sport Pilot & Ultralights**
Challenge Publications, Inc.
7950 Deering Ave.   Phone: (818)887-0550
Canoga Park, CA 91304-5063   Fax: (818)884-1343
Publication E-mail: office@challengeweb.com
Publisher E-mail: mail@challengeweb.com

Consumer magazine covering sport aviation. **Freq:** Monthly. **Subscription Rates:** $18.95 individuals; $30.95 two years; $30.95 out of country individual.

📖 **56 Warbirds International**
Challenge Publications, Inc.
7950 Deering Ave.   Phone: (818)887-0550
Canoga Park, CA 91304-5063   Fax: (818)884-1343
Publication E-mail: office@challengeweb.com
Publisher E-mail: mail@challengeweb.com

Consumer magazine covering vintage and veteran military aircraft. **Freq:** 9/year. **Subscription Rates:** $23.95 individuals; $35.95 two years; $41.95 out of country individual.

CERRITOS

📖 **57 The National KAGRO Journal**
Korean American Grocers Assoc.
17320 Marquardt Ave.   Phone: (310)921-6883
Cerritos, CA 90703   Fax: (310)921-8272

Korean language trade magazine of the National Korean American Grocers Association. **Founded:** 1989. **Freq:** Bimonthly. **Key Personnel:** Mindy Cho, Editor; Jessica Lee, Acct. Exec. **Subscription Rates:** Free to qualified subscribers. **Remarks:** Accepts advertising.
Ad Rates: BW: $3,500   **Circ:** Combined 23,000
             4C: $4,250

CHICO

📖 **58 Smart TV**
Videomaker, Inc.
920 Main St.   Phone: (530)891-8410
PO Box 4591   Fax: (530)891-8443
Chico, CA 95927   Free: (800)284-3226
Publisher E-mail: editor@videomaker.com

Trade magazine covering interactive television, Web television, and the Internet. **Freq:** Bimonthly. **Key Personnel:** Matt York, Publisher/Editor; Stephen Muratore, Exec. Editor; Karen Mele, Director/Managing Editor. **Subscription Rates:** $14.97 individuals. **URL:** http://www.smarttvmag.com.

CITY OF INDUSTRY

📖 **59 Travel & Recreation Magazine**
IDS Publishing, Inc.
15709 E. Valley Blvd.   Phone: (818)333-2346
City of Industry, CA 91744   Fax: (818)961-7056

Chinese language consumer magazine covering travel, recreation and entertainment. **Founded:** 1994. **Freq:** Monthly. **Subscription Rates:** $2.95 single issue; $24 individuals. **Remarks:** Accepts advertising.
Ad Rates: BW: $2,500   **Circ:** Combined 20,000

CORTE MADERA

📖 **60 The Slant**
PO Box 629
Corte Madera, CA 94976

Gay and lesbian community newspaper. **Freq:** Monthly. **Subscription Rates:** $24 individuals. **URL:** http://www.theslant.org.

COSTA MESA

📖 **61 OC Weekly**
PO Box 10788
Costa Mesa, CA 92627

Community newspaper. **Freq:** Weekly. **URL:** http://www.ocweekly.com.

CUPERTINO

📖 **62 The Spirit of Woman in the Moon**
Woman in the Moon Publications (W.I.M.)
PO Box 2087   Phone: (408)279-6626
Cupertino, CA 95015-2087   Fax: (408)279-6636
Publisher E-mail: womaninmoon@earthlink.net

Literary magazine covering New Age topics. **Freq:** Triennial. **Trim Size:** 8 x 10. **Key Personnel:** Diane Adamz-Bogus, Editor and Publisher; Jamie Wright, Pubs. Asst.; Mary Pascual, Assoc. Editor. **Subscription Rates:** $24 individuals; $5 single issue. **Remarks:** Accepts advertising. **URL:** http://www.womaninthemoon.com.
Ad Rates: BW: $900   **Circ:** Combined 3,000
                PCI: $75

DALY CITY

📖 **63 Manila Mail**
Carmen H. Bunag
12 Avalon Dr.   Phone: (650)992-5474
Daly City, CA 94015   Fax: (650)997-0673

Community newspaper for Filipino-Americans. **Freq:** Bimonthly. **Key Personnel:** Carmen H. Bunag, Editor-in-Chief. **Subscription Rates:** Free; $39 by mail. **Remarks:** Accepts advertising.
Ad Rates: BW: $1,548   **Circ:** Combined 12,000

DOWNEY

📖 **64 Manila Times Journal**
Steven Marquez
10842 Paramount Blvd.   Phone: (310)904-1500
Downey, CA 90241   Fax: (310)904-6457

Community newspaper for Filipino-Americans. **Freq:** Weekly. **Key Personnel:** Steven Marquez, Pub./Pres. **Subscription Rates:** Free; $45 by mail. **Remarks:** Accepts advertising.
Ad Rates: BW: $1,500   **Circ:** Combined 50,000

EL MONTE

📖 **65 Chinese Free Daily News**
9639 Telstar Ave.   Phone: (818)453-8800
El Monte, CA 91731   Fax: (818)453-8822

Chinese language general newspaper. **Founded:** 1990. **Freq:** Daily. **Key Personnel:** Walter Chang, Contact. **Subscription Rates:** Free. **Remarks:** Accepts advertising.
Ad Rates: BW: $840   **Circ:** Combined 75,000

ELK GROVE

📖 **66 Web Publisher**
Informant Communications Group
10519 E. Stockton Blvd., Ste. 100   Phone: (916)686-6610
Elk Grove, CA 95624-9703   Fax: (916)686-8497

Trade magazine covering web site design. **Freq:** Monthly. **Key Personnel:** Mitchell Koulouris, Publisher, mkoulouris@web-publisher; Jerry Coffey, Editor-in-Chief, jcoffey@web-publisher.com; Lori Ash, Managing Editor, lash@web-publisher.com. **Subscription Rates:** $30 individuals. **URL:** http://www.web-publisher.com.

EUREKA

📖 **67 Comic Relief**
Page One Publishers and Bookworks, Inc.
Box 6606   Phone: (707)443-2820
Eureka, CA 95502   Fax: (707)445-0270

Consumer magazine covering humor. **Founded:** Nov. 1989. **Freq:** Monthly. **Trim Size:** 8 x 10 1/4. **Key Personnel:** Michael Kunz, Editorial Dir., mkunz@tidepool.com; Perry Bradford-Wilson, Sales & Mktg. Dir. **ISSN:** 1055-9639. **Subscription Rates:** $35 individuals; $4.95 single issue. **Remarks:** Accepts advertising.
Ad Rates: PCI: $50   **Circ:** Paid 18,000

GALT

📖 **68 Laguna Citizen**
Herburger Publications, Inc.
604 N. Lincoln Way
PO Box 307   Phone: (209)745-1551
Galt, CA 95632   Fax: (209)745-4492

Community newspaper. **Freq:** Weekly (Thurs.). **Subscription Rates:** Free.
                                     Circ: Non-paid **11,275**

GARDENA

📖 **69 Lighthouse**
1444 W. 178th St.   Phone: (310)715-1713
Gardena, CA 90248   Fax: (310)715-2089
Publisher E-mail: takuyo@up.nttca.com

Japanese language community newspaper. **Founded:** 1989. **Freq:** Biweekly. **Key Personnel:** Yuzo Komiyama, Advertising. **Subscription Rates:** Free; $55 by mail. **Remarks:** Accepts advertising.
Ad Rates: BW: $1,800   **Circ:** Combined 31,200

GLENDORA

📖 **70 OCB Tracker**
657 E. Arrow Hwy., No. M   Phone: (626)914-0306
Glendora, CA 91740   Fax: (626)914-1837

Community newspaper. **Subscription Rates:** Free. **Remarks:** Accepts advertising. **URL:** http://www.ocbtp.com.
Ad Rates: PCI: $12.71   **Circ:** Combined 10,000

IRVINE

📖 **71 Dan Chung News**
10 Winterbranch   Phone: (714)552-7728
Irvine, CA 92604   Fax: (714)552-1791

Vietnamese language community newspaper. **Founded:** 1980. **Freq:** Semiweekly (Thurs. and Sat.). **Key Personnel:** Nancy Tran, Contact. **Subscription Rates:** Free; $11 by mail. **Remarks:** Accepts advertising.
Ad Rates: BW: $550   **Circ:** Combined 10,000

LA JOLLA

72 Linguistic Notes from La Jolla
University of California at San Diego
C-0108
La Jolla, CA 92093
Publication E-mail: lnlj@ling.ucsd.edu

Scholarly journal covering linguistics. **Founded:** 1969. **Freq:** Irregular. **Key Personnel:** Paola Nieddu, Editor; Jude Theriot, Editor. **ISSN:** 0737-6720. **Subscription Rates:** $13 single issue. **Remarks:** Advertising not accepted.
Circ: (Not Reported)

LAGUNA HILLS

73 Agency Sales Magazine
Manufacturers' Agents National Association (MANA)
23016 Mill Creek Rd.
PO Box 3467
Laguna Hills, CA 92654
Phone: (949)859-4040
Fax: (949)855-2973
Publisher E-mail: mana@manaonline.org

Trade magazine covering marketing for manufacturers' agencies and their principals. **Founded:** 1949. **Freq:** Monthly. **Key Personnel:** Jack Foster, Editor; Bert Holtje, Editor; Jane Holm, Advertising Dir. **ISSN:** 0749-2332. **Subscription Rates:** $49 individuals; $55.50 Canada; $61.50 elsewhere; $7.50 single issue. **Remarks:** Accepts advertising. **URL:** http://www.manaonline.org. **Alt. Formats:** CD-ROM.
Ad Rates: BW: $2074
4C: $3171
Circ: (Not Reported)

74 Fleet Maintenance Supervisor
Cygnus Publishing
25401 Cabot Rd., Ste. 209
Laguna Hills, CA 92653
Phone: (949)830-7520
Fax: (949)830-7523

Trade magazine for vehicle class three or larger repairing and maintenance supervisors. **Print Method:** Web offset. **Trim Size:** 7 3/4 x 10 3/4. **Cols./Page:** 3. **Key Personnel:** Rudy Wolf, Publisher, phone (949)830-7520, fax (949)830-7523, rudy.wolf@cygnuspub.com; Robert Swenson, Assoc. Pub., phone (847)981-0007, fax (847)981-0025, bob.swenson@cygnuspub.com; Anton Ross, Exec. Editor, phone (949)830-7520, fax (949)830-7523, anton.ross@cygnuspub.com. **Subscription Rates:** Free to qualified subscribers. **Remarks:** Accepts advertising.
Ad Rates: BW: $6,020
4C: $9,570
Circ: Controlled ●44,018

LOS ALAMITOS

75 Computer Magazine
IEEE Computer Society
10662 Los Vaqueros Circle
Los Alamitos, CA 90720
Phone: (714)821-8380
Fax: (714)821-4010
Publication E-mail: service@computer.org
Publisher E-mail: csbooks@computer.org

Trade magazine for the IEEE Computer Society. **Freq:** Monthly. **Key Personnel:** Edward A. Parrish, Editor-in-Chief, computer@wpi.edu; Matthew S. Loeb, Publisher, mloeb@computer.org; Angela Burgess, Managing Editor, aburgess@computer.org. **Subscription Rates:** $31 members. **URL:** http://www.computer.org/pubs/computer.
Circ: Combined 90,000

76 IEEE Internet Computing
IEEE Computer Society
10662 Los Vaqueros Circle
Los Alamitos, CA 90720
Phone: (714)821-8380
Fax: (714)821-4010
Publication E-mail: iworld@computer.org
Publisher E-mail: csbooks@computer.org

Trade magazine covering the Internet. **Freq:** Bimonthly. **Key Personnel:** Charles J. Petrie, Editor-in-Chief, petrie@cdr.stanford.edu; Linda World, Managing Editor, lworld@computer.org; Ted Lewis, Assoc. Editor-in-Chief, tedglewis@aol.com. **URL:** http://www.computer.org/Internet.

LOS ALTOS

77 Los Altos Town Crier
The Town Crier Co., Inc.
138 Main St.
Los Altos, CA 94022
Phone: (650)948-9000
Publication E-mail: towncrier@losaltosonline.com

Community newspaper. **Freq:** Weekly. **Subscription Rates:** $20 individuals. **Remarks:** Accepts advertising. **URL:** http://www.losaltosonline.com.
Ad Rates: BW: $1,212.90
4C: $1,727.90
Circ: Combined 16,500

LOS ANGELES

78 Chevy Truck
Petersen Publishing Co., L.L.C.
6420 Wilshire Blvd.
Los Angeles, CA 90048-5515
Phone: (323)782-2350
Fax: (323)782-2704

Consumer magazine covering Chevrolet trucks. **Remarks:** Accepts advertising. **URL:** http://www.d-p-g.com/chevytruck.
Ad Rates: BW: $2,135
4C: $3,245
Circ: Combined 100,000

79 Corvette Fever
Petersen Publishing Co., L.L.C.
6420 Wilshire Blvd.
Los Angeles, CA 90048-5515
Phone: (323)782-2350
Fax: (323)782-2704

Consumer magazine covering automobiles. **Key Personnel:** Ronnie Hartman, Editor; Kim Cook, Managing Editor. **URL:** http://www.d-p-g.com/corvette-fever.

80 El Clasificado
1125 Goodrich Blvd.
Los Angeles, CA 90022
Phone: (213)278-5310

Spanish language community newspaper. **Freq:** Weekly (Wed.). **Subscription Rates:** Free.
Circ: Non-paid **69,467**

81 Electronic Retailing
GPG Publishing Inc.
9200 Sunset Blvd., No. 612
Los Angeles, CA 90069
Phone: (310)724-6750

Trade magazine covering the electronic commerce industry. **Freq:** Bimonthly. **Key Personnel:** Kurt Indvik, Publisher, kindvik@rjgordon.com; Brett Bush, Editor, bbush@rjgordon.com; Josh Moscov, Assoc. Editor, jmoscov@rjgordon.com. **URL:** http://www.eretail.com.

82 Investor's Business Daily
12655 Beatrice St.
Los Angeles, CA 90066
Phone: (310)448-6000

Business and financial newspaper. **Founded:** Apr. 9, 1984. **Freq:** Daily. **Print Method:** Offset. **Trim Size:** 13 3/4 x 22. **Cols./Page:** 6. **Col. Width:** 13 picas. **Col. Depth:** 21 1/8 inches. **Subscription Rates:** $197 individuals. **Remarks:** Accepts advertising. **URL:** http://www.investors.com. **Formerly:** Investor's Daily (1992).
Ad Rates: BW: $10,034.80
PCI: $79.17
Circ: Mon.-Fri. ★**251,172**

83 JP
Petersen Publishing Co., L.L.C.
6420 Wilshire Blvd.
Los Angeles, CA 90048-5515
Phone: (323)782-2350
Fax: (323)782-2704

Consumer magazine for Jeep owners and enthusiasts. **Remarks:** Accepts advertising. **URL:** http://www.d-p-g.com/jp.
Ad Rates: BW: $1,980
4C: $2,940
Circ: Combined 80,000

📖 **84 Korean Sunday News**
4950 Wilshire Blvd.   Phone: (213)954-7500
Los Angeles, CA 90010   Fax: (213)954-7503

Korean language community newspaper. **Freq:** Weekly. **Key Personnel:** Sung Lee, Contact. **Subscription Rates:** $60 individuals. **Remarks:** Accepts advertising.
Ad Rates: BW: $700   **Circ:** Combined 22,000

📖 **85 LA Children Magazine**
Siwol Media Group
11835 Olympic Blvd., Ste. 425-E
Los Angeles, CA 90064   Phone: (310)477-2526

Local, consumer magazine covering parenting. **Freq:** Monthly. **Subscription Rates:** Free.
                                Circ: Non-paid **150,520**

📖 **86 Los Angeles Downtown News**
1264 W. 1st St.   Phone: (213)481-1448
Los Angeles, CA 90026   Fax: (213)250-4617
Publication E-mail: realpeople@downtownnews.com

Community newspaper. **Freq:** Weekly. **Key Personnel:** Sue Laris-Eastin, Editor and Publisher. **Remarks:** Accepts advertising. **URL:** http://www.downtownnews.com.
Ad Rates: PCI: $45   **Circ:** (Not Reported)

📖 **87 Mopar Muscle**
Petersen Publishing Co., L.L.C.
6420 Wilshire Blvd.   Phone: (323)782-2350
Los Angeles, CA 90048-5515   Fax: (323)782-2704

Consumer magazine covering automobiles. **Key Personnel:** Jerry Pitt, Editor; D. Fanatia, Managing Editor. **URL:** http://www.d-p-g.com/moparmuscle.

📖 **88 Muscle Car Review**
Petersen Publishing Co., L.L.C.
6420 Wilshire Blvd.   Phone: (323)782-2350
Los Angeles, CA 90048-5515   Fax: (323)782-2704

Consumer magazine covering automobiles. **Key Personnel:** Tom Shaw, Editor; Kim Cook, Managing Editor. **URL:** http://www.d-p-g.com/musclecar.

📖 **89 Mustang Monthly**
Petersen Publishing Co., L.L.C.
6420 Wilshire Blvd.   Phone: (323)782-2350
Los Angeles, CA 90048-5515   Fax: (323)782-2704

Consumer magazine covering automobiles. **Freq:** Monthly. **Key Personnel:** Jeff Ford, Editor; Jana Huss, Managing Editor. **URL:** http://www.d-p-g.com/mustang.

📖 **90 NetProfit$**
GPG Publishing Inc.
9200 Sunset Blvd., No. 612
Los Angeles, CA 90069   Phone: (310)724-6750

Trade magazine for Internet entrepreneurs. **Freq:** Bimonthly. **Key Personnel:** Kurt Indvik, Publisher, kindvik@rjgordon.com; Brett Bush, Editor, bbush@rjgordon.com; Josh Moscov, Assoc. Editor, jmoscov@rjgordon.com. **Subscription Rates:** $24 individuals. **URL:** http://www.netprofits.mag.com.

📖 **91 The Study USA**
Organization for International Friendship (OIF)
624 S. Grand Ave., Ste. 1201   Phone: (213)629-0086
Los Angeles, CA 90017-9805   Fax: (213)629-0198

Japanese language newspaper for Japanese students studying the U.S. colleges and universities. **Founded:** 1993. **Freq:** Monthly. **Key Personnel:** Yasoji Matsuoka, Advertising Dir. **Subscription Rates:** $15 individuals; $35 out of country. **Remarks:** Accepts advertising.
Ad Rates: BW: $3,500   **Circ:** Combined 50,000

📖 **92 Super Ford**
Petersen Publishing Co., L.L.C.
6420 Wilshire Blvd.   Phone: (323)782-2350
Los Angeles, CA 90048-5515   Fax: (323)782-2704

Consumer magazine covering automobiles. **Key Personnel:** Tom Wilson, Editor; Jana Huss, Managing Editor; John W. Cobb, Group Publisher. **URL:** http://www.d-p-g.com/superford.

📖 **93 U.S. Japan Business News**
256 S. Los Angeles St.   Phone: (213)626-5001
Los Angeles, CA 90012   Fax: (213)613-1187

Japanese language business newspaper. **Founded:** 1975. **Freq:** Weekly. **Key Personnel:** Toshio Mitsuishi, President. **Subscription Rates:** $52 individuals; $90 two years. **Remarks:** Accepts advertising.
Ad Rates: BW: $2,500   **Circ:** Combined 40,000

📖 **94 World Reporter**
4515 Eagle Rook Bldg.   Phone: (213)344-3500
Los Angeles, CA 90041   Fax: (213)344-3501

Community newspaper for Filipino-Americans. **Founded:** 1987. **Freq:** Weekly. **Key Personnel:** Monette A. Maglaya, VP/Gen. Mgr. **Subscription Rates:** Free; $20 by mail. **Remarks:** Accepts advertising.
Ad Rates: BW: $1,500   **Circ:** Combined 50,000

MILPITAS

📖 **95 Vietnam Liberty News**
1811 Houret Ct.   Phone: (408)262-8183
Milpitas, CA 95035   Fax: (408)262-8185

Vietnamese language community newspaper. **Founded:** 1987. **Freq:** Daily (Tues.-Fri.). **Key Personnel:** Do Mui, Contact. **Subscription Rates:** Free. **Remarks:** Accepts advertising.
Ad Rates: BW: $500   **Circ:** Combined 26,000

MONTEREY

📖 **96 Mortuary Management**
Abbott & Hast Publications
761 Lighthouse Ave., Ste. A
Monterey, CA 93940-1033

Trade magazine for the funeral service industry. **Founded:** 1914. **Subscription Rates:** $33 individuals; $55 two years; $39 out of country. **URL:** http://www.abbottandhast.com/mm.html. **Alt. Formats:** Microfiche, UMI.

MONTEREY PARK

📖 **97 Chinese American Daily News**
673 Monterey Pass Rd.   Phone: (626)281-8989
Monterey Park, CA 91754   Fax: (626)281-0859

Chinese language general newspaper. **Founded:** 1989. **Freq:** Mon.-Sat. **Key Personnel:** Catherine Smith, Contact. **Subscription Rates:** Free; $144 by mail. **Remarks:** Accepts advertising.
Ad Rates: BW: $500   **Circ:** Combined 30,000

MOUNTAIN VIEW

📖 **98 Global Technology Business**
Global Technology Business Publishing Inc.
1157 San Antonio Rd.   Phone: (650)937-1418
Mountain View, CA 94043   Fax: (650)934-2306
Publication E-mail: gtbed@computerwire.com

Trade magazine covering computers, electronics, and telecommunications worldwide. **Freq:** Monthly. **Key Personnel:** Alex Vieux, Publisher; Andrew Lawrence, Editor-in-Chief; Kenny MacIver, Editor. **Subscription Rates:** $64 individuals.

NOVATO

99 Somatics
Novato Institute for Somatic Research and Training
1516 Grant Ave., Ste. 212
Novato, CA 94945
Phone: (415)892-0617

Magazine covering health and fitness, movement, dance, yoga, and philosophy for professionals and a general audience. **Subtitle:** Magazine-Journal of the Mind/Body Arts and Sciences. **Freq:** Semiannual. **Key Personnel:** Eleanor Criswell Hanna, Editor, phone (415)897-0336; Allegra Hiner, Managing Editor, fax (415)892-4388. **ISSN:** 0147-5231. **Subscription Rates:** $20 individuals; $25 institutions. **URL:** http://www.somaticsed.com.

OAKLAND

100 The Blitz
Oakland Football Marketing Association
7901 Oakport St., Ste. 4300
Oakland, CA 94621
Phone: (510)615-4830
Fax: (510)615-4826
Publication E-mail: blitz@ofma.com

Magazine for Oakland Raiders season-ticket holders covering the Oakland Raiders team, players, and fans. **Founded:** 1996. **Freq:** Bimonthly. **Print Method:** Sheetfed offset. **Trim Size:** 8 1/2 x 11. **Col. Width:** 3 3/4 inches. **Col. Depth:** 10 inches. **Key Personnel:** Christopher Weills, Publisher; Michael Fanelli, Editor. **Subscription Rates:** Free to qualified subscribers. **Remarks:** Accepts advertising. **URL:** http://www.ofma.com.
Ad Rates: 4C: $1500
Circ: Controlled 15,000

PALO ALTO

101 Annual Review of Earth and Planetary Sciences
Annual Reviews, Inc.
4139 El Camino Way
PO Box 10139
Palo Alto, CA 94303-0139
Phone: (650)493-4400
Fax: (650)424-0910
Free: (800)523-8635
Publisher E-mail: service@annurev.org

Scholarly journal covering earth sciences, geology, and astronomy. **Founded:** 1973. **Freq:** Annual. **Print Method:** Offset. **Trim Size:** 6 x 8 1/2. **Cols./Page:** 1. **Col. Width:** 26 picas. **Col. Depth:** 42 picas. **Key Personnel:** Ike Burke, Publications Dir. **ISSN:** 0084-6597. **Subscription Rates:** $70 individuals. **Remarks:** Advertising not accepted. **URL:** http://www.annualreviews.org.
Circ: (Not Reported)

102 Java Pro
Fawcette Technical Publications
209 Hamilton Ave.
Palo Alto, CA 94301-2530
Phone: (650)833-7100
Fax: (650)853-0230
Free: (800)848-5523

Trade magazine for Java programmers. **Key Personnel:** James E. Fawcette, Editor and Publisher. **Subscription Rates:** $30 individuals. **URL:** http://www.windx.com.

103 Microsoft Interactive Developer
Fawcette Technical Publications
209 Hamilton Ave.
Palo Alto, CA 94301-2530
Phone: (650)833-7100
Fax: (650)853-0230
Free: (800)848-5523
Publication E-mail: 75451.2343@compuserve.com

Trade magazine covering Internet development. **Freq:** Monthly. **Key Personnel:** Eric J. Maffei, Editor-in-Chief; Joanne Steinhart, Senior Managing Editor; Lynne Matthes, Publisher. **Subscription Rates:** $33 individuals. **URL:** http://www.windx.com.

PASADENA

104 Journal of the Los Angeles International Fern Society
Los Angeles International Fern Society
1404 La Loma Rd.
Pasadena, CA 91105
Phone: (626)441-3148

Journal covering ferns worldwide. **Founded:** 1973. **Freq:** Bimonthly. **Trim Size:** 5 1/2 x 8 1/2. **Cols./Page:** 2. **Col. Width:** 2 1/8 inches. **Col. Depth:** 7 1/

4 inches. **Key Personnel:** Janet A. Keyes, Editor, janifern@aol.com. **Subscription Rates:** $20 individuals; $3.75 single issue. **Remarks:** Accepts advertising. **URL:** http://www.southwest.net/users/mrmcd/laifsl.htm.
Ad Rates: PCI: $10
Circ: Combined 400

ROSEMEAD

105 Saigon Times
9129 E. Valley Blvd.
Rosemead, CA 91770
Phone: (818)286-9798
Fax: (818)286-3293

Vietnamese language community newspaper. **Founded:** 1985. **Freq:** Weekly. **Key Personnel:** Sam Choy, Contact. **Subscription Rates:** Free. **Remarks:** Accepts advertising.
Ad Rates: BW: $500
4C: $800
Circ: Combined 20,000

SACRAMENTO

106 New & Review
News & Review
1015 20th St.
Sacramento, CA 95814
Publication E-mail: daves@newsreview.com

Community newspaper. **Freq:** Weekly (Thurs.). **URL:** http://www.newsreview.com/sacto/.
Circ: Combined 93,000

SAN DIEGO

107 Databased Web Advisor
Advisor Publications, Inc.
5675 Ruffin Rd.
San Diego, CA 92123
Phone: (619)278-5600
Fax: (619)278-0300
Free: (800)336-6060
Publication E-mail: editors@advisor.com

Trade magazine covering Internet and intranet database solutions. **Freq:** Monthly. **Key Personnel:** William T. Ota, President; John L. Hawkins, Editor-in-Chief; Jeanne Banfield, Exec. Managing Editor. **Subscription Rates:** $39 individuals. **URL:** http://www.advisor.com.

108 E-business Advisor
Advisor Publications, Inc.
5675 Ruffin Rd.
San Diego, CA 92123
Phone: (619)278-5600
Fax: (619)278-0300
Free: (800)336-6060
Publication E-mail: editors@advisor.com

Trade magazine covering electronic business information. **Freq:** Bimonthly. **Subscription Rates:** $39 individuals. **URL:** http://www.advisor.com.

109 Internet Java & ActiveX Advisor
Advisor Publications, Inc.
5675 Ruffin Rd.
San Diego, CA 92123
Phone: (619)278-5600
Fax: (619)278-0300
Free: (800)336-6060
Publication E-mail: editors@advisor.com

Trade magazine covering Java and ActiveX software development. **Freq:** Monthly. **Key Personnel:** William T. Ota, Pub./Pres./CEO; David Kodama, Managing Editor, david_ kodama@advisor.com; Chris Maroney, Technical Editor, chris_ maroney@advisor.com. **Subscription Rates:** $49 individuals. **URL:** http://www.advisor.com.

110 Lotus Notes & Domino Advisor
Advisor Publications, Inc.
5675 Ruffin Rd.
San Diego, CA 92123
Phone: (619)278-5600
Fax: (619)278-0300
Free: (800)336-6060
Publication E-mail: editors@advisor.com

Trade magazine for Lotus Notes users. **Freq:** Bimonthly. **Key Personnel:** William T. Ota, Publisher, 71154.3123@compuserve.com; Steve Cardill, Editor. **Subscription Rates:** $39 individuals. **URL:** http://www.advisor.com.
Circ: Combined 25,000

111 On the Avenue
3305 Adams Ave.
Box 86
San Diego, CA 92116
Publisher E-mail: ota@tlcnet.com
Phone: (619)640-4420
Fax: (619)280-1835

Community newspaper. **Freq:** Monthly. **Key Personnel:** S. J. Lynnes, Publisher/Business Mgr.; Brian Rangeley, Editor and Publisher. **Subscription Rates:** $22 individuals. **Remarks:** Accepts advertising. **URL:** http://www.gothere.com/onthe avenue.
Ad Rates: BW: $360 **Circ:** (Not Reported)

112 Security Advisor
Advisor Publications, Inc.
5675 Ruffin Rd.
San Diego, CA 92123
Phone: (619)278-5600
Fax: (619)278-0300
Free: (800)336-6060
Publication E-mail: editors@advisor.com

Trade magazine covering Internet and computer security information. **Freq:** Monthly. **URL:** http://www.advisor.com.

SAN FRANCISCO

113 Bay Area Reporter
Benro Enterprises, Inc.
395 Ninth St.
San Francisco, CA 94103-3831
Phone: (415)861-5019

Community newspaper. **Freq:** Weekly (Thurs.). **Subscription Rates:** Free.
Circ: Non-paid **34,735**

114 ChinMusic Magazine
Kevin Chanel
PO Box 225029
San Francisco, CA 94122
Publication E-mail: girlchin@sirius.com

Consumer magazine covering baseball and punk rock music. **Freq:** Triennial. **Trim Size:** 8 1/2 x 11. **Key Personnel:** Kevin Chanel, Editor and Publisher. **Subscription Rates:** $15 individuals; $20 Canada and Mexico; $25 elsewhere; $3 single issue. **URL:** http://www.girlyhead.com/chinmusic.html.

115 NeTProfessional
612 Howard St., 6th Fl.
San Francisco, CA 94105
Phone: (415)957-1911

Trade magazine covering Macintosh solutions for the Internet. **Freq:** Bimonthly. **Key Personnel:** James Capparell, Publisher, publisher@netprolive.com; Raines Cohen, Editor, editor@netprolive.com; Susan Ford, Assoc. Pub., susan@netprolive.com. **Subscription Rates:** $20 individuals. **URL:** http://www.netprolive.com.
Circ: Combined 60,000

116 Nichi Bei Times
2211 Bush St.
San Francisco, CA 94115
Phone: (415)921-6820
Fax: (415)921-0770

General newspaper in Japanese and English. **Freq:** Daily (Tues.-Sun.). **Key Personnel:** Keiko Asano, Contact. **Subscription Rates:** $130 individuals. **Remarks:** Accepts advertising.
Ad Rates: BW: $2,000 **Circ:** Combined 8,000

117 oboe
Night Horn Books
PO Box 424906
San Francisco, CA 94142-4906
Publisher E-mail: nighthornb@aol.com
Phone: (415)440-2442
Fax: (415)440-2442

Literary and fine arts journal. **Key Personnel:** Robert Anbian, Editor and Publisher.

118 Peep
Peep Magazine
3666-F 20th St.
San Francisco, CA 94110
Publication E-mail: mikeque@aol.com

Consumer magazine covering alternative art and literature. **Founded:** Apr. 1994. **Freq:** Semiannual. **Print Method:** Sheetfed offset. **Trim Size:** 8 1/2 x 11. **Key Personnel:** Michael Kay, Editor and Publisher. **Remarks:** Accepts advertising. **URL:** http://www.peep.org.
Ad Rates: BW: $200 **Circ:** Paid 4000

119 The Red Herring
Herring Communications Inc.
1550 Bryant St., No. 450
San Francisco, CA 94103
Publisher E-mail: info@herring.com
Phone: (415)865-2277
Fax: (415)865-2280

Trade magazine covering financial and investment news for high-tech companies. **Freq:** Monthly. **Key Personnel:** Christopher J. Alden, Editorial Dir., chris@herring.com; Anthony B. Perkins, Editor-in-Chief/Publisher, tony@herring.com; Jason Pontin, Editor. **Subscription Rates:** $69 individuals. **URL:** http://www.redherring.com.

120 KDNZ-FM - 88.7
2130 Fulton St., UC 402
San Francisco, CA 94117
E-mail: kdnz@usfca.edu
Phone: (415)422-6880
Fax: (415)422-2898

Format: Educational. **Owner:** University of San Francisco, at above address. **Operating Hours:** 8 a.m.-12 a.m. **Key Personnel:** Patrick Lagreid, GM/Urban Music Dir. **Ad Rates:** Noncommercial. **URL:** http://dons.usfca.edu/~lagrpa00/kdnz/.

121 KNBR-AM - 680
55 Hawthorne St.
San Francisco, CA 94105
Phone: (415)995-6868
Fax: (415)995-6867

Format: Sports.

122 KVTO-AM - 1400
728 Pacific Ave., No. 302
San Francisco, CA 94133
Phone: (415)986-8878
Fax: (415)288-8655

Format: Ethnic. **Founded:** 1994. **Operating Hours:** Continuous. **Wattage:** 1000. **Ad Rates:** $15-40 for 30 seconds; $18-50 for 45 seconds; $20-60 for 60 seconds.

SAN JOSE

123 Thi Truong Tu Do
255 N. Market St., Ste. 124
San Jose, CA 95110
Phone: (408)977-0586
Fax: (408)977-0588

Vietnamese language consumer magazine covering news and entertainment. **Freq:** Biweekly. **Key Personnel:** Nam Pham, Contact. **Subscription Rates:** Free. **Remarks:** Accepts advertising.
Ad Rates: BW: $450 **Circ:** Combined 10,000

124 Thoi Bao
447 E. Santa Clara St.
San Jose, CA 95113
Phone: (408)292-2276
Fax: (408)292-0346

Vietnamese language community newspaper. **Founded:** 1989. **Freq:** Daily (Tues.-Sat.). **Key Personnel:** Ly Vu, Contact. **Remarks:** Accepts advertising.
Ad Rates: BW: $380 **Circ:** Combined 12,000

125 Viet Magazine
255 N. Market St., Ste. 124
San Jose, CA 95110
Phone: (408)977-0586
Fax: (408)977-0588

Vietnamese language consumer magazine for Vietnamese-Americans. **Found-**

Ad Rates: GLR = general line rate; BW = one-time black & white page rate; 4C = one-time four color page rate; SAU = standard advertising unit rate; CNU = Canadian newspaper advertising unit rate; PCI = per column inch rate.
Circulation: ★ = ABC; △ = BPA; ♦ = CAC; ● = CCAB; ▢ = VAC; ⊕ = PO Statement; ‡ = Publisher's Report; Boldface figures = sworn; Light figures = estimated.
Entry type: ▢ = Print; ♠ = Broadcast.

ed: Apr. 1995. **Freq:** Biweekly. **Key Personnel:** Nam Pham, Contact. **Subscription Rates:** $36 individuals. **Remarks:** Accepts advertising.
Ad Rates: BW: $850   **Circ:** Combined 12,000
             4C: $1,200

SAN MARTIN

126 The Filipino Monitor
Pibul Baquirin
PO Box 387   Phone: (408)686-1911
San Martin, CA 95046   Fax: (408)686-1912

Community newspaper for Filipino-Americans. **Freq:** Biweekly. **Key Personnel:** Pibul Baquirin, Editor-in-Chief. **Subscription Rates:** Free; $24 by mail. **Remarks:** Accepts advertising.
Ad Rates: BW: $800   **Circ:** Combined 10,000

SAN MATEO

127 Digital Video
Miller Freeman Inc.
411 Borel Ave., No. 100   Phone: (650)358-9500
San Mateo, CA 94402   Fax: (650)358-8891
                        Free: (888)776-7002

Trade magazine covering digital video, audio, animation, and multimedia. **Freq:** Monthly. **Key Personnel:** Scott Gentry, Publisher, gentry@dv.com; Dominic Milano, Editorial Dir., dmilano@mfi.com; Heidi Carson, Managing Editor, heidi@dv.com. **URL:** http://www.dv.com.

128 NewMedia
HyperMedia Communications Inc.
901 Mariner Island Blvd., No. 365   Phone: (650)573-5170
San Mateo, CA 94404   Fax: (650)573-5131

Trade magazine covering multimedia products and technology. **Freq:** 16/year. **Key Personnel:** Dan Ruby, Editor-in-Chief, druby@newmedia.com; Richard Landry, Pub./CEO, rlandry@newmedia.com; Becy Waring, Exec. Editor, bwaring@newmedia.com. **URL:** http://www.newmedia.com.
                  Circ: Combined 250,000

129 NT Systems
Miller Freeman Inc.
411 Borel Ave., No. 100   Phone: (650)358-9500
San Mateo, CA 94402   Fax: (650)358-8891
                        Free: (888)776-7002
Publication E-mail: ntsys@halldata.com

Trade magazine for Windows NT programmers and users. **Freq:** Monthly. **Key Personnel:** Katie A. Brennan, Publisher, kbrennan@mfi.com; Nicholas Baran, Editor-in-Chief, nbaran@mfi.com. **Subscription Rates:** $39.95 individuals. **URL:** http://www.ntsystems.com.

130 UNIX Review
Miller Freeman Inc.
411 Borel Ave., No. 100   Phone: (650)358-9500
San Mateo, CA 94402   Fax: (650)358-8891
                        Free: (888)776-7002

Technical, trade magazine for software developers. **Freq:** Monthly. **Key Personnel:** John Keough, Publisher, jkeough@mfi.com; Mark Hall, Editor-in-Chief, mhall@mfi.com; Ralph Barker, Sr. Tech. Ed., rbarker@mfi.com. **URL:** http://www.unixreview.com.
                  Circ: Combined 85,000

131 Web Techniques
Miller Freeman Inc.
411 Borel Ave., No. 100   Phone: (650)358-9500
San Mateo, CA 94402   Fax: (650)358-8891
                        Free: (888)776-7002
Publication E-mail: editors@webtechniques.com

Trade magazine for web and Internet developers. **Freq:** Monthly. **Key Personnel:** Manny Sawitt, Publisher; Michael Floyd, Editor-in-Chief; Tami Zemel, Managing Editor. **Subscription Rates:** $35 individuals. **URL:** http://www.webtechniques.com.
                  Circ: Combined 30,000

SANTA BARBARA

132 Nuclear Age Peace Foundation
1187 Coast Village Rd., Ste. 123   Phone: (805)965-3443
Santa Barbara, CA 93108-2794   Fax: (805)568-0466
Publication E-mail: wagingpeace@napf.org

Journal covering peace and nuclear disarmament. **Subtitle:** Journal of the Nuclear Age Foundation. **Founded:** 1985. **Freq:** Triennial. **Print Method:** Offset. **Key Personnel:** David Krieger, President; Laura Lynch, Publications Dir. **ISSN:** 1092-2636. **Subscription Rates:** $12 individuals. **Remarks:** Advertising not accepted. **URL:** http://www.wagingpeace.org. **Former name:** Waging Peace Bulletin; Nuclear Alert.
                  Circ: Combined ‡3000

SANTA CLARA

133 The Filipino-American Headliner
1680 Civic Center Dr., Ste. 101   Phone: (408)272-5862
Santa Clara, CA 95050   Fax: (408)246-1099

Community newspaper for Filipino-Americans. **Freq:** Biweekly. **Key Personnel:** Ben Emata, Editor and Publisher. **Subscription Rates:** Free. **Remarks:** Accepts advertising.
Ad Rates: BW: $800   **Circ:** Combined 7,000

SANTA CRUZ

134 Metro Santa Cruz
Metro Publishing Inc.
111 Union St.
Santa Cruz, CA 95060   Fax: (831)457-5828
Publication E-mail: msc@metcruz.com

Community newspaper. **Freq:** Weekly. **URL:** http://www.metroactive.com/cruz.

135 KZSC-FM - 88.1
KZSC Santa Cruz
UCSC Student Music East   Phone: (831)459-2811
Santa Cruz, CA 95064   Fax: (831)459-4734
E-mail: kzsc@cats.ucsc.edu

Format: Educational. **Operating Hours:** Continuous. **Key Personnel:** Aaron Ikezawa, Station Mgr. **Wattage:** 1250. **Ad Rates:** Noncommercial. **URL:** http://www2.ucsc.edu/~kzsc/.

SANTA MONICA

136 Fax Mainichi U.S.A.
Mainichi Newspapers
2800 28th St., Ste. 103   Phone: (310)664-1666
Santa Monica, CA 90405   Fax: (310)664-1656

Japanese language general newspaper available via fax only. **Founded:** 1994. **Freq:** Daily. **Remarks:** Accepts advertising. **Alt. Formats:** Fax on demand.
Ad Rates: BW: $2,700   **Circ:** Combined 1,500

SONOMA

137 Headliner
The Sonoma Index-Tribune, Inc.
PO Box C   Phone: (707)938-2111
Sonoma, CA 95476   Fax: (707)938-1600

Shopping guide. **Freq:** Weekly (Wed.). **Subscription Rates:** Free.
                 Circ: Non-paid 14,117

138 Rohnert Park Community Voice
The Sonoma Index-Tribune, Inc.
PO Box C   Phone: (707)938-2111
Sonoma, CA 95476   Fax: (707)938-1600

Community newspaper. **Freq:** Semiweekly (Tues. and Fri.). **Subscription Rates:** $18 individuals; $24 by mail.
                  Circ: Paid 14,117

SOUTH SAN FRANCISCO

📖 **139 The Manila Bulletin USA**
362 E. Grand Ave.   Fax: (415)873-4335
South San Francisco, CA 94080   Free: (800)338-5424

Community newspaper for Filipino-Americans. **Founded:** 1993. **Freq:** Weekly. **Key Personnel:** Jenny Montenegro, Advertising Mgr. **Subscription Rates:** Free; $39 by mail. **Remarks:** Accepts advertising.
Ad Rates: BW: $1,300.58   **Circ:** Combined 50,000

THOUSAND OAKS

📖 **140 Public Works Management & Policy**
Sage Publications Inc.
2455 Teller Rd.   Phone: (805)499-0721
Thousand Oaks, CA 91320   Fax: (805)499-0871
Publisher E-mail: info@sagepub.com

Academic journal covering public works and the public infrastructure industry. **Freq:** Quarterly. **Subscription Rates:** $25 members; $48 nonmembers; $135 institutions; $50 members two year; $96 nonmembers two year; $270 institutions two year.

TORRANCE

📖 **141 Bridge U.S.A.**
20300 S. Vermont Ave., No. 200   Phone: (310)532-5921
Torrance, CA 90502   Fax: (310)532-1184

Japanese language consumer magazine. **Founded:** 1989. **Freq:** Biweekly. **Subscription Rates:** Free. **Remarks:** Accepts advertising.
Ad Rates: BW: $1,100   **Circ:** Combined 35,000

📖 **142 Daily Breeze**
5215 Torrance Blvd.
Torrance, CA 90503-4077   Phone: (310)540-5511

General newspaper. **Freq:** Daily. **Key Personnel:** Thomas J. Wafer, Publisher; Jim Box, Editor; Jean Adelsman, Managing Editor. **URL:** http://www.dailybreeze.com.

📖 **143 South Bay Extra**
Copley Los Angeles Newspapers
5215 Torrance Blvd.
Torrance, CA 90509   Phone: (310)540-5511

Community newspaper. **Freq:** Weekly (Sat.). **Subscription Rates:** Free.
                                        Circ: Non-paid **109,515**

VENTURA

📖 **144 PCIM Power Electronic Systems**
Intertec International Inc.
2472 Eastman Ave., No. 33   Phone: (805)650-7070
Ventura, CA 93003-5792   Fax: (805)650-7054
Publication E-mail: sales@powermags.com

Professional magazine for power electronics designers and system integrators. **Freq:** Monthly. **Print Method:** Web offset. **Trim Size:** 8 x 10 3/4. **Remarks:** Accepts advertising. **URL:** http://powermags.com.
Ad Rates: BW: $4,310   **Circ:** (Not Reported)
                 4C: $5,510

📖 **145 Power Quality Assurance**
Intertec International Inc.
2472 Eastman Ave., No. 33   Phone: (805)650-7070
Ventura, CA 93003-5792   Fax: (805)650-7054
Publication E-mail: sales@powerquality.com

Professional magazine covering electrical and electronic power for engineers and managers in the power industry. **Freq:** Bimonthly. **Print Method:** Web offset. **Trim Size:** 8 x 10 3/4. **Key Personnel:** J. Andrew Van Sciver, Publisher; Marsha Lisak, Managing Editor; Fran Dumbach, Production Mgr.;

Theresa Laughlin, Advertising. **ISSN:** 1068-4085. **Subscription Rates:** $44 U.S. and Canada; $88 elsewhere. **Remarks:** Accepts advertising. **URL:** http://www.powerquality.com.
Ad Rates: BW: $4285   **Circ:** (Not Reported)
                 4C: $5485

📖 **146 PowerValue**
Intertec International Inc.
2472 Eastman Ave., No. 33   Phone: (805)650-7070
Ventura, CA 93003-5792   Fax: (805)650-7054
Publication E-mail: sales@powervalue.com

Professional magazine for the electric utilities management industry. **Freq:** Bimonthly. **Trim Size:** 8 1/8 x 10 7/8. **Remarks:** Accepts advertising. **URL:** http://www.powervalue.com.
Ad Rates: BW: $4,285   **Circ:** (Not Reported)
                 4C: $5,485

VICTORVILLE

📖 **147 The Daily Press**
PO Box 1389   Phone: (760)241-7744
Victorville, CA 92393-1389   Fax: (760)241-7145
                                        Free: (800)553-2006

General newspaper. **Freq:** Daily. **Key Personnel:** Ray Marien, Retail Adv. Dir., rmm@vvdailypress.com; Linda Bennett, National Adv. Mgr., ldb@vvdailypress.com; Mike Belles, Circ. Dir., meb@vvdailypress.com. **Remarks:** Advertising accepted; rates available upon request. **URL:** http://www.vvdailypress.com.
                                        Circ: (Not Reported)

WALNUT CREEK

📖 **148 Diablo Arts**
Diablo Publications
2520 Camino Diablo, Ste. 200   Phone: (510)943-1111
Walnut Creek, CA 94596-3944   Fax: (510)943-1045
Publisher E-mail: diablospubs@aol.com

Consumer magazine covering music and the arts. **Freq:** Quarterly. **Key Personnel:** Steven J. Rivera, President. **Subscription Rates:** $2.25 single issue (includes shipping). **URL:** http://www.diablopubs.com.

WESTMINSTER

📖 **149 Viet Bao Kinh Te**
14922 Moran St., No. B   Phone: (714)894-2500
Westminster, CA 92683   Fax: (714)894-7333

Vietnamese language newspaper for Vietnamese-Americans. **Freq:** Daily (Tues.-Sat.). **Key Personnel:** Ann Vu, Mktg. Rep. **Remarks:** Accepts advertising.
Ad Rates: BW: $550   **Circ:** (Not Reported)

Ad Rates: GLR = general line rate; BW = one-time black & white page rate; 4C = one-time four color page rate; SAU = standard advertising unit rate; CNU = Canadian newspaper advertising unit rate; PCI = per column inch rate.
Circulation: ★ = ABC; △ = BPA; ♦ = CAC; ● = CCAB; ❑ = VAC; ⊕ = PO Statement; ‡ = Publisher's Report; Boldface figures = sworn; Light figures = estimated.
Entry type: 📖 = Print; 🎙 = Broadcast.

17

COLORADO

BOULDER

150 Boulder Weekly
Boulder Weekly, Inc.
690 S. Lashley Ln.
Boulder, CO 80303
Publication E-mail: bweditor@tesser.com

Phone: (303)494-5511
Fax: (303)494-2585

Alternative newspaper. **Founded:** Aug. 19, 1994. **Freq:** Weekly. **Print Method:** Web offset. **Trim Size:** 11 3/8. **Key Personnel:** Stewart Sallo, Publisher; Annette Gorence, Assoc. Publisher; Jeff Skoke, Advertising Dir. **Subscription Rates:** Free. **Remarks:** Accepts advertising.
Ad Rates: BW: $825
4C: $1,110

Circ: Non-paid **25,000**

FORT COLLINS

151 The Northern Colorado Business Report
201 S. College Ave., Ste. 300
Fort Collins, CO 80524-2810
Publication E-mail: ncbr@aol.com

Business newspaper. **Key Personnel:** Jeff Nuttall, Publisher, jnuttall@ncbr.com; Christopher Wood, Editor and Publisher, cwood@ncbr.com; Helen Taylor, Managing Editor, htaylor@ncbr.com; Jim Rath, Advertising Mgr., jrath@ncbr.com; Lori Buderus, Circulation Mgr., lbuderus@ncbr.com. **Subscription Rates:** $29.97 individuals; $39.97 out of state; $50 out of country. **Remarks:** Advertising accepted; rates available upon request. **URL:** http://www.ncbr.com.

Circ: Combined **12,000**

152 The Rural Educator Journal
National Rural Education Association
230 Education Bldg.
Fort Collins, CO 80523-1588

Phone: (970)491-7022
Fax: (970)491-1317

Professional journal for rural educators. **Subtitle:** Journal for Rural and Small Schools. **Founded:** 1981. **Freq:** Quarterly. **Key Personnel:** Joseph Newlin, Editor. **Subscription Rates:** $50 individuals. **Remarks:** Accepts advertising.
Circ: Paid **1050**

GOLDEN

153 International Journal of Offshore and Polar Engineering
International Society of Offshore & Polar Engineers (ISOPE)
PO Box 1107
Golden, CO 80402-1107
Publication E-mail: isope@worldnet.att.net

Phone: (303)420-8114
Fax: (303)420-3760

Scholarly journal covering mechanics, materials, energy/resources, engineering, ocean/offshore, marine, polar, and environmental issues. **Founded:** Mar. 1991. **Freq:** Quarterly. **Trim Size:** 8 3/8 x 10 7/8. **Cols./Page:** 2. **Key Personnel:** Prof. Jin S. Chung, Technical Editor. **Subscription Rates:** $130 individuals; $60 single issue.
Circ: Combined **1400**

LOVELAND

154 Windows NT Magazine
Duke Communications International
221 E. 29th St.
Loveland, CO 80538

Phone: (970)663-4700
Fax: (970)667-2321
Free: (800)621-1544

Publication E-mail: winntmag@duke.com

Consumer magazine for Windows NT users. **Freq:** Monthly. **Key Personnel:** Mark Smith, Publisher, mark@winntmag.com; John Enck, Managing Tech. Editor, john@winntmag.com; Karen Forster, Managing Editor, karen@winntmag.com. **Subscription Rates:** $40 individuals. **URL:** http://www.winntmag.com.

Circ: Combined **50,000**

SALIDA

155 The Herald Democrat
Arkansas Valley Publishing Co.
125 E. 2nd St.
PO Box 189
Salida, CO 81201-0189

Phone: (719)539-6691
Fax: (719)539-6630

Community newspaper. **Freq:** Weekly (Wed.). **Key Personnel:** Jeff Dick, Editor; Amy Murphy, Advertising Mgr.; Sandy Griffith, Office Mgr. **Subscription Rates:** $19 individuals; $27 out of area. **URL:** http://www.leadvilleherald.com.

TELLURIDE

156 Mountainfreak
Lungta, LLC
PO Box 4149
Telluride, CO 81435

Phone: (970)728-9731
Fax: (970)728-9821

Publication E-mail: freaks@mountainfreak.com

Consumer magazine covering sports, outdoor activities and lifestyle. **Founded:** Oct. 1995. **Freq:** Quarterly. **Key Personnel:** Hilary White, Publisher, hilary@mountainfreak.com; Suzanne Cheavens, Sr. Editor, freaks@mountainfreak.com. **ISSN:** 1524-2579. **Subscription Rates:** $4.20 individuals. **Remarks:** Accepts advertising. **URL:** http://www.mountainfreak.com.

Circ: Combined **25,000**

Ad Rates: GLR = general line rate; BW = one-time black & white page rate; 4C = one-time four color page rate; SAU = standard advertising unit rate; CNU = Canadian newspaper advertising unit rate; PCI = per column inch rate.
Circulation: ★ = ABC; △ = BPA; ♦ = CAC; ● = CCAB; ❏ = VAC; ⊕ = PO Statement; ‡ = Publisher's Report; Boldface figures = sworn; Light figures = estimated.
Entry type: ▢ = Print; ● = Broadcast.

19

CONNECTICUT

HARTFORD

📖 **157 Connecticut Housing Production and Permit Authorized Construction**
Connecticut Department of Economic and Community Development
505 Hudson St.   Phone: (860)270-8000
Hartford, CT 06106   Fax: (860)270-8100
                                    Free: (888)860-GOCT

Publisher E-mail: decd@po.state.ct.us

Report on Connecticut housing permits authorized. **Freq:** Annual. **Key Personnel:** Kolie S. Chang, Project Mgr., kolie.chang@po.state.ct.us. **Subscription Rates:** Free.

NEW HAVEN

📖 **158 CT LIFE**
Millbrook Publishing Company
5 Edward St.
New Haven, CT 06511   Phone: (203)498-5120

Community newspaper. **Freq:** Monthly. **Subscription Rates:** Free.
Circ: Combined **74,363**

NEW MILFORD

📖 **159 Bethel Beacon**
Housatonic Publications
65 Bank St.   Phone: (860)354-2261
New Milford, CT 06776   Fax: (860)354-2645
Publisher E-mail: housvalpub@aol.com

Community newspaper. **Founded:** 1995. **Freq:** Weekly (Fri.). **Key Personnel:** Fred Hartwell, Circulation Mgr.
Circ: Combined ♦**1,829**

📖 **160 Business Digest**
Housatonic Publications
65 Bank St.   Phone: (860)354-2261
New Milford, CT 06776   Fax: (860)354-2645
Publisher E-mail: housvalpub@aol.com

Community newspaper. **Founded:** 1985. **Freq:** Monthly. **Key Personnel:** Fred Hartwell, Circulation Mgr. **Subscription Rates:** Free.
Circ: Combined ♦**5,235**

📖 **161 Fairfield Minuteman**
Housatonic Publications
65 Bank St.   Phone: (860)354-2261
New Milford, CT 06776   Fax: (860)354-2645
Publisher E-mail: housvalpub@aol.com

Community newspaper. **Founded:** 1995. **Freq:** Weekly (Thurs.). **Key Personnel:** Fred Hartwell, Circulation Mgr. **Subscription Rates:** Free.
Circ: Combined ♦**24,916**

📖 **162 Housatonic Weekend**
Housatonic Publications
65 Bank St.   Phone: (860)354-2261
New Milford, CT 06776   Fax: (860)354-2645
Publisher E-mail: housvalpub@aol.com

Community newspaper. **Founded:** 1993. **Freq:** Weekly (Fri.). **Key Personnel:** Fred Hartwell, Circulation Mgr.
Circ: Combined ♦**17,427**

📖 **163 Litchfield Weekend**
Housatonic Publications
65 Bank St.   Phone: (860)354-2261
New Milford, CT 06776   Fax: (860)354-2645
Publisher E-mail: housvalpub@aol.com

Community newspaper. **Founded:** 1995. **Freq:** Weekly (Fri.). **Key Personnel:** Fred Hartwell, Publisher. **Subscription Rates:** Free.
Circ: Non-paid ♦**5,537**

📖 **164 Westport Minuteman**
Housatonic Publications
65 Bank St.   Phone: (860)354-2261
New Milford, CT 06776   Fax: (860)354-2645
Publisher E-mail: housvalpub@aol.com

Community newspaper. **Founded:** 1993. **Freq:** Weekly (Thurs.). **Key Personnel:** Fred Hartwell, Circulation Mgr. **Subscription Rates:** Free.
Circ: Combined ♦**16,312**

NORWALK

📖 **165 CTI**
Technology Marketing Corp.
1 Technology Plaza   Phone: (203)852-6800
Norwalk, CT 06854   Fax: (203)853-2845
                                   Free: (800)243-6002

Publisher E-mail: tmc@tmcnet.com

Trade magazine covering computer, network, and Internet telephony. **Freq:** 9/year. **Key Personnel:** Richard Tehrani, Publisher, rtehrani@tmcnet.com; Kevin M. Mayer, Editor, kmayer@tmcnet.com; Tom Keating, Technical Editor, tkeating@tmcnet.com. **URL:** http://www.tmcnet.com.

RIDGEFIELD

📖 **166 Acorn Press**
Acorn Press, Inc.
16 Bailey Ave.   Phone: (203)438-6544
Ridgefield, CT 06877   Fax: (203)438-3395

Community newspaper. **Founded:** 1875. **Freq:** Weekly (Wed.). **Key Personnel:** Thomas B. Nash, Publisher. **Subscription Rates:** $30 individuals; $38 out of area.
Circ: Combined ♦**21,708**

SHELTON

📖 **167 The Amity Observer**
Hometown Publications, Inc.
1000 Bridgeport Ave.   Phone: (203)926-2080
Shelton, CT 06484   Fax: (203)926-2092
Publisher E-mail: homepubl@aol.com

Community newspaper. **Founded:** 1995. **Freq:** Weekly (Wed.). **Key Personnel:** Alfred Pullo, Jr., Business Mgr. **Subscription Rates:** Free. **Remarks:** Accepts advertising.
    Circ: Non-paid ♦9,678

📖 **168 The Hamden Journal**
Hometown Publications, Inc.
1000 Bridgeport Ave.   Phone: (203)926-2080
Shelton, CT 06484   Fax: (203)926-2092
Publisher E-mail: homepubl@aol.com

Community newspaper. **Founded:** 1998. **Freq:** Weekly (Wed.). **Key Personnel:** Alfred Pullo, Jr., Business Mgr. **Subscription Rates:** Free. **Remarks:** Accepts advertising.
    Circ: Non-paid ♦17,170

📖 **169 The Milford Mirror**
Hometown Publications, Inc.
1000 Bridgeport Ave.   Phone: (203)926-2080
Shelton, CT 06484   Fax: (203)926-2092
Publisher E-mail: homepubl@aol.com

Community newspaper. **Founded:** 1986. **Freq:** Weekly (Wed.). **Key Personnel:** Alfred Pullo, Jr., Business Mgr. **Subscription Rates:** Free. **Remarks:** Accepts advertising.
    Circ: Non-paid ♦17,867

📖 **170 The Valley Gazette**
Hometown Publications, Inc.
1000 Bridgeport Ave.   Phone: (203)926-2080
Shelton, CT 06484   Fax: (203)926-2092
Publisher E-mail: homepubl@aol.com

Community newspaper. **Founded:** 1992. **Freq:** Weekly (Wed.). **Key Personnel:** Alfred Pullo, Jr., Business Mgr. **Subscription Rates:** Free. **Remarks:** Accepts advertising.
    Circ: Non-paid ♦17,791

STAMFORD

📖 **171 Connecticut Ancestry**
Connecticut Ancestry Society, Inc.
Box 249
Stamford, CT 06904

Professional journal covering local genealogy. **Founded:** 1954. **Freq:** Quarterly. **Trim Size:** 8 1/2 x 11. **Cols./Page:** 1. **Col. Width:** 6 1/2 inches. **Col. Depth:** 9 inches. **Key Personnel:** Robert A. Ferry, Editor; Robert W. Spiers, Subscription Mgr. **ISSN:** 0197-2103. **Subscription Rates:** $25 individuals; $8 single issue. **Remarks:** Advertising not accepted.
    Circ: Combined 310

STONINGTON

📖 **172 Historical Footnotes**
Stonington Historical Society
c/o James Boylan
PO Box 288   Phone: (860)535-4059
Stonington, CT 06378   Fax: (860)535-8322

Scholarly journal covering local history. **Founded:** 1962. **Freq:** Quarterly. **Print Method:** Offset. **Cols./Page:** 3. **Col. Width:** 2 1/8 inches. **Col. Depth:** 10 inches. **Key Personnel:** James Boylan, Editor, james.r.boylan@snct.net. **ISSN:** 0886-5272. **Subscription Rates:** $15 members; $2.25 single issue. **Remarks:** Accepts advertising.
Ad Rates: PCI: $25
    Circ: Paid 900

STRATFORD

📖 **173 Golf Resort News**
The Publishing Group
PO Box 1219
Stratford, CT 06615   Phone: (203)279-0149

Consumer magazine covering golf products and resorts worldwide. **Founded:** May 1992. **Freq:** Monthly. **Print Method:** Sheetfed offset. **Trim Size:** 8 1/2 x 11. **Cols./Page:** 3. **Key Personnel:** John Mortimer, Editor; Robert Foley, Editor; John Chrostowsky, Travel Ed.; Sean McDonogh, Advertising Mgr. **Subscription Rates:** $36 individuals; $5 single issue. **Remarks:** Accepts advertising.
Ad Rates: BW: $4,975   **Circ:** Combined 36,680
            4C: $6,650

WESTPORT

📖 **174 Internet Shopper**
Mecklermedia
20 Ketchum St.   Phone: (203)226-6967
Westport, CT 06880   Fax: (203)454-5840
Publication E-mail: editor@internetshopper.com

Consumer magazine covering Internet shopping. **Freq:** Quarterly. **Key Personnel:** Dan Rosenbaum, Editor-in-Chief; Tricia Curry, Senior Editor, tcurry@internetshopper.com; Paul L. Bonington, Publisher, bonington@iw.com. **Subscription Rates:** $16 individuals. **URL:** http://www.internetshopper.com.
    Circ: Combined 160,000

📖 **175 Internet World**
Mecklermedia
20 Ketchum St.   Phone: (203)226-6967
Westport, CT 06880   Fax: (203)454-5840
Publication E-mail: iwedit@iw.com

Trade magazine covering the Internet industry. **Freq:** 41/year. **Key Personnel:** Bill Besch, Publisher, bbesch@mecklermedia.com; Robert Hertzberg, Editor-in-Chief, rob@iw.com; Tony Silber, Exec. Editor. **URL:** http://www.iw.com.
    Circ: Combined 100,000

DELAWARE

DOVER

🎙 **176 WQVL-AM - 1600**
400 Walker Rd.
PO Box 553
Dover, DE 19901
E-mail: heaven1600@juno.com

Phone: (302)730-1600
Fax: (302)730-9398

Format: Gospel; Religious; News. **Networks:** Sun Radio. **Owner:** Vin-Lor Broadcasting, Inc., at above address. **Formerly:** WKEN-AM (1997). **Operating Hours:** Continuous. **Key Personnel:** Pastor Latt, General Mgr.; Harvey Bullock, Program Dir.

WILMINGTON

📖 **177 Yakuza**
Dave McGurgan
PO Box 26039
Wilmington, DE 19899-6039
Publication E-mail: yakuza@voicenet.com

Phone: (302)651-0203
Fax: (302)651-0206

Consumer magazine covering alternative music, entertainment, and travel. **Key Personnel:** Dave McGurgan, Editor and Publisher. **ISSN:** 1083-8538. **Subscription Rates:** $4.50 single issue. **Remarks:** Advertising accepted; rates available upon request.

Circ: (Not Reported)

Ad Rates: GLR = general line rate; BW = one-time black & white page rate; 4C = one-time four color page rate; SAU = standard advertising unit rate; CNU = Canadian newspaper advertising unit rate; PCI = per column inch rate.
Circulation: ★ = ABC; △ = BPA; ♦ = CAC; • = CCAB; ❑ = VAC; ⊕ = PO Statement; ‡ = Publisher's Report; Boldface figures = sworn; Light figures = estimated.
Entry type: 📖 = Print; 🎙 = Broadcast.

23

DISTRICT OF COLUMBIA

WASHINGTON

📖 **178 Afro-American Historical and Genealogical Society Journal**
Afro-American Historical and Genealogical Society
Box 73086
Washington, DC 20056-3086   Phone: (202)234-5350

Scholarly journal covering Afro-American history and genealogy. **Founded:** 1980. **Key Personnel:** Margo Williams, Editor.

📖 **179 Budget Watch**
National Center for Public Policy Research
777 N. Capitol St. NE, Ste. 803   Phone: (202)371-1400
Washington, DC 20002   Fax: (202)408-7773
Publisher E-mail: info@nationalcenter.org

Periodical covering budget policy in Washington, D.C. **Key Personnel:** David Ridenour, Editor, dridenour@nationalcenter.org. **Remarks:** Advertising not accepted. **URL:** http://www.nationalcenter.org.
Circ: (Not Reported)

📖 **180 The Chemical Bond**
Synthetic Organic Chemical Manufacturers Association (SOCMA)
1850 M St. NW, Ste. 700   Phone: (202)721-4100
Washington, DC 20036   Fax: (202)296-8548

Trade magazine for chemical manufacturers. **Founded:** 1964. **Freq:** 10/year. **Trim Size:** 8 1/2 x 11. **Key Personnel:** Dawn M. Shiley, Editor, phone (202)721-4137, shiley@socma.com. **Subscription Rates:** Free to qualified subscribers; $50 nonmembers. **Remarks:** Accepts advertising. **Available Online. URL:** http://www.socma.com. **Formerly:** SOCMA Newsletter.
Circ: Combined 3000

📖 **181 Cotton**
International Cotton Advisory Committee
1629 K St. NW, Ste. 702   Phone: (202)463-6660
Washington, DC 20006   Fax: (202)463-6950
Publisher E-mail: publications@icac.org

Trade journal covering cotton worldwide. Available in English, French, or Spanish. **Subtitle:** Review of the World Situation. **Freq:** Bimonthly. **Subscription Rates:** $135 individuals. **URL:** http://www.icac.org.

📖 **182 Executive Intelligence Review**
EIR News Service
Box 17390   Phone: (703)777-9451
Washington, DC 20041   Fax: (703)777-9492

Professional magazine covering economics. **Founded:** 1974. **Freq:** Weekly. **Key Personnel:** Susan Welsh, Assoc. Editor; Marsha Freeman, Advertising Dir. **ISSN:** 0273-6314. **Subscription Rates:** $396 individuals; $10 single issue. **Remarks:** Accepts advertising.
Circ: Combined ⊕15,000

📖 **183 Legal Briefs**
National Center for Public Policy Research
777 N. Capitol St. NE, Ste. 803   Phone: (202)371-1400
Washington, DC 20002   Fax: (202)408-7773
Publisher E-mail: info@nationalcenter.org

Periodical covering lawsuit activity. **Key Personnel:** Amy Ridenour, Editor, aridenour@nationalcenter.org. **Remarks:** Advertising not accepted. **URL:** http://www.nationalcenter.org.
Circ: (Not Reported)

📖 **184 Mediterranean Quarterly**
Duke University Press
National Press Bldg., Ste. 984
14th & F St. N.W.
Washington, DC 20045
Publisher E-mail: dukepress@duke.edu

Scholarly journal covering the Mediterranean region. **Freq:** Quarterly. **Key Personnel:** Nikolaos A. Stavrou, Editor; Amy Hartzler, Advertising, phone (919)687-3636. **Subscription Rates:** $24 individuals; $44 institutions; $12 students. **Remarks:** Accepts advertising.
Ad Rates: BW: $500   **Circ:** Paid 800

📖 **185 Political Money Monitor**
National Center for Public Policy Research
777 N. Capitol St. NE, Ste. 803   Phone: (202)371-1400
Washington, DC 20002   Fax: (202)408-7773
Publisher E-mail: info@nationalcenter.org

Magazine covering politics. **Founded:** Oct. 24, 1997. **Key Personnel:** David W. Almasi, Editor, dalmasi@nationalcenter.org. **Remarks:** Advertising not accepted. **URL:** http://www.nationalcenter.org.
Circ: (Not Reported)

📖 **186 Relief Report**
National Center for Public Policy Research
777 N. Capitol St. NE, Ste. 803   Phone: (202)371-1400
Washington, DC 20002   Fax: (202)408-7773
Publisher E-mail: info@nationalcenter.org

Periodical covering government regulation. **Key Personnel:** David Ridenour, Editor, dridenour@nationalcenter.org. **Remarks:** Advertising not accepted. **URL:** http://www.nationalcenter.org.
Circ: (Not Reported)

📖 **187 Scoop**
National Center for Public Policy Research
777 N. Capitol St. NE, Ste. 803   Phone: (202)371-1400
Washington, DC 20002   Fax: (202)408-7773
Publisher E-mail: info@nationalcenter.org

Periodical covering political activity in Washington, D.C. **Founded:** July 19, 1993. **Key Personnel:** Amy Ridenour, Editor, aridenour@nationalcenter.org. **Remarks:** Advertising not accepted. **URL:** http://www.nationalcenter.org.
Circ: (Not Reported)

📖 **188 SpeciaList**
Special Libraries Association
1700 18th St. NW   Phone: (202)234-4700
Washington, DC 20009-2514   Fax: (202)234-2442
Publisher E-mail: sla@sla.org

Professional magazine for members of the Special Libraries Association. **Founded:** July 1, 1980. **Freq:** Monthly. **Trim Size:** 8 1/2 x 11. **Key Personnel:** Shaise Esh, Editor. **ISSN:** 0273-9399. **Subscription Rates:** Free to qualified subscribers; $65 nonmembers U.S. and Canada; $75 nonmembers elsewhere. **Remarks:** Accepts advertising.

Circ: Combined 15,000

📖 **189 Troubling Company Reporter**
Beard Group, Inc.
PO Box 9867   Phone: (301)951-6400
Washington, DC 20016   Fax: (301)951-3621

Magazine covering businesses showing financial strain. **Founded:** 1996. **Freq:** Daily. **Key Personnel:** Christopher Beard, Publisher, chris@beard.com. **ISSN:** 1520-9474. **Subscription Rates:** $1150 individuals. **Remarks:** Advertising not accepted.

Circ: (Not Reported)

📖 **190 Women in the Arts**
The National Museum of Women in the Arts
1250 New York Ave. NW   Phone: (202)783-5000
Washington, DC 20005   Fax: (202)393-3235
                                     Free: (800)222-7270

Art magazine covering women artists in all areas. **Freq:** Quarterly.

FLORIDA

CANTONMENT

☙ 191   WRFP-AM - 1610
450 S. Highway 29
Cantonment, FL 32533

Phone: (850)432-9298
Fax: (850)937-1077

Format: Contemporary Christian; News; Talk. **Simulcasts:** WRFP-FM. **Owner:** X-Static Enterprises, at above address. **Operating Hours:** Continuous. **Key Personnel:** Jon Arthur, General/Traffic Mgr.; Carlyse Cosmas, Program Dir.

☙ 192   WRFP-FM - 107.7
450 S. Hwy. 29
Cantonment, FL 32533

Phone: (850)432-9298
Fax: (850)937-1077

Format: Contemporary Christian; News; Talk. **Simulcasts:** WRFP-AM. **Owner:** X-Static Enterprises, at above address. **Operating Hours:** Continuous. **Key Personnel:** Jon Arthur, General/Traffic Mgr.; Carlyse Cosmas, Program Dir.

CRESTVIEW

☐ 193   Crestview News Leader
Okaloosa Publishing Co.
301 N. Main St.
PO Box 447
Crestview, FL 32536

Phone: (850)682-6524
Fax: (850)682-2246

Community newspaper. **Founded:** 1992. **Freq:** Weekly (Wed.). **Key Personnel:** Jim Knudsen, Publisher. **Subscription Rates:** $18.50 individuals; $28.50 out of area.

Circ: Combined ♦**3,014**

DEERFIELD BEACH

☐ 194   Pompano Times
SFNN, Inc.
601 Fairway Dr.
Deerfield Beach, FL 33441

Phone: (954)574-5300
Fax: (954)429-1207
Free: (800)275-8820

Publisher E-mail: bukley@gate.net

Shopping guide. **Freq:** Weekly (Wed.). **Key Personnel:** Scott Patterson, Publisher.

Circ: Combined 21,000

FORT LAUDERDALE

☐ 195   New Times Broward-Palm Beach
PO Box 14128
Fort Lauderdale, FL 33302-4128

Phone: (954)233-1600

Community newspaper. **Remarks:** Advertising accepted; rates available upon request. **URL:** http://www.newtimespb.com.

Circ: (Not Reported)

GAINESVILLE

☙ 196   WKTK-FM - 98.5
1440 NE Waldo Rd.
Gainesville, FL 32641

Phone: (352)377-0985
Fax: (352)377-1884

Format: Adult Contemporary. **Owner:** Entercom, 401 City Ave., Ste. 409, Bala Cynwyd, PA 19004, (610)660-5610. **Founded:** Apr. 1, 1986. **Former name:** WRYO-FM (1985). **Operating Hours:** Continuous. **ADI:** Gainesville (Ocala), FL. **Key Personnel:** Gary Granger, VP/GM; Briton Jon, Program Dir.; Paula Elf, Office Mgr. **Wattage:** 100,000. **Ad Rates:** Advertising accepted; rates available upon request.

MIAMI

☐ 197   The Bulletin of Marine Science
Rosenstiel School of Marine and Atmospheric Science
4600 Rickenbacker Causeway
Miami, FL 33149-1098

Phone: (305)361-4624
Fax: (305)361-4600

Publisher E-mail: bms@rsmas.miami.edu

Professional journal covering marine science. **Freq:** Bimonthly. **Key Personnel:** Prof. Samuel C. Snedaker, Editor. **Subscription Rates:** $225 institutions; $235 Canada and Mexico; $245 elsewhere; $85 individuals; $45 students. **URL:** http://www.rsmas.miami.edu/bms.

☐ 198   The Florida News
Japan Society of South Florida
80 S.W. 8th St., Ste. 2809
Miami, FL 33130

Phone: (305)358-6006
Fax: (305)374-1030

Japanese language newspaper covering Florida travel, industry and tourism for Japanese residents, visitors and tourists. **Founded:** 1989. **Freq:** Monthly. **Key Personnel:** Akiko Endo, Contact, endo@fl-news.com. **Subscription Rates:** Free. **Remarks:** Accepts advertising. **URL:** http://www.fl-news.com. **Ad Rates:** BW: $600

Circ: Combined 10,000

☐ 199   Herald Values
The Miami Herald Publishing Co.
One Herald Plaza
Miami, FL 33132

Phone: (305)376-3271
Fax: (305)376-3201
Free: (800)376-3324

Shopping guide.

Circ: Combined **735,286**

☐ 200   Vida Social
The Miami Herald Publishing Co.
One Herald Plaza
Miami, FL 33132

Phone: (305)376-3271
Fax: (305)376-3201
Free: (800)376-3324

Spanish language community newspaper.

Circ: Combined **277,385**

OAKLAND PARK

📖 **201 Swap Shop News**
Scott Patterson
3115 N.W. 10th Terrace, Ste. 105
Oakland Park, FL 33309

Newspaper covering shopping news. **Freq:** Monthly. **Key Personnel:** Scott Patterson, Publisher; Lori York, Classified Dir. **Subscription Rates:** Free. **URL:** http://florida-news.com/swapshop.htm.
         Circ: Combined 20,000

ORLANDO

📖 **202 Flying Physician**
Flying Physicians Association, Inc.
PO Box 677427   Phone: (407)359-1423
Orlando, FL 32867-7427   Fax: (407)359-1167
Publisher E-mail: 75114.1632@compuserve.com

Professional journal covering aviation and medical education. **Founded:** 1956. **Freq:** Monthly. **Trim Size:** 8 1/4 x 10 3/4. **Key Personnel:** Patricia A. Nodecker, Managing Editor. **Subscription Rates:** $50 individuals. **Remarks:** Accepts advertising.
Ad Rates: BW: $200
             4C: $750   **Circ:** (Not Reported)

STUART

📖 **203 Fort Pierce News**
Scripps Howard Group
PO Box 9009
Stuart, FL 34995-9009   Phone: (561)287-1550

Community newspaper. **Freq:** Weekly (Fri.). **Subscription Rates:** Free.
         Circ: Non-paid **22,950**

TALLAHASSEE

📖 **204 Orange Seed Technical Bulletin**
Florida Department of State
R.A. Gray Bldg.   Phone: (850)487-2651
Tallahassee, FL 32399-0250   Fax: (850)488-2746

Professional magazine for library and information professionals. **Founded:** 1993. **Freq:** Bimonthly. **Key Personnel:** Larry Nash White, Editor. **Subscription Rates:** Free to qualified subscribers. **Remarks:** Advertising not accepted. **URL:** http://www.dos.state.fl.us/dlls/orange/index.htm.
         Circ: Non-paid 2000

TAMPA

📖 **205 Tampa Review**
University of Tampa Press
401 W. Kennedy Blvd.
Tampa, FL 33606-1490
Publisher E-mail: utpress@alpha.utampa.edu

Literary magazine covering poetry, fiction, nonfiction and art. **Founded:** 1988. **Freq:** Semiannual. **Trim Size:** 7 1/2 x 10 1/2. **Cols./Page:** 2. **Col. Width:** 5 7/8 inches. **Col. Depth:** 8 3/4 inches. **ISSN:** 0896-064X. **Subscription Rates:** $10 individuals. **Remarks:** Advertising not accepted. **URL:** http://www.utampa.edu.
         Circ: Paid 500

THE VILLAGES

📖 **206 The Daily Sun**
1153 Main St.   Phone: (352)753-1119
The Villages, FL 32159   Fax: (352)753-2380

General newspaper. **Freq:** Daily. **Subscription Rates:** $26.75 individuals. **URL:** http://www.thevillagesdailysun.com.

WEST PALM BEACH

📖 **207 Palm Beach Times**
222 Lakeview Ave., Ste. 160-262   Phone: (561)833-5129
West Palm Beach, FL 33401   Fax: (561)659-2893
Publication E-mail: info@palmbeachtimes.com

Community newspaper. **Trim Size:** 9 1/4 x 12 1/4. **Key Personnel:** Audrey Diamond, Publisher. **Remarks:** Accepts advertising. **URL:** http://palmbeach-times.com.
Ad Rates: BW: $1,500   **Circ:** Combined 100,000

WINTER PARK

📖 **208 Orlando Weekly**
Alternative Media, Inc.
807 S. Orlando Ave., Ste. R   Phone: (407)645-5888
Winter Park, FL 32789   Fax: (407)645-2547
Publication E-mail: feedback@orlandoweekly.com

Community newspaper. **Freq:** Weekly. **Key Personnel:** Jeff Truesdell, Editor; Theresa Everline, Managing Editor; Edward Ericson, JR., New Editor; Rick Wohleber, Operations Mgr.; Mike Johnson, Advertising Dir.; Dawn Petree, Production Mgr.; Karen Keane, Circulation Mgr. **Remarks:** Advertising accepted; rates available upon request. **URL:** http://www.orlandoweekly.com.
         Circ: (Not Reported)

GEORGIA

AMERICUS

209 Americus Times-Recorder
Thomson South Georgia
101 Hwy. 27 E.
Americus, GA 31709
Phone: (912)244-3400
Fax: (912)244-2560

Daily newspaper. **Founded:** 1879. **Freq:** Daily and Sunday. **Key Personnel:** Cody Graves, Circ. Dir. **Subscription Rates:** $96.20 individuals.
Circ: Combined ♦**7,450**

ATLANTA

210 Ashrae Journal
American Society of Heating, Refrigerating and Air-Conditioning
  Engineers, Inc. (ASHRAE)
1791 Tullie Circle NE
Atlanta, GA 30329
Phone: (404)636-8400
Fax: (404)321-5478
Free: (800)5AS-HRAE

Publisher E-mail: orders@ashrae.org

Trade journal covering engineering applications in heating, refrigeration, and air-conditioning engineering. **Founded:** 1959. **Freq:** Monthly. **Cols./Page:** 2. **Key Personnel:** Fred Turner, Editor; W. Stephen Comstock, Publisher, comstock@ashrae.org. **ISSN:** 0001-2491. **Subscription Rates:** $59 individuals; $79 Canada; $149 elsewhere. **Remarks:** Accepts advertising. **URL:** http://www.ashrae.org.
Ad Rates: BW: $4760 **Circ:** Paid 55,000
4C: $5960

211 EconSouth
Federal Reserve Bank of Atlanta
104 Marietta St.
Atlanta, GA 30303-2713
Phone: (404)521-8269
Fax: (404)521-8050

Trade magazine covering regional and national economic issues. **Founded:** Dec. 1998. **Freq:** Quarterly.

212 Korean Journal
5455 Buford Hwy., No. 207-A
Atlanta, GA 30340
Phone: (404)451-6946
Fax: (404)451-6956

Korean language community newspaper. **Founded:** 1983. **Freq:** Weekly. **Key Personnel:** Mike Lee, Contact. **Subscription Rates:** Free. **Remarks:** Accepts advertising.
Ad Rates: BW: $400 **Circ:** Combined 30,600

213 WKXC-FM - 99.5
1776 Briarcliff Rd. NE
Atlanta, GA 30306

Format: Country. **Owner:** GBH Broadcasting Corp., at above address. **Founded:** 1992. **Operating Hours:** Continuous. **Key Personnel:** George H. Buck, Jr., President; Nancy H. Walker, Vice President. **Wattage:** 50,000. **URL:** http://www.kicks99.com.

214 WLTA-AM - 1400
2970 Peachtree Rd., 8th Fl.
Atlanta, GA 30305
Phone: (404)365-0970
Fax: (404)816-0748
E-mail: wniv@wniv.com

Format: Talk. **Networks:** UPI; Sun Radio; AP. **Owner:** Genesis Communications, Inc., at above address. **Founded:** May 17, 1988. **Operating Hours:** Continuous. **ADI:** Atlanta (Athens & Rome), GA. **Key Personnel:** Sandra Culver, General Mgr.; James Sutton, Operations Mgr.; Kay Jones, Sales Mgr.; Jonathan Schaffer, News Dir. **Wattage:** 3,000. **Ad Rates:** $30-75 per unit. **URL:** http://www.wniv.com.

215 WNIV-AM - 970
2970 Peachtree Rd., 8th Fl.
Atlanta, GA 30305
Phone: (404)365-0970
Fax: (404)816-0748
E-mail: wniv@wniv.com

Format: Talk. **Networks:** UPI; Sun Radio; AP. **Owner:** Genesis Communications, Inc., at above address. **Founded:** May 17, 1988. **Operating Hours:** Continuous. **ADI:** Atlanta (Athens & Rome), GA. **Key Personnel:** Sandra Culver, General Mgr.; James Sutton, Operations Mgr.; Kay Jones, Sales Mgr.; Jonathan Schaffer, News Dir. **Wattage:** 3,000. **Ad Rates:** $30-75 per unit. **URL:** http://www.wniv.com.

CARROLLTON

216 WCKS-FM - 102.7
102 Parkwood Cir.
Carrollton, GA 30117
Phone: (770)834-KISS

Format: Contemporary Hit Radio (CHR). **Operating Hours:** Continuous. **URL:** http://www.wcks.com.

DORAVILLE

217 Korean Southeast News
5725 Buford Hwy., No. 211
Doraville, GA 30340
Phone: (770)454-9655
Fax: (770)454-6191

Korean language community newspaper. **Freq:** Weekly (Fri.). **Key Personnel:** Simon Han, Contact. **Subscription Rates:** Free; $20 by mail. **Remarks:** Accepts advertising.
Ad Rates: BW: $300 **Circ:** Combined 20,000

ELLIJAY

218 WLJA-AM - 1560
PO Box 545
Ellijay, GA 30540
Phone: (706)276-2016
Fax: (706)635-1018

Format: Country; Gospel. **Networks:** USA Radio; Georgia Radio. **Owner:** Tri-State Communications, Inc., at above address. **Formerly:** WLEJ-AM (1985). **Operating Hours:** Sunrise-sunset. **Key Personnel:** Byron Dobbs, General Mgr.; Randy Gravley, Sales Mgr.; Linda Slajer, Office Mgr.; Jackie Grizzle, Chief Engineer. **Wattage:** 1,000. **Ad Rates:** $5 for 30 seconds; $6 for 60 seconds.

219 WLJA-FM - 93.5
PO Box 545
Ellijay, GA 30540
Phone: (706)276-2016
Fax: (706)635-1018

Format: Country; Gospel. **Networks:** USA Radio; Georgia Radio. **Owner:** Tri-State Communications, Inc., at above address. **Founded:** 1985. **Formerly:** WLEJ-FM (1986). **Operating Hours:** Continuous. **Key Personnel:** Byron Dobbs, General Mgr.; Randy Gravley, Sales Mgr.; Linda Slajer, Office Mgr.;

Jackie Grizzle, Chief Engineer. **Wattage:** 6,000. **Ad Rates:** $12 for 30 seconds; $15 for 60 seconds.

NORCROSS

📖 **220 The Weekly**
PO Box 921441   Phone: (770)263-7400
Norcross, GA 30010-1141   Fax: (770)263-7003
Publication E-mail: weeklypub1@mindspring.com

Community newspaper. **Freq:** Weekly. **URL:** http://theweekly.com.

STATESBORO

📖 **221 Statesboro Herald**
Statesboro Publishing Co. Inc.
1 Herald Sq.
PO Box 888   Phone: (912)764-9031
Statesboro, GA 30459   Free: (888)764-9031

General newspaper. **Freq:** Daily and Sunday. **Key Personnel:** Randy Morton, Publisher, phone (912)489-9431; Amelia Morrison Hall, Exec. Editor, phone (912)489-9402; Joe Hotchkiss, Editor, phone (912)489-9442; Jan Melton, Advertising Dir., phone (912)489-9401; Jamie Lawson, Circulation Mgr., phone (912)489-9425. **URL:** http://www.statesboroherald.com.

HAWAII

HONOLULU

📖 **222 East West Journal**
1150 S. King St., Ste. 209
Honolulu, HI 96814

Phone: (808)596-0099
Fax: (808)596-2292

Japanese language business, news and entertainment newspaper for Japanese residents and businesspeople in Hawaii. **Founded:** 1976. **Freq:** Biweekly. **Key Personnel:** Yuji Nagai, Pres./Pub. **Subscription Rates:** $26 individuals. **Remarks:** Accepts advertising.
Ad Rates: BW: $1,500   **Circ:** Combined 5,000

📖 **223 Hawaii Hochi**
917 Kokea St.
Honolulu, HI 96817-4528

Phone: (808)845-2255
Fax: (808)847-7215

Japanese language newspaper for Japanese Americans in Hawaii. **Founded:** 1912. **Freq:** Mon.-Sat. **Key Personnel:** Mamoru Tanji, Advertising Sales. **Subscription Rates:** $120 individuals. **Remarks:** Accepts advertising.
Ad Rates: BW: $1,876.88   **Circ:** Combined 8,000
                4C: $2,294.88

🎙 **224 KOHO-AM - 1170**
500 Ala Moana Blvd., Ste. 400
Honolulu, HI 96813

Phone: (808)951-1170
Fax: (808)585-8899

Format: Ethnic. **Owner:** Legacy Communications Corp., 210 N. 1000 E., PO Box 1450, St. George, UT 84771-1450, (435)628-1000, Fax: (435)628-6636. **Founded:** 1959. **Key Personnel:** E. Morgan Skinner, President; Lavon Randall, Chairman; R. Machael Bull, Controller. **Wattage:** 5000.

KANEOHE

📖 **225 Midweek Magazine**
RFD Publications, Inc.
45-525 Luluku Rd.
Kaneohe, HI 96744-1945

Phone: (808)235-5881
Fax: (808)247-7246

Consumer magazine covering local news and entertainment. **Freq:** Weekly (Wed.). **Key Personnel:** Karen Berry, Advertising, phone (808)235-5881. **Remarks:** Advertising accepted; rates available upon request. **URL:** http://www.midweek.com.

Circ: (Not Reported)

IDAHO

DEARY

226 Talk of the Town
Talk of the Town Publications
PO Box 286
Deary, ID 83823-0286   Phone: (208)877-1550
Publication E-mail: tot@turbonet.com

Community newspaper. **Freq:** Bimonthly. **Subscription Rates:** $25 individuals. **URL:** http://www.home.turbonet.com/tot/.

LEWISTON

227 KVTY-FM - 105.1
805 Stewart Ave.   Phone: (208)746-5056
Lewiston, ID 83501   Fax: (208)743-4440

Format: Classic Rock. **Networks:** AP. **Owner:** IDAVEND Co., at above address. **Founded:** 1998. **Operating Hours:** Continuous. **Key Personnel:** Robert Prasil, General Mgr., rprasil@valley-internet.net; Melva Prasil, Station Mgr.; Steve Kingsly, News Dir.; Darin Seibert, Program Dir.; Ben Bonfield, Sales Mgr. **Wattage:** 500. **Ad Rates:** $12-18 for 30 seconds; $15-23 for 60 seconds.

ILLINOIS

ARLINGTON HEIGHTS

📖 **228 California Fairways**
Adams Business Media
2101 S. Arlington Heights Rd., Ste. 150
Arlington Heights, IL 60005

Phone: (847)427-9512
Fax: (847)427-2006

Professional magazine for golf course and country club operators in California. **Freq:** Bimonthly. **Print Method:** Web offset. **Trim Size:** 8 x 10 3/4. **Key Personnel:** Mark Adams, President; Colleen Murphy, VP/Group Publisher; John Fultz, Editor; Deanna Morgan, Advertising Sales. **Remarks:** Accepts advertising. **URL:** http://www.greenindustry.com/.
Ad Rates: BW: $1,385   **Circ:** (Not Reported)
4C: $1,970

📖 **229 Repair Shop Product News**
Adams Business Media
2101 S. Arlington Heights Rd., Ste. 150
Arlington Heights, IL 60005

Phone: (847)427-9512
Fax: (847)427-2006

Trade magazine for the automobile industry. **Freq:** Bimonthly. **Trim Size:** 10 7/8 x 16. **Key Personnel:** James L. Gillespie, Publisher, jgillespie@adamsinterctive.com; Eric Schroder, Editor-in-Chief, eschroder@adamsinteractive.com. **Remarks:** Accepts advertising. **URL:** http://www.autotruck.net/.
Ad Rates: BW: $4305   **Circ:** Combined 35,000
4C: $5320

📖 **230 sportsTURF**
Adams Business Media
2101 S. Arlington Heights Rd., Ste. 150
Arlington Heights, IL 60005

Phone: (847)427-9512
Fax: (847)427-2006

Trade magazine of the Sports Turf Managers Association for groundskeepers. **Freq:** Monthly. **Print Method:** Web offset. **Trim Size:** 8 x 10 3/4. **Key Personnel:** Mark Adams, President; Colleen Murphy, VP/Group Publisher; Steve Berens, Editor; Deanna Morgan, Adv. Sales. **Remarks:** Accepts advertising. **URL:** http://www.greenindustry.com/.
Ad Rates: BW: $2,940   **Circ:** Combined 18,431
4C: $3,845

BOURBONNAIS

📖 **231 The-A-Ki-Ki**
Kankakee Valley Genealogical Society
Box 442
Bourbonnais, IL 60914

Local genealogical journal. **Founded:** 1970. **Freq:** Quarterly. **Subscription Rates:** $12 individuals. **Remarks:** Advertising not accepted.
Circ: (Not Reported)

CAROL STREAM

📖 **232 Christian Parenting Today**
Christianity Today, Inc.
465 Gundersen Dr.
Carol Stream, IL 60188
Publication E-mail: cptmag@aol.com

Phone: (630)260-6200
Fax: (630)260-0114

Consumer magazine covering parenting for a Christian audience. **Founded:** 1988. **Freq:** Bimonthly. **Print Method:** Offset. **Trim Size:** 8 x 10 3/4. **Cols./Page:** 3. **Col. Width:** 2 1/4 inches. **Col. Depth:** 10 inches. **Key Personnel:** Harold L. Myra, Publisher; Linda Schembach, VP, Sales; Ron R. Lee, Exec. Editor, ronraylee@aol.com; Kevin A. Miller, Editorial Dir., kevincpt@aol.com. **ISSN:** 1066-7215. **Subscription Rates:** $17.95 individuals; $3.95 single issue. **Remarks:** Accepts advertising. **URL:** http://www.christianparenting.net.
Ad Rates: BW: $3,171   **Circ:** Paid ‡87,194
4C: $3,805   Non-paid ‡23,889

📖 **233 Computing Today**
Christianity Today, Inc.
465 Gundersen Dr.
Carol Stream, IL 60188
Publication E-mail: computingt@aol.com

Phone: (630)260-6200
Fax: (630)260-0114

Trade magazine covering computers, technology and the internet for Christians. **Subtitle:** A Guide to the Internet and Software from Christianity Online. **Founded:** 1997. **Freq:** Bimonthly. **Print Method:** Offset. **Trim Size:** 8 x 10 3/4. **Cols./Page:** 3. **Col. Width:** 2 1/4 inches. **Col. Depth:** 10 inches. **Key Personnel:** Harold L. Myra, Publisher; Linda Schembach, VP, Sales; Mark Moring, Managing Editor, markm@aol.com. **ISSN:** 1092-9020. **Subscription Rates:** $14.95 individuals; $2.95 single issue. **Remarks:** Accepts advertising. **URL:** http://www.computingtoday.net.
Ad Rates: BW: $2575   **Circ:** Paid 100,000
4C: $3090

📖 **234 Men of Integrity**
Christianity Today, Inc.
465 Gundersen Dr.
Carol Stream, IL 60188
Publication E-mail: pkmenmag@aol.com

Phone: (630)260-6200
Fax: (630)260-0114

Consumer magazine covering religious issues for men. **Founded:** July 1998. **Freq:** Bimonthly. **Print Method:** Offset. **Trim Size:** 4 x 6 3/8. **Cols./Page:** 2. **Col. Width:** 1 1/2 inches. **Col. Depth:** 5 7/8 inches. **Key Personnel:** Harold L. Myra, Publisher; Harry Genet, Editor; Ashley Neam, Editor. **Subscription Rates:** Free donation suggested. **Remarks:** Advertising not accepted. **URL:** http://www.christianity.net/menofintegrity.
Circ: Non-paid 25,000

CENTRALIA

📖 **235 Morning Sentinel**
Centralia Press, Ltd.
232 E. Broadway
PO Box 627
Centralia, IL 62801

Phone: (618)532-5604
Fax: (618)533-1212
Free: (800)371-9892

Community newspaper. **Founded:** 1863. **Freq:** Daily and Sunday. **Key Personnel:** Dan Nichols, General Mgr. **Subscription Rates:** $85.80 individuals; $105 by mail.
Circ: Combined ♦17,122

CHICAGO

236 America's Family Support Magazine
Family Resource Coalition
20 N. Wacker Dr., No. 1100
Chicago, IL 60606
Publisher E-mail: frca@frca.org

Phone: (312)338-0900
Fax: (312)338-1522

Consumer magazine covering family issues. **Freq:** Quarterly.

237 Chicago Shimpo
4670 N. Manor Ave.
Chicago, IL 60625

Phone: (773)478-6170
Fax: (773)478-9360

Japanese language community newspaper. **Founded:** 1945. **Freq:** Semiweekly (Wed. and Fri.). **Key Personnel:** Akiko Sugano, Contact. **Subscription Rates:** $55 individuals. **Remarks:** Accepts advertising.
Ad Rates: BW: $1,100   **Circ:** Combined 5,000

238 Dziennik Chicagowski
Chemigraph Graphic Arts, Printing, Publishing Co.
5242 W. Diversey Ave.
Chicago, IL 60639

Phone: (773)283-1898
Fax: (773)685-7762

Polish and English language daily newspaper for Polish-Americans. **Founded:** 1991. **Freq:** Daily and Sunday. **Trim Size:** 11 1/2 x 16. **Cols./Page:** 5. **Col. Width:** 12.5 picas. **Col. Depth:** 14.5 inches. **Key Personnel:** Michal Kuchejda, Publisher. **Remarks:** Accepts advertising.
Ad Rates: BW: $1800   **Circ:** Combined 25,000
4C: $2225

239 MidAmerica Guide
Japan Arts & Communications
203 N. Wabash Ave., No. 1520
Chicago, IL 60621

Phone: (312)419-0111
Fax: (312)419-0112

Consumer magazine covering U.S.-Japan relations in Japanese. **Founded:** 1983. **Freq:** Monthly. **Key Personnel:** Masaru Uehara, Contact. **Subscription Rates:** Free; $30 by mail. **Remarks:** Accepts advertising.
Ad Rates: BW: $900   **Circ:** Combined 4,000
4C: $1,500

240 N'DIGO
Hartman Group Publishing, Inc.
401 N. Wabash, Ste. 534
Chicago, IL 60611

Phone: (312)822-0202

Newspaper covering lifestyle, entertainment, and other issues for an upscale, middle-class, African-American audience. **Freq:** Weekly (Thurs.). **Subscription Rates:** Free; $63 by mail.

Circ: Combined **100,098**

241 New Asian Americans Magazine
Shi Young
417 S. Dearborn St.
Chicago, IL 60605
Publisher E-mail: naam@mcs.com

Phone: (312)431-0900
Fax: (312)431-0990

Consumer magazine covering social, political and civil rights issues concerning and for Asian Americans in Chinese and English. **Freq:** Bimonthly. **Key Personnel:** Shi Young, Publisher. **Subscription Rates:** $4.95 single issue; $36 individuals; $70 two years. **Remarks:** Accepts advertising.
Ad Rates: BW: $3,475   **Circ:** Combined 57,800
4C: $4,413

242 Other Voices
University of Illinois at Chicago
601 S. Morgan St.
Chicago, IL 60607-7120

Phone: (312)413-2209

Literary journal covering fiction. **Founded:** 1984. **Freq:** Semiannual. **Key Personnel:** Lois Hauselman, Exec. Editor. **ISSN:** 8756-4696. **Subscription Rates:** $20 two years; $7 single issue. **Remarks:** Advertising not accepted.
Circ: (Not Reported)

243 Public Culture
Duke University Press
University of Chicago
124 Wieboldt Hall
1010 E. 59th St.
Chicago, IL 60637
Publisher E-mail: dukepress@duke.edu

Scholarly journal covering cultural studies. **Freq:** Triennial. **Key Personnel:** Carol A. Breckenridge, Editor; Amy Hartzler, Advertising, phone (919)687-3636. **Subscription Rates:** $30 individuals; $75 institutions. **Remarks:** Accepts advertising.
Ad Rates: BW: $325   **Circ:** Combined 1000

244 Via Times Newsmagazine
PO Box 138155
Chicago, IL 60613

Phone: (312)866-0811
Fax: (312)866-9207

Consumer magazine for Filipino-Americans in English and some Tagalog. **Founded:** 1984. **Freq:** Monthly. **Key Personnel:** Veronica Leighton, Contact. **Subscription Rates:** Free; $20 by mail. **Remarks:** Accepts advertising.
Ad Rates: BW: $600   **Circ:** Combined 60,000

DECATUR

245 Mystery Time
Hutton Publications
PO Box 2907
Decatur, IL 62524

Consumer journal covering fiction and poetry related to mystery and suspense. **Founded:** 1972. **Freq:** Semiannual. **Trim Size:** 5 x 8. **Key Personnel:** Linda Hutton, Editor. **ISSN:** 0886-2958. **Subscription Rates:** $10 individuals. **Remarks:** Advertising not accepted.
Circ: Paid 100

246 Rhyme Time
Hutton Publications
PO Box 2907
Decatur, IL 62524

Poetry journal. **Founded:** 1971. **Freq:** Quarterly. **Trim Size:** 5 x 8. **Key Personnel:** Linda Hutton, Editor. **ISSN:** 0886-0211. **Subscription Rates:** $24 individuals. **Remarks:** Advertising not accepted.
Circ: Paid 100

DOWNERS GROVE

247 Lemont Reporter
Reporter/Progress Newspapers
922 Warren Ave.
Downers Grove, IL 60515

Phone: (630)969-0188
Fax: (630)969-0228

Community newspaper. **Founded:** 1990. **Freq:** Weekly (Wed.). **Key Personnel:** Christopher Winter, Publisher.
Circ: Combined ♦5275

248 Lisle Reporter
Reporter/Progress Newspapers
922 Warren Ave.
Downers Grove, IL 60515

Phone: (630)969-0188
Fax: (630)969-0228

Community newspaper. **Founded:** 1995. **Freq:** Weekly (Wed.). **Key Personnel:** Christopher Winter, Publisher.
Circ: Combined ♦7148

249 Willowbrook Progress
Reporter/Progress Newspapers
922 Warren Ave.
Downers Grove, IL 60515

Phone: (630)969-0188
Fax: (630)969-0228

Community newspaper. **Founded:** 1995. **Freq:** Weekly (Thurs.). **Key Personnel:** Christopher Winter, Publisher.
Circ: Combined ♦2,369

ELK GROVE VILLAGE

250 Aftermarket Today
Automotive Service Industry Association (ASIA)
25 Northwest Pt., Ste. 425
Elk Grove Village, IL 60007-1035
Publisher E-mail: asia@aftmktusa.org
Phone: (847)228-1310
Fax: (847)228-1510

Trade magazine of the Automotive Service Industry Association. **Freq:** Quarterly. **Subscription Rates:** Free to qualified subscribers; $40 nonmembers. **Remarks:** Advertising not accepted. **URL:** http://www.aftmkt.com.
Circ: (Not Reported)

FREEPORT

251 Freeport Shopping News
Woodward Communications
1342 S. Harlem Ave.
PO Box 607
Freeport, IL 61032-0604
Phone: (815)235-4106
Fax: (815)235-7077
Free: (800)343-6419

Shopping guide. **Freq:** Weekly (Wed.). **Subscription Rates:** Free.
Circ: Non-paid 22,861

GALESBURG

252 The Zephyr
Norm Winick
251 E. Main St.
PO Box 1
Galesburg, IL 61402
Publication E-mail: zephyr@misslink.net
Phone: (309)342-2010

Community newspaper. **Founded:** 1989. **Freq:** Weekly (Thurs.). **Print Method:** Offset. **Trim Size:** 11 x 17. **Cols./Page:** 6. **Col. Width:** 1 5/8 inches. **Key Personnel:** Norm Winick, Editor and Publisher. **USPS:** 004-515. **Subscription Rates:** $16 individuals; $19 out of area; $24 out of state. **Remarks:** Accepts advertising. **URL:** http://www.thezephyr.com.
Ad Rates: PCI: $3.75
Circ: Paid 2,000

GENESEO

253 Orion Gazette
Terry Newspapers
108 W. 1st St.
Geneseo, IL 61254-0209
Phone: (309)944-2119
Fax: (309)944-6161
Free: (888)837-7963
Publication E-mail: editor@terrynews.com

Community newspaper. **Freq:** Weekly (Thurs.). **Remarks:** Advertising accepted; rates available upon request. **URL:** http://www.terrynews.com.
Circ: (Not Reported)

LIBERTYVILLE

254 FacilityCare
IHS Publishing Group
17730 W. Peterson Rd.
PO Box 159
Libertyville, IL 60048-0159
Publication E-mail: facilitycare@ihspubs.com
Publisher E-mail: ihs@ihspubs.com
Phone: (847)362-8711
Fax: (847)362-3484

Professional magazine covering design, construction, and maintenance of healthcare facilities for facility managers. **Subtitle:** Design, Operation & Maintenance of Healthcare Facilities. **Founded:** Nov. 1996. **Freq:** 10/year. **Print Method:** Web offset. **Trim Size:** 11 x 15 3/4. **Cols./Page:** 4. **Col. Width:** 2 1/8 inches. **Col. Depth:** 14 3/4 inches. **Key Personnel:** Marsha Robertson, Group Publisher, marshar@ihspubs.com; Lauren Guthrie, Publisher, laureng@ihspubs.com. **ISSN:** 1090-7475. **Subscription Rates:** $55 individuals; $10 single issue. **Remarks:** Accepts advertising.
Ad Rates: BW: $5309
4C: $6359
Circ: Paid 35,560

255 Vacuum & Thinfilm
IHS Publishing Group
17730 W. Peterson Rd.
PO Box 159
Libertyville, IL 60048-0159
Publication E-mail: vt@ihspubs.com
Publisher E-mail: ihs@ihspubs.com
Phone: (847)362-8711
Fax: (847)362-3484

Professional magazine covering vacuum, thin film deposition, and other technologies for the development and manufacture of electronic products for researchers, engineers, managers, and technicians. **Freq:** Monthly. **Print Method:** Web offset. **Trim Size:** 7 7/8 x 10 7/8. **Cols./Page:** 3. **Col. Width:** 2 1/8 inches. **Col. Depth:** 10 inches. **Key Personnel:** Marsha Robertson, Group Publisher, marshar@ihspubs.com; Amy Knutson-Strack, Exec. Editor; David Mount, Editor; Kathy Tierney, Asst. Editor. **ISSN:** 1521-3684. **Subscription Rates:** $65 individuals; $10 single issue. **Remarks:** Accepts advertising.
Circ: Controlled **20,000**

MACOMB

256 WIUS-FM - 88.3
1 University Circle
Macomb, IL 61455
E-mail: wius@ccmail.wiu.edu
Phone: (309)298-3217
Fax: (309)298-2829

Format: Eclectic. **Owner:** Western Illinois University, at above address. **Founded:** Jan. 1982. **Operating Hours:** 8 a.m.-1 a.m. Mon.-Fri.; 12 p.m.-2 a.m. Sat.-Sun. **Key Personnel:** Chris Wahlberg, Station Mgr., mucw@wiu.edu; Tiffany Strietelmeier, Asst. Mgr./Music Dir., mutms@wiu.edu; Brent Clair, Music Dir., brentclair@hotmail.com; Stacey Rogers, Promotions Dir., muser1@wiu.edu. **Wattage:** 100. **Ad Rates:** Underwriting available. **URL:** http://www.wiu.edu/users/miwius/wiu/.

MOUNT PROSPECT

257 Program TV
Allied Management
PO Box 9121
Mount Prospect, IL 60056
Phone: (847)797-9051
Fax: (847)797-9075

Polish language television, movie and entertainment guide. **Founded:** May 1, 1999. **Freq:** Weekly. **Print Method:** Web offset. **Trim Size:** 7 3/8 x 10. **Key Personnel:** Kinga trojan, Managing Editor; Lidia Chodzen, General Mgr.; Zaneta Yankowiak, Editor-in-Chief. **Subscription Rates:** $52 individuals. **Remarks:** Accepts advertising.
Ad Rates: BW: $548
Circ: Combined 28,000

NASHVILLE

258 WNSV-FM - 104.7
186 E. St. Louis St.
Nashville, IL 62263
Phone: (618)327-4444
Fax: (618)327-3716

Format: Adult Contemporary. **Networks:** Westwood One Radio. **Owner:** Dana R. Withers, at above address. **Founded:** July 1, 1994. **Operating Hours:** Continuous. **Key Personnel:** Brad Meyer, Sales Mgr.; Nick Howes, News Dir.; Gina Droege, Business Mgr. **Wattage:** 3,000. **Ad Rates:** $11-20 for 30 seconds; $13-22 for 60 seconds.

OAK BROOK

259 Suburban Life Citizen
Life Newspapers
709 Enterprise Dr.
Oak Brook, IL 60523
Phone: (630)368-1100

Community newspaper. **Freq:** Semiweekly (Wed. and Sat.). **Key Personnel:** Trever Bricker, Circ. Dir. **Subscription Rates:** $31.50 individuals; $40 by mail.
Circ: Combined **27,219**

260 Suburban Life Elmhurst
Life Newspapers
709 Enterprise Dr.
Oak Brook, IL 60523   Phone: (630)368-1100

Community newspaper. **Freq:** Weekly (Thurs.). **Key Personnel:** Trever Bricker, Circ. Dir. **Subscription Rates:** Free.
     Circ: Combined **14,180**

261 Suburban Life Lombard/Villa Park
Life Newspapers
709 Enterprise Dr.
Oak Brook, IL 60523   Phone: (630)368-1100

Community newspaper. **Freq:** Weekly (Thurs.). **Key Personnel:** Trever Bricker, Circ. Dir. **Subscription Rates:** Free.
     Circ: Combined **29,632**

OAK PARK

262 EDI Forum
EDI Group Ltd.
221 Lake St.   Phone: (708)848-0135
Oak Park, IL 60302-0710   Fax: (708)848-0270
Publication E-mail: edigroup@worldnet.att.net

Trade magazine covering information on EDI and electronic commerce. **Subtitle:** The Journal of Electronic Commerce. **Freq:** Quarterly. **URL:** http://www.edigroup.com.

RIVER FOREST

263 INTV-TV -
705 Keystone Ave.   Phone: (708)488-0914
River Forest, IL 60305   Fax: (708)488-0914

Format: News. **Networks:** Public Broadcasting Service (PBS). **Owner:** Internet Television Network, at above address. **Operating Hours:** Continuous. **Key Personnel:** Fredric Golman, Pres./Exec. Prod., fgolman@mindspring.com. **URL:** http://intv.net.

ROBINSON

264 Robinson Daily News
302 S. Cross St.
PO Box 639
Robinson, IL 62454   Phone: (618)544-2101
     Fax: (618)544-9533
Publication E-mail: robdnad@midwest.net

General newspaper. **Founded:** 1919. **Freq:** Daily. **Remarks:** Accepts advertising. **URL:** http://www.robdailynew.com.
     Circ: (Not Reported)

SCHAUMBURG

265 North American Actuarial
Society of Actuaries
475 N. Martingale Rd., Ste. 800   Phone: (847)706-3500
Schaumburg, IL 60173-2226   Fax: (847)706-3599
Publisher E-mail: bhaynes@soa.org

Scholarly journal covering actuarial practice, including life and health insurance, pensions, employee benefits, property and casualty insurance, and finance and investments for professionals and others. **Founded:** Jan. 1997. **Freq:** Quarterly. **Print Method:** Web offset. **Trim Size:** 8 1/2 x 11. **Cols./Page:** 2. **Col. Width:** 3 1/2 inches. **Col. Depth:** 9 inches. **Key Personnel:** Samuel H. Cox, Editor; Michael J. Cowell, Editor; Cheryl L. Enderlein, Submissions & Reviews, cenderlein@soa.org. **ISSN:** 1092-0277. **Subscription Rates:** $95 individuals; $25 single issue. **Remarks:** Advertising not accepted. **Former name:** Transactions.
     Circ: Non-paid **17,000**

SPRINGFIELD

266 Journal of Illinois History
Illinois Historic Preservation Agency
1 Old State Capitol Plaza
Springfield, IL 62701-1507   Phone: (217)524-6045

Journal covering local history. **Freq:** Quarterly. **Key Personnel:** Evelyn R. Taylor, Editor. **ISSN:** 1522-0532. **Subscription Rates:** $18 individuals; $5 single issue.

267 The Post-Abortion Review
Elliot Institute
PO Box 7348
Springfield, IL 62791-7348   Phone: (217)525-8202
     Fax: (217)525-8212

Professional journal covering the physical and psychological effects of abortion. **Founded:** 1993. **Freq:** Quarterly. **Print Method:** Offset. **Trim Size:** 8 1/2 x 11. **Key Personnel:** David Reardon, Editor; Amy Sobie, Asst. Editor. **ISSN:** 1083-9496. **Subscription Rates:** $20 individuals. **Remarks:** Advertising not accepted. **URL:** http://www.afterabortion.org.
     Circ: Controlled **1050**

WEST FRANKFORT

268 West Frankfort Daily American
Liberty Group Publishing Co.
PO Box 617
West Frankfort, IL 62896

General newspaper. **Freq:** Daily. **Key Personnel:** G. David Green, Publisher; Diann Walthes, Business Mgr.; Shannon Woodworth, Managing Editor; Jeremy Norris, Production Mgr.; Kathy Eldridge, Circulation Mgr. **Remarks:** Advertising accepted; rates available upon request. **URL:** http://www.dailyamericannews.com.
     Circ: (Not Reported)

WOODSTOCK

269 The Woodstock Independent
671 E. Calhoun St.
Woodstock, IL 60098

Community newspaper. **Freq:** Weekly (Wed.). **Remarks:** Accepts advertising. **URL:** http://www.inde-news.com.
Ad Rates: PCI: $8   **Circ:** (Not Reported)

INDIANA

BLOOMINGTON

📖 **270 The Bloomington Voice**
Bloomington Voice Ltd.
3900 S. Old State Rd., No. 37   Phone: (812)331-0963
Bloomington, IN 47401   Fax: (812)337-3308
Publication E-mail: lsorg@bvoice.com

Community newspaper. **Founded:** Jan. 1992. **Freq:** Weekly. **Key Personnel:** Diane Aden Hayes, Editor and Publisher; Barbara Glaze, Advertising Dir.; Nancy Magel, Circulation Mgr. **Subscription Rates:** $52 individuals. **Remarks:** Accepts advertising.
Circ: (Not Reported)

BUTLER

📖 **271 The National Stock Dog**
Juan-Jer Corporation
PO Box 402
Butler, IN 46721-0402

Periodical covering dogs for breeders and others. **Key Personnel:** J. R. Russell, Editor and Publisher; R. Gorney, Subscriptions. **Subscription Rates:** $22 individuals; $3 single issue. **Remarks:** Accepts advertising.
Ad Rates: BW: $100   **Circ:** (Not Reported)
                    4C: $300

FISHERS

📖 **272 Center Grove Gazette**
Topics Newspapers, Inc.
13095 Publisher's Dr.   Phone: (317)598-6397
Fishers, IN 46038   Fax: (317)598-6340
Publisher E-mail: topics@inetdirect.net

Community newspaper. **Freq:** Weekly (Thurs.). **Key Personnel:** Chip Gallagher, Circulation Dir. **Subscription Rates:** Free.
Circ: Combined ♦**10,899**

📖 **273 Lawrence Topics**
Topics Newspapers, Inc.
13095 Publisher's Dr.   Phone: (317)598-6397
Fishers, IN 46038   Fax: (317)598-6340
Publisher E-mail: topics@inetdirect.net

Community newspaper. **Freq:** Weekly (Wed.). **Key Personnel:** Chip Gallagher, Circulation Dir. **Subscription Rates:** Free.
Circ: Combined ♦**9,068**

📖 **274 Westfield Enterprise**
Topics Newspapers, Inc.
13095 Publisher's Dr.   Phone: (317)598-6397
Fishers, IN 46038   Fax: (317)598-6340
Publisher E-mail: topics@inetdirect.net

Community newspaper. **Freq:** Weekly (Wed.). **Key Personnel:** Chip Gallagher, Circulation Dir. **Subscription Rates:** Free.
Circ: Combined ♦**4,876**

📖 **275 White River Gazette**
Topics Newspapers, Inc.
13095 Publisher's Dr.   Phone: (317)598-6397
Fishers, IN 46038   Fax: (317)598-6340
Publisher E-mail: topics@inetdirect.net

Community newspaper. **Freq:** Weekly (Thurs.). **Key Personnel:** Chip Gallagher, Circulation Dir. **Subscription Rates:** Free.
Circ: Combined ♦**8,768**

FRANKLIN

📖 **276 Access (Greenwood)**
American Safe Deposit Association
PO Box 519   Phone: (317)738-4432
Franklin, IN 46131   Fax: (317)738-5267

Trade magazine covering safe deposit procedures and security for members. **Remarks:** Accepts advertising.
Ad Rates: BW: $160   **Circ:** Controlled 3,000

GOSHEN

📖 **277 El Puente**
PO Box 553   Phone: (219)533-9082
Goshen, IN 46527-0553   Fax: (219)553-3611

Spanish language community newspaper. **Founded:** Mar. 1992. **Freq:** Monthly. **Print Method:** Offset. **Trim Size:** 11 x 13 1/2. **Cols./Page:** 4. **Col. Width:** 2 1/2 inches. **Col. Depth:** 12 1/2 inches. **Key Personnel:** Zulma Prieto, Editor and Publisher; Jodi Magallanes, Advertising Mgr., jodim@gte.net; Jimmer Prieto, Editor. **Subscription Rates:** $15 individuals. **Remarks:** Accepts advertising.
Ad Rates: BW: $420   **Circ:** Combined 6,050
                    4C: $520
                    PCI: $8.40

LA PORTE

📖 **278 Families in Michiana**
DiJon Publications
PO Box 748   Phone: (219)362-3225
La Porte, IN 46350   Fax: (219)324-0086
Publisher E-mail: info@dijonpublications.com

Consumer magazine covering regional travel. **Freq:** Annual. **Subscription Rates:** Free. **URL:** http://www.dijonpublications.com.

📖 **279 The LaPorte County Magazine**
DiJon Publications
PO Box 748   Phone: (219)362-3225
La Porte, IN 46350   Fax: (219)324-0086
Publisher E-mail: info@dijonpublications.com

Consumer magazine covering local travel and tourism. **Freq:** Annual. **Subscription Rates:** Free. **URL:** http://www.dijonpublicatons.com.

Ad Rates: GLR = general line rate; BW = one-time black & white page rate; 4C = one-time four color page rate; SAU = standard advertising unit rate; CNU = Canadian newspaper advertising unit rate; PCI = per column inch rate.
Circulation: ★ = ABC; △ = BPA; ♦ = CAC; • = CCAB; ❑ = VAC; ⊕ = PO Statement; ‡ = Publisher's Report; Boldface figures = sworn; Light figures = estimated.
Entry type: 📖 = Print; 🎙 = Broadcast.

280   LaPorte Herald-Argus
701 State. St.
La Porte, IN 46350   Fax: (219)362-2166

General newspaper. **Freq:** Daily. **Key Personnel:** Clem T. Otolski, Publisher; Mark Johnson, Managing Editor; Robert Rehlander, Business Mgr.; Carol Kuta, Retail Adv. Mgr.; John Schulz, Circ. Dir. **Remarks:** Accepts advertising. **URL:** http://www.heraldargus.com.
Ad Rates: PCI: $7.33   **Circ:** (Not Reported)

ROCHESTER

281   The Rochester Sentinel
118 E. 8th St.   Phone: (219)223-2111
PO Box 260   Fax: (219)223-5782
Rochester, IN 46975   Free: (800)686-2112

General newspaper. **Founded:** 1858. **Freq:** Daily. **Key Personnel:** Jack K. Overmyer, President, phone (219)223-5316; Sarah Overmyer Wilson, Publisher, phone (219)224-5331, show@rochsent.com; W. S. Wilson, Editor, phone (219)224-5329, wsw@rochsent.com; Karen Vojtasek, Advertising Mgr., phone (219)224-5322, ads@rochsent.com. **Subscription Rates:** $93 individuals; $108 by mail. **URL:** http://www.rochsent.com.

WABASH

282   WKUZ-FM - 95.9
PO Box 342   Phone: (219)563-4111
Wabash, IN 46992   Fax: (219)563-4425

Format: Country. **Networks:** USA Radio; Brownfield. **Owner:** Upper Wabash Broadcasting Corp., at above address. **Founded:** 1966. **Operating Hours:** Continuous. **ADI:** Fort Wayne (Angola), IN. **Key Personnel:** Chuck Adams, President; Toni Adams, Vice President; Andy Melton, Acct. Rep.; Tara Lyons, Office Mgr. **Wattage:** 4,200. **Ad Rates:** $15 for 30 seconds. **URL:** http://www.wkuz.com.

IOWA

DAVENPORT

283 River Cities Reader
315 Brady St.
Davenport, IA 52801
Phone: (319)324-0049
Fax: (319)323-3101
Publication E-mail: rcreader@rcreader.com

Community newspaper. **Freq:** Weekly (Wed.). **Key Personnel:** Todd McGreevy, Pub./Web Sales; Kathleen McCarthy, Editor; Tim Read, Production Mgr. **Subscription Rates:** Free. **Remarks:** Advertising accepted; rates available upon request. **URL:** http://www.rcreader.com.
Circ: (Not Reported)

DES MOINES

284 Cityview
Business Publications Corp.
The Depot at Fourth
100 4th St.
Des Moines, IA 50309
Phone: (515)288-3336
Fax: (515)288-0309
Publisher E-mail: bpc@mail.common.link.com

Alternative community newspaper. **Freq:** Weekly. **Print Method:** Web offset. **Trim Size:** 11 1/2 x 12 3/4. **Cols./Page:** 4. **Col. Width:** 2 3/10 inches. **Key Personnel:** Jennifer Wilson, Editor, jenniferwilson@bpcdm.com; Lon Matejczyk, VP Sales/Mktg., lonmatejezyk@bpcdm.com; Mark Elliott, Circulation Mgr., markelliott@bpcdm.com. **Subscription Rates:** $156 individuals.
Remarks: Accepts advertising.
Circ: Non-paid 33,000

285 Cuisine
August Home Publishing
2200 Grand Ave.
Des Moines, IA 50312
Phone: (515)282-7000
Fax: (515)283-0447
Free: (800)311-3991

Consumer magazine covering cooking. **Freq:** Bimonthly. **Subscription Rates:** $19.95 individuals; $29.95 out of country. **Remarks:** Advertising not accepted. **URL:** http://www.augusthome.com/cooking/cuisine/.
Circ: (Not Reported)

286 Garden Gate
August Home Publishing
2200 Grand Ave.
Des Moines, IA 50312
Phone: (515)282-7000
Fax: (515)283-0447
Free: (800)311-3991
Publication E-mail: gardengate@gardengatemag.com

Consumer magazine covering gardening. **Freq:** Bimonthly. **Subscription Rates:** $19.95 individuals; $29.95 out of country. **URL:** http://www.augusthome.com/gardening/gardengate/.

287 Intro
Business Publications Corp.
The Depot at Fourth
100 4th St.
Des Moines, IA 50309
Phone: (515)288-3336
Fax: (515)288-0309
Publisher E-mail: bpc@mail.common.link.com

Consumer magazine covering local travel and tourism. **Freq:** Semiannual.

Trim Size: 8 1/8 x 10 7/8. **Key Personnel:** Loretta Sieman, Editor, lorettasieman@bpcdm.com; Lon Matejczyk, VP Sales/Mktg., lonmatejczyk@bpcdm.com; Mark Elliott, Circulation Mgr., markelliott@bpcdm.com. **Subscription Rates:** Free. **Remarks:** Accepts advertising.
Ad Rates: 4C: $5,787
Circ: Controlled 170,000

288 Iowa Small Business Resource Guide
Business Publications Corp.
The Depot at Fourth
100 4th St.
Des Moines, IA 50309
Phone: (515)288-3336
Fax: (515)288-0309
Publisher E-mail: bpc@mail.common.link.com

Trade magazine covering small business. **Founded:** June 1996. **Freq:** Annual. **Trim Size:** 8 1/8 x 10 7/8. **Key Personnel:** Loretta Sieman, Editor, lorettasieman@bpcdm.com; Lon Matejczyk, VP Sales/Mktg., lonmatejczyk@bpcdm.com; Mark Elliott, Circulation Mgr., markelliott@bpcdm.com. **Remarks:** Accepts advertising.
Circ: Combined 15,000

289 Lyrical Iowa
Iowa Poetry Assoc.
2325 61st St.
Des Moines, IA 50322
Phone: (515)279-1106

Poetry journal. **Founded:** 1945. **Freq:** Annual. **Print Method:** Offset. **Trim Size:** 6 x 9. **Cols./Page:** 1. **Key Personnel:** Lucille Morgan Wilson, Editor. **ISSN:** 0076-1699. **Subscription Rates:** $9 individuals. **Remarks:** Advertising not accepted.
Circ: (Not Reported)

290 Metropolitan Des Moines
Business Publications Corp.
The Depot at Fourth
100 4th St.
Des Moines, IA 50309
Phone: (515)288-3336
Fax: (515)288-0309
Publisher E-mail: bpc@mail.common.link.com

Consumer magazine covering relocation and home improvement. **Founded:** 1988. **Freq:** Annual. **Trim Size:** 8 1/8 x 10 7/8. **Key Personnel:** Loretta Sieman, Editor, lorettasieman@bpcdm.com; Lon Matejczyk, VP Sales/Mktg., lonmatejczyk@bpcdm.com; Mark Elliott, Circulation Mgr., markelliott@bpcdm.com. **Remarks:** Accepts advertising.
Circ: Controlled 30,000

291 The Midday Record
Business Publications Corp.
The Depot at Fourth
100 4th St.
Des Moines, IA 50309
Phone: (515)288-3336
Fax: (515)288-0309
Publisher E-mail: bpc@mail.common.link.com

Business newspaper. **Founded:** 1995. **Freq:** Daily. **Key Personnel:** Bill Day, Editor, phone (515)288-0309, billday@bpcdm.com; Lon Matejczyk, VP Sales/Mktg., lonmatejczyk@bpcdm.com; Mark Elliott, Circulation Mgr., markelliott@bpcdm.com. **Subscription Rates:** $99 individuals. **Remarks:** Accepts advertising.
Ad Rates: BW: $250
Circ: Combined 500

292 more
Meredith Corp.
1716 Locust St.
Des Moines, IA 50309-3023

Phone: (515)284-3000
Fax: (515)284-3697
Free: (800)678-2674

Consumer magazine covering health, beauty, lifestyle, and other issues for women. **Freq:** Monthly. **Key Personnel:** Michael Brownstein, Publisher; Myrna Blyth, Editor-in-Chief; Susan Crandell, Exec. Editor; Ikla Stanger, Managing Editor; Julie Pinkwater, Advertising Dir. **URL:** http://www.moremag.com.

293 Northwest Shopper
Shopper-News Network
PO Box 4826
Des Moines, IA 50306

Phone: (515)262-1190

Shopping guide. **Freq:** Weekly (Wed.). **Subscription Rates:** Free.

Circ: Non-paid **22,034**

294 ShopNotes
August Home Publishing
2200 Grand Ave.
Des Moines, IA 50312

Phone: (515)282-7000
Fax: (515)283-0447
Free: (800)311-3991

Publication E-mail: shopnotes@shopnotes.com

Trade magazine covering woodworking. **Freq:** Bimonthly. **Subscription Rates:** $19.95 individuals; $29.95 out of country. **URL:** http://www.augusthome.com/woodworking/shopnotes.

295 Shopper-News Network
PO Box 4826
Des Moines, IA 50306

Phone: (515)262-1190

Shopper. **Freq:** Weekly. **Print Method:** Offset. **Trim Size:** 11 1/2 x 17. **Cols./Page:** 7. **Col. Width:** 1 3/8 inches. **Subscription Rates:** Free. **Remarks:** Accepts advertising.
Ad Rates: GLR: $5
  BW: $3,808 **Circ:** Non-paid **145,764**
  4C: $4,508
  SAU: $47.60
  PCI: $34

EDGEWOOD

296 Eastern Iowa Shopping News
Woodward Communications
103 N. Washington
PO Box 327
Edgewood, IA 52042-0327

Phone: (319)928-6214
Fax: (319)928-7028
Free: (800)658-3406

Shopping guide. **Freq:** Weekly (Wed.). **Subscription Rates:** Free.

Circ: Non-paid 17,003

FAIRFIELD

297 Handheld PC Magazine
Thaddeus Computing, Inc.
110 North Court
PO Box 869
Fairfield, IA 52556

Phone: (515)472-6330
Fax: (515)472-1879
Free: (800)373-6114

Publisher E-mail: orders@thaddeus.com

Consumer magazine covering usages and products for HP 100/2002X handheld computers. **Founded:** 1997. **Freq:** Bimonthly. **Print Method:** Web offset. **Trim Size:** 8 3/8 x 10 7/8. **Key Personnel:** Hal Goldstein, Exec. Editor; Rich Hall, Editor. **ISSN:** 1093-2585. **Subscription Rates:** $19.95 individuals; $4.95 single issue. **Remarks:** Accepts advertising. **URL:** http://www.hpcmag.com.
Ad Rates: BW: $2400 **Circ:** Paid 18108
  4C: $3150

LE MARS

298 Daily Sentinel
Le Mars Daily Sentinel
41 1st Ave. N.E.
Le Mars, IA 51031

Phone: (712)546-7031
Fax: (712)546-7035

Publication E-mail: sentinel@pionet.net

General newspaper. **Freq:** Daily. **Key Personnel:** Barbara Trimble, Publisher; Tom Stangl, General Mgr./Editor; Susan Kirwin, Marketing Dir.; Erica Baxter, Circulation Mgr.; Joyce Kneip, Business Mgr. **Subscription Rates:** $81.75 individuals; $109.50 by mail. **URL:** http://www.lemarssentinel.com.

MUSCATINE

299 Muscatine Journal
301 E. 3rd St.
PO Box 809
Muscatine, IA 52761

Phone: (319)263-2331
Fax: (319)262-8042
Free: (800)383-3198

Community newspaper. **Freq:** Mon.-Sat. **Key Personnel:** Mark Roby, Publisher; Jeff Tecklenburg, Editor. **URL:** http://www.muscatinejournal.com.

OSCEOLA

300 Osceola Sentinel-Tribune
Clarke County Publishing
PO Box 447
Osceola, IA 50213

Community newspaper. **Freq:** Weekly (Thurs.). **Print Method:** Web offset. **Subscription Rates:** $20 students. **Remarks:** Accepts advertising. **URL:** http://www.osceolaiowa.com.
Ad Rates: BW: $564.38 **Circ:** (Not Reported)
  PCI: $4.69

TAMA

301 KZAT-FM - 95.5
303 McClellan St.
Tama, IA 52339

Phone: (515)484-5958
Fax: (515)484-5962
Free: (888)484-5955

E-mail: kzat@kzat.com

Format: Classical. **Networks:** CBS. **Owner:** Camrory Broadcasting, Inc., at above address. **Founded:** May 31, 1997. **Operating Hours:** Continuous. **ADI:** Cedar Rapids-Waterloo-Dubuque, IA. **Key Personnel:** Cathy Campbell, Pres./General Mgr., ccampbell@kzat.com; Adam Abrams, News Dir., adam@kzat.com; Eric Thompson, Program Dir.; Mindy Schmidt, Office Mgr., mimi@kzat.com. **Wattage:** 6,000. **Ad Rates:** $7.25-14.50 for 30 seconds. **URL:** http://www.kzat.com.

KANSAS

GARDEN CITY

🎙 302 KANZ-FM - 91.1
201 N. 7th St.
Garden City, KS 67846   Phone: (316)275-7444

Format: Public Radio. **Networks:** National Public Radio (NPR); Public Radio International (PRI). **Owner:** Kanza Society, Inc., at above address. **Founded:** Oct. 4, 1979. **Operating Hours:** Continuous. **Key Personnel:** Brian T. Ajjas, Exec. Dir., hpprexec@pld.com; Lynn Boitano, Program Dir.; Nate Wald, News Dir.; Diana Aqular-Sinclar, Marketing. **Wattage:** 100,000. **Ad Rates:** Noncommercial; underwriting available.

GOODLAND

📖 303 Sherman County Star
Box 599   Phone: (785)899-5500
Goodland, KS 67735   Fax: (785)899-6260
                                           Free: (800)583-8677

Community newspaper. **Freq:** Weekly (Wed.). **Key Personnel:** Eric Yonkey, Publisher; Roxie Yonkey, Editor, roxie@scstar.com. **Subscription Rates:** $26 individuals; $32 out of state. **Remarks:** Accepts advertising. **URL:** http://www.scstar.com. **Feature Editors:** Fred Kester, *Sports*.
Ad Rates: BW: $600   **Circ:** (Not Reported)
                 PCI: $4.25

KINSLEY

📖 304 Kinsley Graphic
Vallene Immenschuh
522 Marsh   Phone: (316)659-2244
Kinsley, KS 67547   Fax: (316)659-2444

Community newspaper. **Freq:** Weekly. **Key Personnel:** Vallene Immenschuh, Publisher; Carl Immenschuh, Editor. **Subscription Rates:** $26.25 individuals. **URL:** http://www.thepelicanpress.com/graphic.htm.
                                           Circ: Paid 3,215

LAWRENCE

📖 305 The Lawrence Journal-World
PO Box 888   Phone: (785)832-7136
Lawrence, KS 66044   Free: (800)578-8748
Publication E-mail: sales@ljworld.com

General newspaper. **Freq:** Mon.-Sun. **Subscription Rates:** $210 individuals; $230 out of state. **Remarks:** Advertising accepted; rates available upon request. **URL:** http://www.ljworld.com.
                                           Circ: (Not Reported)

LENEXA

📖 306 Fresh Trends
Vance Publishing Corp.
10901 W. 84th Terrace   Phone: (913)438-8700
Lenexa, KS 66214   Fax: (913)438-0690
                                           Free: (800)252-1925

Publication E-mail: new@thepacker.com

Trade journal covering survey results of produce consumers. **Freq:** Annual. **Cols./Page:** 3. **Key Personnel:** Lori Fairchild, Editor; Jenny Herron, Advertising Mgr.; Cathy Donahue, Circulation Mgr. **ISSN:** 0030-9168. **Subscription Rates:** $20 individuals. **Remarks:** Accepts advertising.
                                           Circ: (Not Reported)

MANHATTAN

📖 307 Lifestory
Letter Rock Publications
3591 Letter Rock Rd.   Phone: (785)539-0910
Manhattan, KS 66502   Fax: (785)539-4169
Publisher E-mail: lifestor@kansas.net

Consumer magazine covering history and genealogy. **Freq:** Monthly. **Trim Size:** 8 1/2 x 11. **Key Personnel:** Charley Kempthorne, Editor; Steve Hoffman, Business Mgr.; Kathleen Oldfather, Office Mgr.; June Kempthorne, Advertising Dir. **ISSN:** 1967-9243. **Subscription Rates:** $24 individuals; $28 Canada and Mexico; $40 elsewhere. **Remarks:** Accepts advertising.
Ad Rates: BW: $260   **Circ:** (Not Reported)

OVERLAND PARK

📖 308 Cellular & Mobile International
Intertec Publishing Corp.
PO Box 12901   Phone: (913)967-7303
Overland Park, KS 66212-2901   Fax: (913)967-1901
                                           Free: (800)262-1954

Trade magazine covering mobile communication. **Freq:** 29/year. **Key Personnel:** Mercy Contrevas, Publisher; Ramona Isbell, Editor, ramona_isbell@intertec.com. **URL:** http://www.intertec.com.
                                           Circ: Combined 10,000

SHAWNEE

📖 309 Shawnee Journal Herald
Liberty Group Publishing
11004 Johnson Dr.
Shawnee, KS 66203-2869
Publication E-mail: editor@shawneejournalherald.com

Community newspaper. **Freq:** Weekly. **Subscription Rates:** $22.50 individuals; $27.50 out of area; $32.50 out of state. **Remarks:** Advertising accepted; rates available upon request. **URL:** http://www.shawneejournalherald.com.
                                           Circ: (Not Reported)

WICHITA

📖 310 Multivariate Experimental Clinical Research
Wichita State University
1845 Fairmount
Wichita, KS 67260-0034   Phone: (316)978-3170

Scholarly journal covering psychological research. **Freq:** Irregular. **Key Personnel:** Dr. Charles Burdsal, Editor, burdsal@wsuhub.uc.twsu.edu. **ISSN:** 0147-3964. **Subscription Rates:** $29 individuals; $35 out of country; $50 institutions; $56 institutions out of country.

KENTUCKY

BARDSTOWN

📖 **311 Computer Times**
Louisville Computer Times
3206 Kings Ct.   Phone: (502)348-0295
Bardstown, KY 40004   Free: (800)211-6542

Trade magazine covering computer trends and other issues for SOHO users. **Freq:** Monthly. **Key Personnel:** Terry Kibiloski, Editor; Sean Kibiloski, Managing Editor; Charlene Jones, Exec. Editor. **Subscription Rates:** $12 individuals. **URL:** http://www.computertimes.com.

Circ: Combined 60,000

BOWLING GREEN

📖 **312 Psychology**
Institute for Leadership and Organization Effectiveness
1409 Mt. Ayre
Bowling Green, KY 42101

Professional journal covering behavioral sciences and education. **Subtitle:** A Journal of Human Behavior. **Founded:** 1964. **Freq:** Quarterly. **Key Personnel:** Dr. Joseph P. Cangemi, Editor; Dr. Casimir J. Kowalski, Managing Editor. **Subscription Rates:** $22 individuals; $6 single issue. **Remarks:** Accepts advertising.

Circ: (Not Reported)

HAROLD

🎙 **313 WXLR-FM - 104.9**
US Highway 23 Main St.   Phone: (606)478-1200
Paulsboro Row   Fax: (606)478-1040
Harold, KY 41635   Free: (800)635-7052
E-mail: radio@thedoublex.com

Format: Classic Rock. **Networks:** CBS; Westwood One Radio. **Owner:** Adam D. Gearheart, 99 Church St., PO Box 1049, Harold, KY 41635. **Founded:** Jan. 14, 1994. **Operating Hours:** Continuous. **Key Personnel:** Barry Boyd, Sales Mgr.; Debi Manuel, Program Dir.; Brandi Gearheart, Traffic Mgr.; Michael Thomas, Production Mgr. **Wattage:** 3,000. **Ad Rates:** $10 for 30 seconds; $15 for 60 seconds. **URL:** http://www.thedoublex.com.

LOUISVILLE

📖 **314 Louisville Eccentric Observer (LEO)**
Louisville Eccentric Observer
3900 Shelbyville Rd., Ste. 14A
Louisville, KY 40207   Phone: (502)895-9770

Community newspaper. **Freq:** Weekly (Wed.). **Subscription Rates:** Free.
Circ: Combined **31,251**

🎙 **315 WTFX-FM - 100.5**
4000 Radio Dr., No. 1   Phone: (502)479-2222
Louisville, KY 40218   Fax: (502)479-2234

Format: Album-Oriented Rock (AOR). **Owner:** Clear Channel Broadcasting Inc., 200 Concord Plaza, Ste. 600, San Antonio, TX 78216. **Operating Hours:** Continuous. **ADI:** Louisville, KY. **Key Personnel:** Doug James, Vice President/General Mgr.; Michael Lee, Operations Mgr.; Kevin Hughes, General Sales Mgr.; Keith Kraus, Sales Mgr. **Wattage:** 50,000.

RUSSELLVILLE

📖 **316 News-Democrat & Leader**
120 Public Sq.
PO Box 270
Russellville, KY 42276

Community newspaper. **Founded:** 1806. **Key Personnel:** Randall G. Fuqua, Publisher; Jim Turner, Editor; Nancy Allen, Advertising Mgr.; Rita Stuart, Business Mgr.; Steve Justice, Production Mgr. **URL:** http://www.newdemocratleader.com.

LOUISIANA

FRANKLINTON

317 WFCG-FM - 98.9
PO Box 604
Franklinton, LA 70438
Phone: (504)839-4110
Fax: (504)839-4800

Format: Country. **Owner:** Gaco Broadcasting Corp., at above address. **Operating Hours:** Continuous. **Key Personnel:** Vickie DeCarlo, Contact.

METAIRIE

318 New Orleans CityBusiness
111 Veterans Blvd., Ste. 1810
Metairie, LA 70005
Phone: (504)834-9292
Publication E-mail: sales@neworleans.com

Business newspaper. **Freq:** Weekly. **Key Personnel:** Carolyn W. McLellan, Publisher; Kathy Finn, Editor; Judi Russell, Managing Editor. **Subscription Rates:** $49.95 individuals. **Remarks:** Advertising accepted; rates available upon request. **URL:** http://www.neworleans.com/citybusiness.
Circ: (Not Reported)

NEW ORLEANS

319 Louisiana Music Directory
Offbeat Publications
333 St. Charles Ave., Ste. 614
New Orleans, LA 70130-3117
Phone: (504)522-5533
Fax: (504)522-1159

Trade directory magazine covering music, entertainment-related business, and musicians in Louisiana. **Founded:** 1990. **Freq:** Annual. **Print Method:** Web offset. **Trim Size:** 8 1/4 x 10 3/4. **Cols./Page:** 4. **Col. Width:** 1 11/16 inches. **Col. Depth:** 9 13/16 inches. **Key Personnel:** Jan V. Ramsey, Editor and Publisher. **ISSN:** 1072-4427. **Subscription Rates:** $28 individuals. **Remarks:** Accepts advertising. **URL:** http://www.offbeat.com.
Ad Rates: BW: $1,890
4C: $2,590
Circ: Non-paid 13,000

320 Offbeat Magazine
Offbeat Publications
333 St. Charles Ave., Ste. 614
New Orleans, LA 70130-3117
Phone: (504)522-5533
Fax: (504)522-1159
Publication E-mail: editor@offbeat.com

Consumer magazine covering music and entertainment in New Orleans, Louisiana. **Subtitle:** New Orleans' and Louisiana's Music Magazine. **Founded:** Aug. 1988. **Freq:** Monthly. **Print Method:** Web offset. **Trim Size:** 8 1/4 x 10 3/4. **Cols./Page:** 4. **Col. Width:** 1 11/16 inches. **Col. Depth:** 9 13/16 inches. **Key Personnel:** Jan V. Ramsey, Publisher; David H. Jones, Editor. **ISSN:** 1090-0810. **Subscription Rates:** $35 individuals; $73 out of country; $2.95 single issue. **Remarks:** Accepts advertising. **URL:** http://www.offbeat.com.
Ad Rates: BW: $1,685
4C: $2,185
Circ: Combined **50,000**

SHREVEPORT

321 Q.J.I.
Louisiana State University, Shreveport
1 University Pl.
Shreveport, LA 71115-2399
Phone: (318)797-5235
Fax: (318)797-5122

Scholarly journal covering philosophy. **Founded:** 1977. **Freq:** Quarterly. **Print Method:** Offset. **Key Personnel:** Norman A. Dolch, Ph.D., Editor, ndolch@pilot.lsus.edu; Laura Marron, Ph.D., Editor. **ISSN:** 0783-9752. **Subscription Rates:** $20 individuals; $35 libraries. **Remarks:** Advertising not accepted.
Circ: Paid 100

Ad Rates: GLR = general line rate; BW = one-time black & white page rate; 4C = one-time four color page rate; SAU = standard advertising unit rate; CNU = Canadian newspaper advertising unit rate; PCI = per column inch rate.
Circulation: ★ = ABC; △ = BPA; ♦ = CAC; ● = CCAB; ❏ = VAC; ⊕ = PO Statement; ‡ = Publisher's Report; Boldface figures = sworn; Light figures = estimated.
Entry type: ▯ = Print; ✇ = Broadcast.

47

MAINE

NEW GLOUCESTER

📖 **322 New Gloucester News**
PO Box 102
New Gloucester, ME 04260

Community newspaper. **Founded:** 1972. **Freq:** Weekly. **Key Personnel:** Catherine Cooper, Editor; Jackie Rybeck, Advertising Mgr. **Subscription Rates:** $30 individuals. **URL:** http://www.newgloucesternews.com.

PORTLAND

📖 **323 Casco Bay Weekly**
Maine Publishing Corp.
561 Congress St.
Portland, ME 04101   Phone: (207)775-6601

Community newspaper. **Freq:** Weekly (Thurs.). **Subscription Rates:** Free.
                                                    Circ: Combined **29,423**

WINDHAM

📖 **324 The Suburban News**
733 Roosevelt Trl.   Phone: (207)892-1166
Windham, ME 04062   Fax: (207)892-1171

Community newspaper. **Freq:** Weekly. **Subscription Rates:** $52 by mail.
Remarks: Accepts advertising. **URL:** http://www.suburbanews.com.
Ad Rates: BW: $525   **Circ:** Combined 8000
                4C: $750

MARYLAND

BALTIMORE

325 World Federation for Mental Health Annual Report
World Federation for Mental Health
Sheppard & Enoch Pratt Hospital
Box 6815   Phone: (410)938-3180
Baltimore, MD 21285-6815   Fax: (410)938-3183
Publisher E-mail: wfmh@erols.com

Professional journal covering mental health. **Freq:** Annual. **Key Personnel:** Prof. Eugene B. Brody, M.D., Editor-in-Chief. **Remarks:** Advertising not accepted. **URL:** http://www.wfmh.org.
                                              Circ: Paid 2500

COLUMBIA

326 Korea Post
9505 Berger Rd.   Phone: (410)381-6633
Columbia, MD 21046   Fax: (410)290-9335

Korean language newspaper. **Founded:** 1989. **Freq:** Weekly. **Key Personnel:** Jung Kyun Yi, Contact. **Subscription Rates:** Free; $40 by mail. **Remarks:** Accepts advertising.
Ad Rates: BW: $300   **Circ:** Combined 13,000

327 Towson Times
Patuxent Publishing Co.
10750 Little Patuxent Pkwy.
Columbia, MD 21044   Phone: (410)730-3990

Community newspaper. **Available Online.**

FROSTBURG

328 Journal of the Alleghenies
Council of the Alleghenies Inc.
Box 514
Frostburg, MD 21532

Journal covering local history. **Founded:** 1962. **Freq:** Annual. **Remarks:** Advertising not accepted.
                                              Circ: Paid 200

GAITHERSBURG

329 Aspen Hill Gazette
The Gazette Newspapers
1200 Quince Orchard Blvd.   Phone: (301)253-6161
Gaithersburg, MD 20878   Fax: (301)670-7183

Community newspaper. **Freq:** Weekly (Wed.). **Subscription Rates:** Free.
                                        Circ: Combined 8,324

330 Business Gazette
The Gazette Newspapers
1200 Quince Orchard Blvd.   Phone: (301)253-6161
Gaithersburg, MD 20878   Fax: (301)670-7183

Community business newspaper. **Freq:** Monthly. **Subscription Rates:** Free.
                                      Circ: Non-paid 28,332

331 College Park Gazette
The Gazette Newspapers
1200 Quince Orchard Blvd.   Phone: (301)253-6161
Gaithersburg, MD 20878   Fax: (301)670-7183

Community newspaper. **Freq:** Weekly (Thurs.). **Subscription Rates:** Free.
                                       Circ: Combined 17,460

332 Frederick Gazette
The Gazette Newspapers
1200 Quince Orchard Blvd.   Phone: (301)253-6161
Gaithersburg, MD 20878   Fax: (301)670-7183

Community newspaper. **Freq:** Weekly (Thurs.). **Subscription Rates:** Free.
                                       Circ: Combined 27,098

333 Kensington Gazette
The Gazette Newspapers
1200 Quince Orchard Blvd.   Phone: (301)253-6161
Gaithersburg, MD 20878   Fax: (301)670-7183

Community newspaper. **Freq:** Weekly (Wed.). **Subscription Rates:** Free.
                                        Circ: Combined 7,158

334 Montgomery Village Gazette
The Gazette Newspapers
1200 Quince Orchard Blvd.   Phone: (301)253-6161
Gaithersburg, MD 20878   Fax: (301)670-7183

Community newspaper. **Freq:** Weekly (Wed.). **Subscription Rates:** Free.
                                        Circ: Combined 9,888

335 New Market/Urbana Gazette
The Gazette Newspapers
1200 Quince Orchard Blvd.   Phone: (301)253-6161
Gaithersburg, MD 20878   Fax: (301)670-7183

Community newspaper. **Freq:** Weekly (Thurs.). **Subscription Rates:** Free.
                                        Circ: Combined 8,905

336 North Potomac Gazette
The Gazette Newspapers
1200 Quince Orchard Blvd.   Phone: (301)253-6161
Gaithersburg, MD 20878   Fax: (301)670-7183

Community newspaper. **Freq:** Weekly (Wed.). **Subscription Rates:** Free.
                                        Circ: Combined 4,079

337 Takoma Park
The Gazette Newspapers
1200 Quince Orchard Blvd.   Phone: (301)253-6161
Gaithersburg, MD 20878   Fax: (301)670-7183

Community newspaper. **Freq:** Weekly (Wed.). **Subscription Rates:** Free.
                                        Circ: Combined 5,720

Ad Rates: GLR = general line rate; BW = one-time black & white page rate; 4C = one-time four color page rate; SAU = standard advertising unit rate;
CNU = Canadian newspaper advertising unit rate; PCI = per column inch rate.
Circulation: ★ = ABC; △ = BPA; ♦ = CAC; • = CCAB; ❏ = VAC; ⊕ = PO Statement; ‡ = Publisher's Report; Boldface figures = sworn; Light figures = estimated.
Entry type: ▯ = Print; ✽ = Broadcast.

📖 **338　Tech Gazette**
The Gazette Newspapers
1200 Quince Orchard Blvd.　　　　　　Phone: (301)253-6161
Gaithersburg, MD 20878　　　　　　　Fax: (301)670-7183

Community newspaper covering technology. **Freq:** Monthly. **Subscription Rates:** Free.
　　　　　　　　　　　　　　　　　Circ: Non-paid **30,987**

📖 **339　Walkersville/Thurmont Gazette**
The Gazette Newspapers
1200 Quince Orchard Blvd.　　　　　　Phone: (301)253-6161
Gaithersburg, MD 20878　　　　　　　Fax: (301)670-7183

Community newspaper. **Freq:** Weekly (Thurs.). **Subscription Rates:** Free.
　　　　　　　　　　　　　　　　　Circ: Combined **9,961**

POTOMAC

📖 **340　Potomac/Bethesda Almanac**
Connection Publishing, Inc.
10220 River Rd., No. 303
Potomac, MD 20854　　　　　　　　Phone: (301)983-3350

Community newspaper. **Freq:** Weekly (Wed.). **Key Personnel:** Peter C. Labovitz, Pres./Pub. **Subscription Rates:** Free.
　　　　　　　　　　　　　　　　　Circ: Combined ◆**26,240**

📖 **341　Wireless Networks**
Phillips Business Information, Inc.
1201 Seven Locks Rd., Ste. 300　　　　Phone: (301)340-1520
Potomac, MD 20854　　　　　　　　Fax: (301)340-3847
　　　　　　　　　　　　　　　　　Free: (888)707-5809
Publication E-mail: orders@acm.org
Publisher E-mail: clientservices.pbi@phillips.com

Technical trade magazine covering the wireless industry. **Freq:** Quarterly. **Key Personnel:** Mark Mandelbaum, Publications Dir. **Subscription Rates:** $170 individuals; $47 single issue. **URL:** http://www.acm.org.

SILVER SPRING

📖 **342　Montessori News**
International Montessori Society
912 Thayer Ave.
Silver Spring, MD 20910　　　　　　Phone: (301)589-1127
Publication E-mail: havis@erols.com

Newspaper of the International Montessori Society covering education. **Freq:** Semiannual. **ISSN:** 0889-6720. **Subscription Rates:** Free to qualified subscribers. **URL:** http://www.wdn.com/trust/ims.

WALDORF

📖 **343　Accident Investigation Quarterly**
Victor T. Craig
PO Box 234
Waldorf, MD 20604-0234　　　　　　Phone: (301)843-1371

Professional journal. **Founded:** 1994. **Freq:** Quarterly. **Key Personnel:** Victor T. Craig, Editor and Publisher. **ISSN:** 1082-6521. **Subscription Rates:** $27 individuals U.S. & Canada; $49 two years. **Remarks:** Advertising accepted; rates available upon request.
　　　　　　　　　　　　　　　　　Circ: Combined 2100

📖 **344　Accident Reconstruction Journal**
Victor T. Craig
PO Box 234
Waldorf, MD 20604-0234　　　　　　Phone: (301)843-1371

Professional journal. **Founded:** 1989. **Freq:** Bimonthly. **Key Personnel:** Victor T. Craig, Editor. **ISSN:** 1057-8153. **Subscription Rates:** $39 individuals U.S. and Canada; $69 two years. **Remarks:** Advertising accepted; rates available upon request.
　　　　　　　　　　　　　　　　　Circ: Combined 3550

WHEATON

📖 **345　Lexicon**
Ninthwave Records and Publishing
PO Box 1734
Wheaton, MD 20915
Publication E-mail: guerue@erols.com

Consumer magazine covering music. **Subtitle:** New Wave and Beyond. **Freq:** Quarterly. **Key Personnel:** David Richards, Managing Editor. **Subscription Rates:** $12 individuals; $15 Canada and Mexico; $18 elsewhere. **Remarks:** Accepts advertising.
　　　　　　　　　　　　　　　　　Circ: (Not Reported)

MASSACHUSETTS

ALLSTON

📖 346 HERMENAUT
PO Box 141
Allston, MA 02134
Phone: (617)522-7100
Publication E-mail: editors@hermanaut.com

Magazine bringing difficult but important philosophical ideas about popular culture. **Subtitle:** The Digest of Heady Philosophy. **Freq:** Quarterly. **Print Method:** Saddle-stitched. **Trim Size:** 7 x 8 1/2. **Key Personnel:** Joshua Glenn, Editor. **Subscription Rates:** $20 individuals; $30 elsewhere. **Remarks:** Advertising accepted; rates available upon request.

Circ: 2,000

AMHERST

📖 347 Hopscotch
Duke University Press
Amherst College
PO Box 5000, Box 2255
Amherst, MA 01002-5000

Scholarly journal covering cultural and ethnic issues. **Freq:** Quarterly. **Key Personnel:** Ilan Stavans, Editor; Antonio Benitez-Rojo, Editor-at-Large; Nancy Kimberly, Advertising, phone (919)687-3653, nancy.kimberly@duke.com. **Subscription Rates:** $24 individuals; $53 institutions. **Remarks:** Accepts advertising. **URL:** http://www.hopscotch.org.
Ad Rates: BW: $1000

Circ: Combined 1500

📖 348 Nineteenth Century Theatre
University of Massachusetts at Amherst
Dept. of English
Amherst, MA 01003

Journal covering theatre and film. **Freq:** Semiannual. **Print Method:** Offset litho. **Key Personnel:** Prof. Jacky Bratton, Editor; Ann Featherstone, Editorial Asst. **ISSN:** 0893-3766. **Subscription Rates:** $18 individuals; $27 institutions. **Remarks:** Accepts advertising.

Circ: Paid 380

BOSTON

📖 349 Critical Sociology
Humanities Press, Inc.
112 Water St., Ste. 400
Boston, MA 02109
Phone: (617)742-5277
Fax: (617)263-2324
Free: (877)999-7575

Publisher E-mail: cs@brillusa.com

Professional journal covering sociology. **Founded:** 1969. **Freq:** Triennial. **Trim Size:** 6 x 9. **Cols./Page:** 1. **Key Personnel:** David Fasenfest, Editor; Elizabeth Cushinsky, VP/General Mgr. **ISSN:** 0896-9205. **Subscription Rates:** $34 individuals; $49 out of country. **Remarks:** Accepts advertising. **Former name:** Insurgent Sociologist.
Ad Rates: BW: $200

Circ: Paid 850

📖 350 Design Times
The Regis Publishing Co., Inc.
1 Design Center Pl., Ste. 249
Boston, MA 02210
Phone: (617)443-0636
Fax: (617)443-0637

Consumer and professional magazine covering interior design. **Freq:** Bimonthly. **Key Personnel:** Louis Postel, Editor and Publisher. **Subscription Rates:** $19.95 individuals. **URL:** http://www.designtimes.net/.

📖 351 J Magazine
Genki Publishing
20 Park Plaza, Ste. 616
Boston, MA 02116
Phone: (617)423-0066
Fax: (617)423-9545

Japadese language consumer magazine covering music and entertainment for Japanese youth. **Founded:** 1991. **Freq:** Monthly. **Key Personnel:** Kiyoko Murashima, Contact. **Subscription Rates:** Free; $30 by mail. **Remarks:** Accepts advertising.
Ad Rates: BW: $1,800
4C: $2,700
Circ: Combined 20,000

📖 352 Journal of Phenomenological Psychology
Humanities Press, Inc.
112 Water St., Ste. 400
Boston, MA 02109
Phone: (617)742-5277
Fax: (617)263-2324
Free: (877)999-7575

Publisher E-mail: cs@brillusa.com

Professional journal covering philosophy, psychology, and phenomenology. **Founded:** 1969. **Freq:** Semiannual. **Trim Size:** 6 x 9. **Cols./Page:** 1. **Key Personnel:** Frederick J. Wertz, Editor; Elizabeth Cushinsky, VP/General Mgr. **ISSN:** 0047-2662. **Subscription Rates:** $65 individuals; $75 out of country. **Remarks:** Accepts advertising.
Ad Rates: BW: $150

Circ: Paid 200

📖 353 Newbury Street and Back Bay Guide
Jacaranda Publishing, Inc.
143 Newbury St.
Boston, MA 02116
Phone: (617)424-9005
Fax: (617)424-8944
Publisher E-mail: info@jacaranda-media.com

Travel and tourist newspaper. **Freq:** Biweekly. **Key Personnel:** Sarie Booy, Advertising. **Subscription Rates:** $25 individuals. **Remarks:** Accepts advertising. **URL:** http://backbayguide.com.
Ad Rates: BW: $810

Circ: Combined 7,500

📖 354 Passages
Humanities Press, Inc.
112 Water St., Ste. 400
Boston, MA 02109
Phone: (617)742-5277
Fax: (617)263-2324
Free: (877)999-7575

Publisher E-mail: cs@brillusa.com

Scholarly, interdisciplinary journal covering sociology and cultural studies. **Subtitle:** Journal of Transnational and Transcultural Studies. **Founded:** 1999. **Freq:** Semiannual. **Trim Size:** 6 x 9. **Cols./Page:** 1. **Key Personnel:** Mohammed A. Bamyeh, Editor; Elizabeth Cushinsky, VP/General Mgr. **ISSN:** 1388-4433. **Subscription Rates:** $42 individuals; $52 out of country. **Remarks:** Accepts advertising.
Ad Rates: BW: $150

Circ: (Not Reported)

📖 **355 Radical Philosophy Review**
Humanities Press, Inc.
112 Water St., Ste. 400
Boston, MA 02109

Phone: (617)742-5277
Fax: (617)263-2324
Free: (877)999-7575

Publisher E-mail: cs@brillusa.com

Professional journal covering philosophy. **Subtitle:** A Journal for Progressive Thought. **Founded:** 1998. **Freq:** Semiannual. **Trim Size:** 6 x 9. **Cols./Page:** 1. **Key Personnel:** Lewis R. Gordon, Editor; Elizabeth Cushinsky, VP/General Mgr. **ISSN:** 1388-4441. **Subscription Rates:** $35 individuals; $45 out of country. **Remarks:** Accepts advertising. **Former name:** Radical Philosophy Review of Books.
Ad Rates: BW: $150　　　　　　**Circ:** (Not Reported)

📖 **356 Research in Phenomenology**
Humanities Press, Inc.
112 Water St., Ste. 400
Boston, MA 02109

Phone: (617)742-5277
Fax: (617)263-2324
Free: (877)999-7575

Publisher E-mail: cs@brillusa.com

Professional journal covering phenomenological philosophy. **Founded:** 1970. **Freq:** Annual. **Trim Size:** 6 x 9. **Cols./Page:** 1. **Key Personnel:** John Sallis, Editor; Elizabeth Cushinsky, VP/General Mgr. **ISSN:** 0085-5553. **Subscription Rates:** $50 individuals; $60 out of country. **Remarks:** Accepts advertising.
Ad Rates: BW: $150　　　　　　**Circ:** Paid 200

📖 **357 Review of Existential Psychology and Psychiatry**
Humanities Press, Inc.
112 Water St., Ste. 400
Boston, MA 02109

Phone: (617)742-5277
Fax: (617)263-2324
Free: (877)999-7575

Publisher E-mail: cs@brillusa.com

Professional journal covering psychotherapy and the human experience. **Subtitle:** A Journal of Ethical and Political Philosophy. **Founded:** 1974. **Freq:** Triennial. **Trim Size:** 6 x 9. **Cols./Page:** 1. **Key Personnel:** Keith Hoeller, Editor; Elizabeth Cushinsky, VP and General Mgr. **ISSN:** 0361-1531. **Subscription Rates:** $39 individuals; $49 out of country; $29.95 single issue. **Remarks:** Accepts advertising.
Ad Rates: BW: $200　　　　　　**Circ:** Paid 320

📖 **358 Studies in Practical Philosophy**
Humanities Press, Inc.
112 Water St., Ste. 400
Boston, MA 02109

Phone: (617)742-5277
Fax: (617)263-2324
Free: (877)999-7575

Publisher E-mail: cs@brillusa.com

Professional journal covering philosophy. **Subtitle:** A Journal of Ethical and Political Philosophy. **Founded:** 1999. **Freq:** Semiannual. **Trim Size:** 6 x 9. **Cols./Page:** 1. **Key Personnel:** Jennifer Hansen, Editor; Michael Collins Hughes, Editor; Malek Moazzam-Doulat, Editor. **ISSN:** 1389-0506. **Subscription Rates:** $35 individuals; $52 out of country. **Remarks:** Accepts advertising.
Ad Rates: BW: $150　　　　　　**Circ:** (Not Reported)

🎤 **359 WNKS-FM - 95.1**
116 Huntington Ave.
Boston, MA 02116

Format: Contemporary Hit Radio (CHR). **Owner:** EZ Charlotte, Inc., at above address. **Founded:** July 15, 1975. **Formerly:** WEOJ-FM. **Operating Hours:** Continuous. **Key Personnel:** Bill Schoening, General Mgr., phone (704)945-3004; Keith Cornwell, Sales Mgr., phone (704)945-3027; Brian Bridgeman, Program Dir., phone (704)945-3006. **Wattage:** 100,000. **URL:** http://www.kiss951.com.

🎤 **360 WYLX-FM - 97.3**
1200 Soldiers Field
Boston, MA 02134

Free: (800)880-9662

E-mail: robbin@alex973.com

Format: Classic Rock. **Owner:** CBS Radio, Inc., 950 W. Main St., Lebanon, OH 45036. **Founded:** Apr. 1994. **Formerly:** WMMA-FM (1994). **Operating Hours:** Continuous. **ADI:** Cincinnati, OH. **Key Personnel:** Robbin Dell, General Mgr., robbin@alex973.com; Deanna K. Sanders, Business Mgr., deanna@alex973.com; Scott Carlisle, pd@alex973.com; Dave Smith, Chief Engineer; Gina Easterly, Traffic Dir. **Wattage:** 6,000. **Ad Rates:** Advertising accepted; rates available upon request. **URL:** http://www.alex@973.com.

BROOKLINE

📖 **361 Cook's Illustrated**
Boston Common Press
17 Station St.
Brookline, MA 02146

Consumer magazine covering cooking. **Founded:** 1991. **Key Personnel:** Keith Powers, Managing Editor.

📖 **362 SunExpert**
Computer Publishing Group, Inc.
320 Washington St.
Brookline, MA 02146-3202

Phone: (617)739-7001
Fax: (617)739-7003

Trade magazine for SPARC and RS/6000 workstation users. **Freq:** Monthly. **Key Personnel:** Douglas Pryor, Editor-in-Chief, dpryor@cpg.com; S. Henry Sacks, Publisher, shs@cpg.com; Lisa Guisbond, Managing Editor, lisa@cpg.com. **URL:** http://www.cpg.com.
Circ: Combined 93,500

CAMBRIDGE

📖 **363 Harvard Education Bulletin**
Harvard Graduate School of Education
35 Longfellow Hall
Appian Way
Cambridge, MA 02138

Magazine for the Harvard Graduate School of Education. **Freq:** Semiannual. **Trim Size:** 8 1/2 x 11. **Cols./Page:** 2. **Key Personnel:** Andrew Hrycyna, Editor. **Subscription Rates:** Free to qualified subscribers.

📖 **364 Harvard Journal of Law and Public Policy**
Harvard Society for Law and Public Policy, Inc.
Cambridge, MA 02138

Phone: (617)495-3105
Fax: (617)496-0620

Professional journal covering law. **Founded:** 1978. **Freq:** Triennial. **Cols./Page:** 1. **ISSN:** 0193-4872. **Subscription Rates:** $32.50 individuals; $38 out of country; $12 single issue; $15 single issue out-of-country. **Remarks:** Accepts advertising. **Online:** LEXIS-NEXIS; Westlaw.
Circ: (Not Reported)

📖 **365 Peacework**
American Friends Service Committee (AFSC)
2161 Massachusetts Ave.
Cambridge, MA 02140

Phone: (617)661-6130
Fax: (617)354-2832

Publication E-mail: pwork@igc.org

Periodical covering social issues, including disarmament, peace and social justice. **Subtitle:** Global Thought and Local Action for Nonviolent Social Change. **Founded:** June 1, 1972. **Freq:** Monthly. **Trim Size:** 8 1/2 x 11. **Key Personnel:** Paticia Watson, Editor. **ISSN:** 0748-0725. **Subscription Rates:** $20 individuals first-class mail; $7 students and low income; $30 out of country. **Remarks:** Advertising not accepted. **Alt. Formats:** Audio tape; Braille; Diskette; Microform.
Circ: Combined 2500

📖 **366 R.L.E. Currents**
Massachusetts Institute of Technology
77 Massachusetts Ave., Rm. 36-412
Cambridge, MA 02139

Phone: (617)253-2566
Fax: (617)253-1301

Publication E-mail: bpassero@rle.mit.edu

Technical journal covering electronics. **Founded:** Dec. 1988. **Freq:** Semiannual. **ISSN:** 1040-2012. **Subscription Rates:** Free to qualified subscribers. **Remarks:** Advertising not accepted.
Circ: (Not Reported)

FRAMINGHAM

367 CIO Web Business
CIO Communications
492 Old Connecticut Path   Phone: (508)872-0080
PO Box 9208   Fax: (508)879-7784
Framingham, MA 01701-9208   Free: (800)788-4605

Trade magazine covering business on the Internet. **Freq:** Bimonthly. **Key Personnel:** Abbie Lundberg, Editor-in-Chief; Richard Pastore, Exec. Editor; Gary J. Beach, Publisher. **Subscription Rates:** $30 individuals. **URL:** http://www.web.master.com.

                                             Circ: Paid 150,000

368 The Industry Standard
International Data Group
5 Speen St.   Phone: (508)879-0700
PO Box 9171   Fax: (508)875-8931
Framingham, MA 01701   Free: (800)343-4935

Business magazine covering the Internet economy. **Freq:** Weekly. **Key Personnel:** Jonathan Weber, Editor-in-Chief. **Subscription Rates:** $84 individuals.

369 IntraNet Magazine
Network World Inc./IDG
161 Worcester Rd.   Phone: (508)875-6400
PO Box 9172   Fax: (508)820-3467
Framingham, MA 01701-9172   Free: (800)622-1108
Publisher E-mail: nwnews@nww.com

Trade magazine covering intranets. **Freq:** Monthly. **Key Personnel:** John Gallant, Editor-in-Chief, jgallant@nww.com; John Dix, Editor, jdix@nww.com; Beth Schultz, Exec. Editor, bschultz@nww.com. **Subscription Rates:** Free. **URL:** http://www.nwfusion.com.

GOSHEN

370 Paths of Learning
Down-to-Earth Books
PO Box 163
Goshen, MA 01032   Phone: (413)628-0227

Journal covering poetry.

HATFIELD

371 Valley Advocate
New Mass. Media, Inc.
87 School St.   Phone: (413)247-9301
Hatfield, MA 01038   Fax: (413)247-5439

Community newspaper. **Freq:** Weekly. **Key Personnel:** Kathy Nylic, Publisher; Dan Caccavaro, Editor-in-Chief; Tom Vannah, Managing Editor; Michael Knapp, Production Mgr.; Jeffrey Owczarski, Circulation Mgr. **URL:** http://www.valleyadvocate.com.

372 Westchester County Weekly
New Mass. Media, Inc.
87 School St.   Phone: (413)247-9301
Hatfield, MA 01038   Fax: (413)247-5439

Community newspaper. **Freq:** Weekly. **Key Personnel:** Eric Benjamin, Publisher; Lorraine Gengo, Editor-in-Chief; Jennifer Ponte Canning, Managing Editor; Amy Pitz, Sales Mgr.; Bill Adams, Production Mgr. **Remarks:** Accepts advertising. **URL:** http://www.westchesterweekly.com.
Ad Rates: BW: $1,055   **Circ:** (Not Reported)

LOWELL

373 Dharma Beat
Box 1753
Lowell, MA 01853-1753
Publication E-mail: karouaczine@aol.com

Literary magazine covering the life and works of Jack Kerouac. **Subtitle:** A Jack Kerouac Newszine. **Founded:** 1993. **Freq:** Semiannual. **Trim Size:** 8 1/2 x 11. **Cols./Page:** 3. **Key Personnel:** Attila Gyenis, Editor. **ISSN:** 1072-4559. **Subscription Rates:** $7 individuals; $10 out of country; $3.50 single issue. **Remarks:** Accepts advertising.
Ad Rates: BW: $250   **Circ:** Combined 400

MALDEN

374 The Malden Milestone
Milestones
51 Pleasant St., Ste. 5
Malden, MA 02148
Publication E-mail: editors@milestones.com

Community newspaper. **Key Personnel:** David Graham Greenlie, Editor. **URL:** http://www.milestones.com/ndotnet/milestone.

MATTAPOISETT

375 The Wanderer
Wanderer Comm., Inc.
55 County Rd.
Mattapoisett, MA 02739   Phone: (508)758-9055

Community newspaper. **Freq:** Weekly (Thurs.). **Subscription Rates:** Free; $28 by mail. **Remarks:** Advertising accepted; rates available upon request. **URL:** http://www.wanderer.com.
                                             Circ: (Not Reported)

MAYNARD

376 Religious Conference Manager
Adams Business Media
60 Main St.   Phone: (978)897-5552
Maynard, MA 01754-2011   Fax: (978)897-6824

Trade magazine for religious meeting planners and executives. **Freq:** Bimonthly. **Print Method:** Web offset. **Trim Size:** 8 x 10 3/4. **Key Personnel:** Susan Abbot Pelletier, Editor. **Remarks:** Accepts advertising. **URL:** http://www.meetingnet.com/media/religious/.
Ad Rates: BW: $2,655   **Circ:** (Not Reported)
                 4C: $4,025

377 Technology Meetings
Adams Business Media
60 Main St.   Phone: (978)897-5552
Maynard, MA 01754-2011   Fax: (978)897-6824

Professional magazine for managers and planners in the technology industry. **Freq:** Bimonthly. **Print Method:** Web offset. **Trim Size:** 8 x 10 3/4. **Cols./Page:** 3. **Col. Width:** 2 1/4 inches. **Key Personnel:** David Erickson, Editor; Karen Waxman, Production Mgr.; Melissa Fromento, Adv./Sales Dir.; Mark Adams, President. **Remarks:** Accepts advertising. **URL:** http://www.meetingnet.com/media/technology/.
Ad Rates: BW: $2,900   **Circ:** (Not Reported)
                 4C: $4,400

NORWOOD

378 Information Security
International Computer Security Assoc.
106 Access Rd.   Phone: (781)255-0200
Norwood, MA 02062   Fax: (781)255-0215

Trade magazine covering Internet and computer security. **Freq:** Monthly. **Key Personnel:** Peter S. Tippett, Publisher, ptippett@icsa.com; Sarah L. Cain, Managing Editor, scain@icsa.com. **Subscription Rates:** $100 individuals. **URL:** http://www.infosecuritymag.com.

PEABODY

379 Lynnfield-Peabody Edition
Suburban Publishing Corp.
PO Box 6039
Peabody, MA 01961-6039
Phone: (978)532-5880
Fax: (978)532-4250

Community newspaper. **Founded:** 1957. **Freq:** Weekly (Wed.). **Key Personnel:** Richard H. Ayer, Publisher. **Subscription Rates:** Free.
Circ: Combined ◆**5,200**

380 Peabody-Lynnfield Edition
Suburban Publishing Corp.
PO Box 6039
Peabody, MA 01961-6039
Phone: (978)532-5880
Fax: (978)532-4250

Community newspaper. **Founded:** 1957. **Freq:** Weekly (Wed.). **Key Personnel:** Richard H. Ayer, Publisher. **Subscription Rates:** Free.
Circ: Combined ◆**20,300**

PITTSFIELD

381 Pittsfield Gazette
The Pittsfield Gazette, Inc.
PO Box 2236
Pittsfield, MA 01202
Phone: (413)443-2010
Fax: (413)443-2445
Publication E-mail: ourgazette@aol.com

Community newspaper. **Freq:** Weekly (Thurs.). **Subscription Rates:** $20 individuals; $30 out of area.

STONEHAM

382 The Stoneham Independent
Woburn Daily Times, Inc.
377 Main St.
Stoneham, MA 02180
Phone: (781)438-1660
Fax: (781)436-6762
Publisher E-mail: news@woburnonline.com

Community newspaper. **Founded:** 1870. **Freq:** Weekly (Wed.). **Key Personnel:** Al Turco, Editor; Mark Haggerty, Business Mgr. **Subscription Rates:** $20 individuals; $38 two years; $22 out of area; $24 out of state. **Remarks:** Accepts advertising. **URL:** http://www.stonhamonline.com.
Ad Rates: PCI: $7.55   **Circ:** Paid 4600

VINEYARD HAVEN

383 Martha's Vineyard Times
PO Box 518
Vineyard Haven, MA 02568
Phone: (508)693-6100
Fax: (508)693-6000
Publication E-mail: mvtimes@vineyard.net

Community newspaper. **Freq:** Weekly (Thurs.). **Subscription Rates:** $95 by mail. **Remarks:** Accepts advertising. **URL:** http://vineyard.net/biz/mvtimes.
Ad Rates: BW: $1,250   **Circ:** (Not Reported)
         PCI: $17.50

WEST SPRINGFIELD

384 Dirt Late Model
Mind Over Media Publications
131 Elm St.
West Springfield, MA 01090
Phone: (413)781-0500
Fax: (413)781-1387

Professional journal covering auto racing. **Freq:** Bimonthly. **Subscription Rates:** $18 individuals; $30 Canada. **Remarks:** Accepts advertising.
Ad Rates: BW: $600   **Circ:** (Not Reported)
         4C: $800

385 Late Model Racer
Mind Over Media Publications
131 Elm St.
West Springfield, MA 01090
Phone: (413)781-0500
Fax: (413)781-1387

Professional magazine covering auto racing. **Freq:** Bimonthly. **Subscription Rates:** $18 individuals; $30 Canada. **Remarks:** Accepts advertising.
Ad Rates: BW: $600   **Circ:** (Not Reported)
         4C: $800

386 Trackside
Mind Over Media Publications
131 Elm St.
West Springfield, MA 01090
Phone: (413)781-0500
Fax: (413)781-1387

Professional magazine covering the auto racing industry. **Freq:** Bimonthly. **Subscription Rates:** $25 individuals; $35 Canada; $45 two years. **Remarks:** Accepts advertising.
Ad Rates: BW: $600   **Circ:** (Not Reported)
         4C: $800

WESTFIELD

387 Historical Journal of Massachusetts
Westfield State College
Westfield, MA 01086
Phone: (413)572-5344
Fax: (413)562-3613

Scholarly journal covering local history. **Founded:** 1972. **Freq:** Semiannual. **Key Personnel:** Martin Kaufman, Editorial Dir. **ISSN:** 0276-8313. **Subscription Rates:** $10 individuals. **Remarks:** Accepts advertising.
Circ: Paid 1000

WORCESTER

388 Science & Engineering Network News
49 Midgley Ln.
Worcester, MA 01604-3564
Phone: (508)755-5242
Fax: (508)795-1636
Publication E-mail: senn@world.std.com

Trade magazine covering Internet resources for scientists and engineers. **Freq:** Monthly. **Subscription Rates:** $194 individuals; $39 single issue. **URL:** http://www.senn.com.

389 The Worcester Phoenix
The Phoenix Media/Communications Group
108 Grove St., Ste. 18
Worcester, MA 01605-2651
Phone: (508)767-9777
Fax: (508)795-0439
Publication E-mail: worcester-feedback@phx.com

Community newspaper. **Founded:** 1993. **Freq:** Weekly (Wed.). **URL:** http://www.worcesterphoenix.com.

MICHIGAN

ALLEGAN

📖 **390 Kalamazoo Flashes**
Flashes Publishers
595 Jenner Dr.
Allegan, MI 49010   Phone: (616)673-2141

Shopping guide. **Freq:** Weekly. **Subscription Rates:** Free.
Circ: Combined **27,133**

📖 **391 Portage Flashes**
Flashes Publishers
595 Jenner Dr.
Allegan, MI 49010   Phone: (616)673-2141

Shopping guide. **Freq:** Weekly. **Subscription Rates:** Free.
Circ: Combined **27,933**

📖 **392 Village Area Flashes**
Flashes Publishers
595 Jenner Dr.
Allegan, MI 49010   Phone: (616)673-2141

Shopping guide. **Freq:** Weekly. **Subscription Rates:** Free.
Circ: Combined **9,017**

📖 **393 Westside Flashes**
Flashes Publishers
595 Jenner Dr.
Allegan, MI 49010   Phone: (616)673-2141

Shopping guide. **Freq:** Weekly. **Subscription Rates:** Free.
Circ: Combined **19,643**

ANN ARBOR

🎙 **394 WDEO-AM - 1290**
24 Frank Lloyd Wright Dr.   Phone: (734)930-5200
Ann Arbor, MI 48106   Fax: (734)930-3179
E-mail: credo@rc.net

Format: Talk; Religious. **Owner:** Cumulus Broadcasting, at above address.
Operating Hours: Sunrise-sunset. **ADI:** Lansing (Ann Arbor), MI. **Key Personnel:** Steve Clarke, Production Dir., phone (734)930-3177, credo@rc.net; Henry Root, Program Dir., phone (734)930-3169, hroot@rc.net. **Wattage:** 500.

BLOOMFIELD HILLS

📖 **395 Woodward**
Woodward Press
PO Box 7085
Bloomfield Hills, MI 48302
Free: (888)878-7591

Consumer magazine covering local lifestyle and issues. **Freq:** Monthly. **Key Personnel:** Leif A. Gruenberg, Editor and Publisher, leif@woodwardmagazine.com; Maureen Feder, Advertising, phone (248)681-6413; Sarah Peters, Editorial, sarah@woodwardmagazine.com. **Subscription**

Rates: $24 individuals; $32 Canada; $48 out of country. **URL:** http://www.woodwardmagazine.com.

BRIGHTON

📖 **396 Insider Business Journal**
HomeTown Communications Network
PO Box 260   Phone: (810)220-1800
Brighton, MI 48116   Fax: (810)220-5320

Trade journal covering business. **Freq:** Monthly. **Subscription Rates:** $18 individuals; $24 two years. **Remarks:** Accepts advertising. **URL:** http://www.insiderbiz.com.
Ad Rates: BW: $1,204   **Circ:** (Not Reported)
             4C: $1,564

CADILLAC

🎙 **397 WLXV-FM - 96.7**
PO Box 520   Phone: (616)775-1263
Cadillac, MI 49601   Fax: (616)779-2844

Format: Adult Contemporary. **Owner:** MacDonald Garber Broadcasting, Inc., PO Box 286, Petoskey, MI 49770, (616)347-8713. **Founded:** 1974. **Formerly:** WITW-FM (1983); WEVZ-FM (1987); WWLZ-FM (1994). **Operating Hours:** Continuous. **Key Personnel:** Kae Ryno, Office Mgr. **Wattage:** 25,000.

DETROIT

📖 **398 The Michigan Post**
2565 W. Grand Blvd., Ste. 603   Phone: (313)894-0078
Detroit, MI 48208   Fax: (313)894-0085

Newspaper covering automotive and motor sports news. **Founded:** Mar. 1997. **Freq:** Monthly. **Trim Size:** 10 x 16. **Cols./Page:** 4. **Col. Width:** 10 inches. **Col. Depth:** 15 inches. **Subscription Rates:** $25 individuals; $35 out of country. **Remarks:** Accepts advertising.
Ad Rates: BW: $560   **Circ:** (Not Reported)
             4C: $765

MOUNT CLEMENS

📖 **399 Inky Trail News**
70 Macomb, Ste. 226
Mount Clemens, MI 48043

Newspaper covering crafts, hobbies, and entertainment for women. **Founded:** 1993. **Freq:** Bimonthly. **Key Personnel:** Wendy Fisher, Editor. **Subscription Rates:** $15 individuals. **URL:** http://pages.prodigy.com/worldlinks.

PETOSKEY

🎙 **400 WLXT-FM - 96.3**
PO Box 286   Phone: (616)347-8713
Petoskey, MI 49770   Fax: (616)347-9920
E-mail: radio1@lite96.com

Format: Adult Contemporary. **Owner:** MacDonald Garber Broadcasting, Inc., at above address. **Operating Hours:** Continuous.

PORT HURON

🎤 **401 WGRT-FM - 102.3**
624 Grand River   Phone: (810)987-3200
Port Huron, MI 48060   Fax: (810)987-3325
E-mail: wgrt@tir.com

Format: Adult Contemporary. **Networks:** ABC. **Owner:** Port Huron Family Radio, Inc., at above address. **Founded:** 1991. **Operating Hours:** Continuous. **Key Personnel:** Cathie Martin, Business Mgr.; Bruce Peterson, Sales Mgr.; Martin Doorn, General Mgr.; Martha Vancamp, Production Mgr. **URL:** http://www.wgrt.com.

ROYAL OAK

📖 **402 Birmingham Mirror**
Mirror Newspapers
410 Cambridge
PO Box 430   Phone: (248)546-4900
Royal Oak, MI 48067-0430   Fax: (248)398-2353
Publication E-mail: mirror@mirrornews.com

Community newspaper. **Freq:** Weekly (Thurs.). **Key Personnel:** Nikki Smith, Circulation Mgr. **Subscription Rates:** Free.
       Circ: Combined ♦ **11,945**

📖 **403 Clawson Mirror**
Mirror Newspapers
410 Cambridge
PO Box 430   Phone: (248)546-4900
Royal Oak, MI 48067-0430   Fax: (248)398-2353
Publication E-mail: mirror@mirrornews.com

Community newspaper. **Freq:** Weekly (Thurs.). **Key Personnel:** Nikki Smith, Circulation Mgr. **Subscription Rates:** Free.
       Circ: Combined ♦ **7,198**

📖 **404 Huntington Woods/Berkley Mirror**
Mirror Newspapers
410 Cambridge
PO Box 430   Phone: (248)546-4900
Royal Oak, MI 48067-0430   Fax: (248)398-2353
Publication E-mail: mirror@mirrornews.com

Community newspaper. **Freq:** Weekly (Thurs.). **Key Personnel:** Nikki Smith, Circulation Mgr. **Subscription Rates:** Free.
       Circ: Combined ♦ **11,093**

📖 **405 Pleasant Ridge/Ferndale Mirror**
Mirror Newspapers
410 Cambridge
PO Box 430   Phone: (248)546-4900
Royal Oak, MI 48067-0430   Fax: (248)398-2353
Publication E-mail: mirror@mirrornews.com

Community newspaper. **Freq:** Weekly (Thurs.). **Key Personnel:** Nikki Smith, Circulation Mgr. **Subscription Rates:** Free.
       Circ: Combined ♦ **14,821**

📖 **406 Royal Oak Mirror**
Mirror Newspapers
410 Cambridge
PO Box 430   Phone: (248)546-4900
Royal Oak, MI 48067-0430   Fax: (248)398-2353
Publication E-mail: mirror@mirrornews.com

Community newspaper. **Freq:** Weekly (Thurs.). **Key Personnel:** Nikki Smith, Circulation Mgr. **Subscription Rates:** Free.
       Circ: Combined ♦ **31,868**

TRAVERSE CITY

📖 **407 Publishing for Entrepreneurs**
Jenkins Group, Inc.
121 E. Front St., 3rd Fl.
Traverse City, MI 49684
Publication E-mail: jgeditorial@northlink.net

Trade magazine covering marketing for the publishing and information industries. **Freq:** Bimonthly. **Key Personnel:** Jerrold R. Jenkins, President & CEO; Phil Murphy, Exec. Editor; Jim Barnes, Assoc. Publisher. **ISSN:** 1098-433X. **Subscription Rates:** $30 individuals; $40 Canada; $46 Europe & Asia; $10 single issue. **URL:** http://www.bookpublishing.com.

TROY

📖 **408 GMC Directions**
Sandy Corp.
1500 W. Big Beaver Rd.   Phone: (800)735-1236
Troy, MI 48084   Fax: (810)649-3614

Consumer magazine covering news for owners of General Motors automobiles. **Subtitle:** An Official General Motors Magazine. **Founded:** Nov. 1997. **Freq:** Triennial. **Print Method:** Web offset. **Trim Size:** 8 1/8 x 10 3/4. **Key Personnel:** Emily Olds, Marketing Assoc., emily.olds@sandycorp.com; Shelley Dowland, Asst. Publisher; Kevin Dempsey, Ad Representative. **Subscription Rates:** Free to qualified subscribers. **Remarks:** Accepts advertising.
Ad Rates: 4C: $23,370   **Circ:** Non-paid 779,000

📖 **409 Pontiac Driving Excitement**
Sandy Corp.
1500 W. Big Beaver Rd.   Phone: (800)735-1236
Troy, MI 48084   Fax: (810)649-3614
Publication E-mail: barry.kluczyk@sandycorp.com

Consumer magazine covering news for Pontiac automobile owners. **Subtitle:** An Official General Motors Magazine. **Founded:** Feb. 1998. **Freq:** Triennial. **Print Method:** Web offset. **Trim Size:** 8 1/8 x 10 3/4. **Key Personnel:** Emily Olds, Marketing Assoc., emily.olds@sandycorp.com; Shelley Dowland, Asst. Publisher; Kevin Dempsey, Advertising Rep., phone (847)705-9660; Barry Kluczyk, Editor. **Subscription Rates:** Free to qualified subscribers. **Remarks:** Accepts advertising.
Ad Rates: BW: $29,000   **Circ:** Non-paid 967,000

WEST BLOOMFIELD

📖 **410 International Journal of Acarology**
Indira Publishing House
Box 250456   Phone: (248)661-2529
West Bloomfield, MI 48325-0456   Fax: (248)661-4066

Professional journal covering mites and ticks. **Founded:** 1975. **Freq:** Quarterly. **Cols./Page:** 2. **Key Personnel:** Vikram Prasad, M.D., Editor-in-Chief, v.prasad@ix.netcom.com. **ISSN:** 0164-7954. **Subscription Rates:** $560 individuals. **Remarks:** Advertising not accepted.
       Circ: (Not Reported)

MINNESOTA

BIG LAKE

411 Clearwater Tribune
West Sherburne Tribune
29 S. Lake St.
PO Box 276   Phone: (612)263-3602
Big Lake, MN 55309   Fax: (612)263-8458

Community newspaper. **Founded:** 1986. **Freq:** Weekly (Fri.). **Key Personnel:** Gary W. Meyer, President. **Subscription Rates:** Free.
Circ: Non-paid ◆**4,408**

FARIBAULT

412 Faribault Area Shopper
Huckle Publishing, Inc.
514 Central Ave.
Faribault, MN 55021   Phone: (507)334-1853

Shopping guide. **Freq:** Weekly (Sun.). **Subscription Rates:** Free.
Circ: Non-paid **13,928**

413 Northfield Area Shopper
Huckle Publishing, Inc.
514 Central Ave.
Faribault, MN 55021   Phone: (507)334-1853

Shopping guide. **Freq:** Weekly (Sun.). **Subscription Rates:** Free.
Circ: Non-paid **10,329**

414 Waseca County Area Shopper
Huckle Publishing, Inc.
514 Central Ave.
Faribault, MN 55021   Phone: (507)334-1853

Shopping guide. **Freq:** Weekly (Sun.). **Subscription Rates:** Free.
Circ: Non-paid **9,201**

FERGUS FALLS

415 The Heartland Shopping News
The Midweek, Inc.
PO Box 651
Fergus Falls, MN 56538   Phone: (218)739-3308

Shopping guide. **Freq:** Weekly (Sun.). **Subscription Rates:** Free.
Circ: Non-paid **13,971**

416 The Midweek
The Midweek, Inc.
PO Box 651
Fergus Falls, MN 56538   Phone: (218)739-3308

Shopping guide. **Freq:** Weekly (Sun.). **Subscription Rates:** Free.
Circ: Non-paid **20,853**

HIBBING

417 KADU-FM - 90.1
12104 Old Highway 169   Phone: (218)263-3000
Hibbing, MN 55746   Fax: (218)263-6752
E-mail: kaduz@kadu.org

Format: Contemporary Hit Radio (CHR). **Owner:** JPI Radio, Inc., at above address. **Founded:** 1994. **Operating Hours:** Continuous. **Key Personnel:** Corey Jenness, Station Mgr. **Wattage:** 18,000. **Ad Rates:** Underwriting available. **URL:** http://www.kadu.org.

MINNEAPOLIS

418 Budstikken
999 41st St. NE, Ste. 205
Minneapolis, MN 55421-3185

Genealogical journal covering Norwegian ethnic news. **Founded:** 1970. **Freq:** Semiannual. **Print Method:** Offset. **Trim Size:** 8 1/2 x 11. **Cols./Page:** 3. **Col. Width:** 2 1/4 inches. **Key Personnel:** Roy Everson, Editor. **Remarks:** Accepts advertising.
Ad Rates: BW: $60   **Circ:** Paid 1400

419 International Affairs
East View Publications
3020 Harbor Ln. N.   Phone: (612)550-0961
Minneapolis, MN 55447   Fax: (612)559-2931
                                        Free: (800)477-1005
Publisher E-mail: eastview@eastview.com

Scholarly journal covering Russian foreign policy for scholars, analysts and students of Russia. **Subtitle:** A Russian Journal of World Politics, Diplomacy and International Relations. **Freq:** Bimonthly. **Key Personnel:** Boris Piadyshev, Editor. **ISSN:** 0130-9641. **Subscription Rates:** $39 individuals; $69 out of country; $245 institutions. **URL:** http://www.eastview.com.

420 Military Thought
East View Publications
3020 Harbor Ln. N.   Phone: (612)550-0961
Minneapolis, MN 55447   Fax: (612)559-2931
                                        Free: (800)477-1005
Publisher E-mail: eastview@eastview.com

Scholarly journal covering military policy in Russia. **Subtitle:** A Russian Journal of Military Theory and Strategy. **Freq:** Bimonthly. **Key Personnel:** Gen. Viacheslav Erokhin, Editor. **ISSN:** 0869-5636. **Subscription Rates:** $79 individuals; $295 institutions. **URL:** http://www.eastview.com.

421 Minnesota Christian Chronicle
7317 Cahill Rd., Ste. 201   Phone: (612)562-1234
Minneapolis, MN 55439   Fax: (612)941-3010
Publication E-mail: editor@mcchronicle.com
Publisher E-mail: publisher@mcchronicle.com

Christian community newspaper. **URL:** http://www.mcchronicle.com.

📖 **422 Minnesota Precision Manufacturing Association Journal**
Hiebel & Associates
3300 Bass Lake Rd.   Phone: (612)566-5696
Minneapolis, MN 55429   Fax: (612)566-5780
Publication E-mail: mpma@mpma.com

Trade magazine covering manufacturing in Minnesota. **Freq:** 8/year. **Key Personnel:** Susan Carter, Editor; Charles Arnold, Sales Mgr.; Colleen LesSard, Assoc. Editor. **Remarks:** Accepts advertising.
       Circ: (Not Reported)

📖 **423 Pillsbury Classic Cookbooks**
Pillsbury Co.
200 6th St., M.S. 28M7   Phone: (612)330-4475
Minneapolis, MN 55402   Fax: (612)330-4875

Consumer magazine covering cooking. **Founded:** 1979. **Freq:** Monthly. **Print Method:** Web offset. **Trim Size:** 5 7/16 x 8 3/4. **Key Personnel:** William Monn, Publication Manager; Jackie Sheehan, Editor; Karen Goodsall, Circulation Mgr. **ISSN:** 1089-0432. **Subscription Rates:** $24.95 individuals; $2.99 single issue. **Remarks:** Accepts advertising.
Ad Rates: 4C: $10,000   **Circ:** Paid 500,000,000

📖 **424 Social Sciences**
East View Publications
3020 Harbor Ln. N.   Phone: (612)550-0961
Minneapolis, MN 55447   Fax: (612)559-2931
       Free: (800)477-1005

Publisher E-mail: eastview@eastview.com

Scholarly journal covering contemporary Russian thought in the social sciences and humanities. **Subtitle:** A Quarterly Journal of the Russian Academy of Sciences. **Freq:** Quarterly. **Key Personnel:** L. Mitrokhin, Editor. **ISSN:** 0134-5486. **Subscription Rates:** $45 individuals; $65 out of country; $195 institutions. **URL:** http://www.eastview.com.

MINNETONKA

📖 **425 Cooking Pleasures**
North American Outdoor Group, Inc.
12301 Whitewater Dr., Ste. 260   Phone: (612)988-7117
Minnetonka, MN 55343   Fax: (612)936-9169
       Free: (800)688-7611

Publisher E-mail: addept@naoginc.com

Consumer magazine covering cooking. **Founded:** Dec. 1998. **Freq:** Bimonthly. **Print Method:** Offset. **Trim Size:** 7 3/4 x 10 1/2. **Cols./Page:** 3. **Col. Width:** 2 1/4 inches. **Col. Depth:** 10 inches. **Key Personnel:** Betsy Wrey, Editor, phone (612)352-7020; Nancy Benedict, Publisher; Russell M. Nolan, Group Publisher. **Remarks:** Accepts advertising.
Ad Rates: BW: $1,753   **Circ:** Paid 100,000
       4C: $2,480

📖 **426 Gardening How-To**
North American Outdoor Group, Inc.
12301 Whitewater Dr., Ste. 260   Phone: (612)988-7117
Minnetonka, MN 55343   Fax: (612)936-9169
       Free: (800)688-7611

Publisher E-mail: addept@naoginc.com

Consumer magazine covering gardening. **Founded:** 1996. **Freq:** Bimonthly. **Print Method:** Offset. **Trim Size:** 7 7/8 x 10 1/2. **Cols./Page:** 3. **Col. Width:** 2 1/4 inches. **Col. Depth:** 10 inches. **Key Personnel:** Kelly O'Hara, Editor, phone (612)988-7475; Jim Bryant, Publisher, phone (612)988-7107; Russell M. Nolan, Group Publisher. **Remarks:** Accepts advertising. **URL:** http://www.gardeningclub.com.
Ad Rates: BW: $12,240   **Circ:** Paid 480,000
       4C: $17,745

📖 **427 PGA Tour Partners**
North American Outdoor Group, Inc.
12301 Whitewater Dr., Ste. 260   Phone: (612)988-7117
Minnetonka, MN 55343   Fax: (612)936-9169
       Free: (800)688-7611

Publisher E-mail: addept@naoginc.com

Consumer magazine covering professional golf. **Founded:** 1997. **Freq:** Bimonthly. **Print Method:** Offset. **Trim Size:** 7 3/4 x 10 1/2. **Cols./Page:** 3.

Col. Width: 2 1/4 inches. **Col. Depth:** 10 inches. **Key Personnel:** Tom Stine, Editor; Scot Ramon, Publisher; Russell M. Nolan, Group Publisher. **Subscription Rates:** $24 individuals. **Remarks:** Accepts advertising. **URL:** http://www.pgatour.com/ropes/partners_ club.html.
Ad Rates: BW: $13,970   **Circ:** Paid 320,000
       4C: $19,950

ROSEVILLE

📖 **428 Focus News**
2819 Hamline Ave. N., Ste. 101   Phone: (651)633-3434
Roseville, MN 55113   Fax: (651)633-9550
Publication E-mail: info@focusnews.com

Community newspaper. **Freq:** Weekly. **Subscription Rates:** $85 individuals. **URL:** http://www.focusnews.com.

ST. PAUL

📖 **429 Hungry Mind Review**
Macalester College
1648 Grand Ave.
St. Paul, MN 55105
Publication E-mail: hmreview@winternet.com

Consumer magazine covering book reviews and news. **Freq:** Quarterly. **Key Personnel:** R. David Unowsky, Publisher; Bart Schneider, Editor; Margaret Todd Maitland, Managing Editor; Diana Katigbak BenJaafar, Marketing Dir. **ISSN:** 0887-5499. **Subscription Rates:** $14 individuals; $22 two years. **URL:** http://www.bookwire.com/hmr.

WILLMAR

📖 **430 The Sunday Reminder**
Forum Communications Co.
PO Box 839
Willmar, MN 56201   Phone: (320)235-1150

Shopping guide. **Freq:** Weekly (Sun.). **Subscription Rates:** Free.
       Circ: Non-paid **27,371**

WORTHINGTON

📖 **431 Worthington Globe**
Forum Communications Company
PO Box 639
Worthington, MN 56187   Phone: (507)376-9711

Daily newspaper. **Freq:** Mon.-Sat. **Subscription Rates:** $105.20 individuals; $116.40 by mail.
       Circ: Combined **12,647**

MISSISSIPPI

SENATOBIA

📖 **432 The Democrat**
North Mississippi Newspapers
219 E. Main St.
PO Box 369   Phone: (601)562-4414
Senatobia, MS 38668-0369   Fax: (601)562-8866

Community newspaper. **Freq:** Weekly. **Remarks:** Advertising accepted; rates available upon request. **URL:** http://www.thedemocrat.com.

Circ: Combined 15,300

VICKSBURG

📖 **433 Dredging Research**
United States Army Corps of Engineers
3909 Halls Ferry Rd.   Phone: (601)634-2349
Vicksburg, MS 39180-6199   Fax: (601)634-3528

Research publication covering dredging activities at the U.S. Army Engineer Research and Development Center. **Founded:** 1998. **Freq:** Quarterly. **Key Personnel:** Elke Briner, Editor, brinere@wes.army.mil; Dr. Robert M. Engler, Program Mgr.; Thomas R. Patin, Program Mgr.; E. Clark McNair, Program Mgr. **Subscription Rates:** Free. **Remarks:** Advertising not accepted. **URL:** http://www.wes.army.mil/el/dots/.

Circ: Non-paid 2200

Ad Rates: GLR = general line rate; BW = one-time black & white page rate; 4C = one-time four color page rate; SAU = standard advertising unit rate; CNU = Canadian newspaper advertising unit rate; PCI = per column inch rate.
Circulation: ★ = ABC; △ = BPA; ◆ = CAC; • = CCAB; ❑ = VAC; ⊕ = PO Statement; ‡ = Publisher's Report; Boldface figures = sworn; Light figures = estimated.
Entry type: 📖 = Print; 🎙 = Broadcast.

61

MISSOURI

CAMDENTON

📖 **434 The Lake Sun Leader**
450 N. Highway 5
Camdenton, MO 65020-9781
Phone: (573)346-2132
Fax: (573)346-4508
Free: (800)373-0287

Publication E-mail: lakesun@is.usmo.com

General newspaper. **Founded:** 1879. **Freq:** Daily. **Key Personnel:** Tom Turner, Publisher; Michael Feeback, Editor. **Subscription Rates:** $95.50 individuals; $99.72 out of area; $105 out of state. **URL:** http://www.lakesunleader.com.

CAPE GIRARDEAU

📖 **435 Southeast Missourian Plus**
Concord Publishing House, Inc.
301 Broadway
PO Box 699
Cape Girardeau, MO 63701
Phone: (573)334-7115
Fax: (573)334-7288
Publisher E-mail: advertising@semissourian.com

Daily newspaper. **Founded:** 1972. **Freq:** Mon.-Sun. **Key Personnel:** Mark Kneer, Circ. Dir. **Subscription Rates:** $143.50 individuals.
Circ: Combined ◆**17,215**

ELDON

📖 **436 Miller County Autogram-Sentinel**
Vernon Publishing, Inc.
409-15 S. Maple
Eldon, MO 65026
Phone: (573)392-5658
Fax: (573)392-7755
Publisher E-mail: advertiser@vernonpublishing.com

Community newspaper. **Freq:** Weekly. **Subscription Rates:** $23.50 individuals; $28.50 out of area; $36.50 out of state. **URL:** http://www.vernonpublishing.com/millercountyweb.htm.
Circ: Paid 1,875

JEFFERSON CITY

📖 **437 Arts'n Crafts Showguide**
ACN Publications
Box 25
Jefferson City, MO 65102
Phone: (573)636-0491
Fax: (573)636-2112
Publisher E-mail: acnpubs@plnet.net

Trade magazine covering arts and crafts. **Founded:** 1985. **Freq:** Bimonthly. **Print Method:** Web offset. **Trim Size:** 8 1/4 x 10 3/4. **Cols./Page:** 3. **Col. Width:** 2 1/4 inches. **Key Personnel:** Dan Engle, Editor and Publisher. **ISSN:** 1071-6289. **Subscription Rates:** $21.95 individuals; $4.50 single issue. **Remarks:** Accepts advertising. **URL:** http://www.acnshowguide.com.
Ad Rates: BW: $550   **Circ:** Paid 9000
4C: $750
PCI: $30

KANSAS CITY

📖 **438 Applicator**
Sealant, Waterproofing and Restoration Institute
2841 Main
Kansas City, MO 64108
Phone: (816)472-SWRI
Fax: (816)472-7765

Trade magazine covering sealing, waterproofing, and restoration. **Freq:** Triennial. **Subscription Rates:** $25 individuals. **Remarks:** Accepts advertising. **URL:** http://www.swrionline.org.
Circ: (Not Reported)

📖 **439 Forensic Quarterly**
National Federation of State High School Associations
11724 NW Plaza Circle
Kansas City, MO 64153-1158
Phone: (816)464-5400
Fax: (816)464-5571

Educational periodical covering debate for high school students. **Freq:** Quarterly two issues in April; two issues in June. **Print Method:** Sheetfed offset. **Trim Size:** 6 x 9. **Cols./Page:** 1. **Col. Width:** 4 1/2 inches. **Col. Depth:** 7 3/4 inches. **Key Personnel:** Treva Dayton, Editor, tkdayton@nfhsmail.org. **Subscription Rates:** $5 single issue. **Remarks:** Advertising not accepted. **URL:** http://www.nfhs.org.
Circ: Paid 5000

ST. LOUIS

📖 **440 Life Insurance Selling**
330 N. 4th St.
St. Louis, MO 63102
Phone: (314)421-5445
Fax: (314)421-1070

Trade magazine for life and health insurance agents. **Freq:** Monthly. **Subscription Rates:** $7 individuals; $14 two years. **Remarks:** Accepts advertising. **URL:** http://www.lifeinsuranceselling.com.
Ad Rates: BW: $3,221   **Circ:** (Not Reported)
4C: $4,216

📖 **441 West End-Clayton Word**
Virginia Publishing Co.
4814 Washington St., Ste. 120
St. Louis, MO 63108
Phone: (314)367-6612

Community newspaper. **Freq:** Weekly. **Remarks:** Accepts advertising. **URL:** http://www.wordnews.com.
Ad Rates: BW: $1,000   **Circ:** (Not Reported)

SPRINGFIELD

🎙 **442 KWTO-FM - 98.7**
3000 E. Chestnut Expressway
Springfield, MO 65808
Phone: (417)860-5300
Fax: (417)867-7675

Format: Classic Rock. **Networks:** Mutual Broadcasting System. **Operating Hours:** Continuous.

WARRENSBURG

📖 **443 Probation and Parole Law Reports**
Knehans-Miller Publications
PO Box 1033
Warrensburg, MO 64093-1033   Phone: (660)429-1102

Professional periodical covering federal and state appellate court decisions dealing with all aspects of probation and parole. **Founded:** 1979. **Freq:** Monthly. **Key Personnel:** Dane C. Miller, Editor. **ISSN:** 0276-6965. **Subscription Rates:** $136 U.S. and Canada.

📖 **444 Traffic Law Reports**
Knehans-Miller Publications
PO Box 1033
Warrensburg, MO 64093-1033   Phone: (660)429-1102

Professional journal covering federal and state appellate court decisions dealing with all aspects of traffic enforcement and administration. **Founded:** 1987. **Freq:** Monthly. **Key Personnel:** Dane C. Miller, Editor. **ISSN:** 0893-3030. **Subscription Rates:** $136 U.S. and Canada.

WARSAW

🎙 **445 KAYQ-FM - 97.7**
PO Box 1420   Phone: (660)438-7343
Warsaw, MO 65355   Fax: (660)438-7159

Format: Country. **Networks:** Jones Satellite; USA Radio; Missouri. **Owner:** Valkyrie Broadcasting, at above address. **Founded:** Mar. 10, 1980. **Operating Hours:** Continuous. **ADI:** Kansas City, MO (Lawrence, KS). **Key Personnel:** Joey Anderson, General Mgr.; Glenna Thrasher, Business Mgr. **Wattage:** 3,300. **Ad Rates:** Advertising accepted; rates available upon request.

WASHINGTON

📖 **446 Anvil's Ring**
Artists-Blacksmith Association of North America
Box 206   Phone: (314)390-2133
Washington, MO 63090   Fax: (314)390-2133
Publication E-mail: jmmac@socketis.net
Publisher E-mail: abana@mail.usmo.com

Trade magazine for blacksmiths. **Freq:** Quarterly. **Remarks:** Accepts advertising.

                                Circ: (Not Reported)

MONTANA

GREAT FALLS

📖 **447 Consumers Press**
Lee Publications
PO Box 6747
Great Falls, MT 59406   Phone: (406)761-2406

Shopping guide. **Freq:** Weekly (Thurs.). **Subscription Rates:** Free.
Circ: Combined **32,720**

LIBBY

📖 **448 The Montanian**
PO Box 946
Libby, MT 59923   Phone: (406)293-8202
Publisher E-mail: montanian@libby.org

Community newspaper. **Founded:** 1989. **Freq:** Weekly (Tues.). **Key Personnel:** Carol Latham, Publisher; David F. Latham, News Editor. **Subscription Rates:** Free; $20 by mail. **Remarks:** Advertising accepted; rates available upon request. **URL:** http://www.libby.org/montanian.
Circ: Combined **5,000**

Ad Rates: GLR = general line rate; BW = one-time black & white page rate; 4C = one-time four color page rate; SAU = standard advertising unit rate;
CNU = Canadian newspaper advertising unit rate; PCI = per column inch rate.
Circulation: ★ = ABC; △ = BPA; ♦ = CAC; ● = CCAB; ❑ = VAC; ⊕ = PO Statement; ‡ = Publisher's Report; Boldface figures = sworn; Light figures = estimated.
Entry type: 📖 = Print; 🎙 = Broadcast.

65

NEBRASKA

COLUMBUS

449 Columbus Area Choice
Morris/Stauffer Communications, Inc.
2917 23rd St.
PO Box 1397   Phone: (402)564-1025
Columbus, NE 68602-1397   Fax: (402)564-1403

Shopper. **Founded:** Mar. 1990. **Freq:** Weekly. **Print Method:** Offset. **Cols./Page:** 7. **Col. Depth:** 16 inches. **Key Personnel:** Kevin L. Bennett, General Mgr. **Subscription Rates:** Free. **Remarks:** Accepts advertising.
Ad Rates: PCI: $6.95   **Circ:** Non-paid ◆**24,940**

LINCOLN

450 Lincoln Journal Star
926 P St.
Lincoln, NE 68508   Phone: (402)475-4200

General newspaper. **Freq:** Mon.-Sun. **Subscription Rates:** $161.20 individuals; $135.20 out of area; $182 by mail. **URL:** http://www.journalstar.com.

451 Smart Computing
Sandhills Publishing
120 W. Harvest Dr.   Phone: (402)479-2181
PO Box 85310   Fax: (402)479-2195
Lincoln, NE 68501-5310   Free: (800)331-4890

Consumer magazine covering tutorial information and news for new users of personal computers. **Freq:** Monthly. **Subscription Rates:** $24 individuals. **URL:** http://www.sandhills.com.

Circ: Combined 310,000

MCCOOK

452 KNGN-AM - 1360
R.R. 3, Box 1360   Phone: (308)345-2006
McCook, NE 69001   Fax: (308)345-2052
                                                    Free: (800)767-1360
E-mail: goodnews@wil.net.com

Format: Religious. **Networks:** SkyLight Satellite; Ambassador Inspirational Radio. **Owner:** Lutheran Church Missouri Synod, 1333 S. Kirkwood Rd., St. Louis, MO 63122. **Founded:** Mar. 1990. **Operating Hours:** 6 a.m.-9:45 p.m. **Key Personnel:** Mike Nielsen, General Mgr., goodnews@wilnet.com; Sandy Stuckwisen, Program Dir. **Ad Rates:** Noncommercial. **URL:** http://www.christianlink.com/kngn.

SIDNEY

453 Sidney Daily Sun
Vincent W. Bodiford
817 12th Ave.   Phone: (308)254-2818
PO Box 193   Fax: (308)254-3925
Sidney, NE 69162   Free: (888)254-2818
Publication E-mail: sydneysun@hamilton.net

Community newspaper. **Founded:** Sept. 1997. **Freq:** Daily Tues. through Sat. **Print Method:** Web offset. **Cols./Page:** 6. **Col. Width:** 2 picas. **Col. Depth:** 21 inches. **Key Personnel:** Vincent W. Bodiford, Publisher, publisher@sidneysun.com; Jason Hackett, Managing Editor; Lana Butts, Advertising Mgr. **Subscription Rates:** $89 individuals. **URL:** http://www.sidneysun.com. **Feature Editors:** Chris Cleveland, *Sports*; Shell Jeffrey Tomjack, *Features*; Bob Moore, *City*.
Ad Rates: PCI: $6.5   **Circ:** Paid ‡2518

SUPERIOR

454 The Superior Express
PO Box 408   Phone: (402)879-3291
Superior, NE 68978   Fax: (402)879-3293

Community newspaper. **Subscription Rates:** $16 individuals; $23 out of state. **URL:** http://www.superior.com/spc/sefrntpg.htm.

Ad Rates: GLR = general line rate; BW = one-time black & white page rate; 4C = one-time four color page rate; SAU = standard advertising unit rate; CNU = Canadian newspaper advertising unit rate; PCI = per column inch rate.
Circulation: ★ = ABC; △ = BPA; ◆ = CAC; • = CCAB; ❑ = VAC; ⊕ = PO Statement; ‡ = Publisher's Report; Boldface figures = sworn; Light figures = estimated.
Entry type: ❑ = Print; 🎙 = Broadcast.

67

NEVADA

LAS VEGAS

455 Las Vegas CityLife
Las Vegas Press
3335 Wynn Rd.
Las Vegas, NV 89102
                    Free: (800)457-3077

Community newspaper. **Subscription Rates:** $50 individuals. **Remarks:** Advertising accepted; rates available upon request. **URL:** http://www.lvcitylife.com.

                                    Circ: Combined 238,000

456 Las Vegas Weekly
Radiant City Publications, LLC
PO Box 230657
Las Vegas, NV 89123-0011
Publication E-mail: lasvegas@lasvegasweekly.com

Community arts and culture newspaper. **Founded:** 1991. **Freq:** Weekly (Wed.). **Key Personnel:** Daniel A. Greenspun, Publisher; Bruce Spotleson, General Mgr.; Chris Rohland, Advertising Dir.; Ron Gannon, Circulation Mgr. **Subscription Rates:** $40 individuals. **URL:** http://www.scopemag.com. **Formerly:** Scope. **Feature Editors:** Richard Abowitz, *Features*; Rob Bhatt, *News*.

                                    Circ: Combined 66,000

457 The Southern Nevada Health Care Journal
Ingram Communications Group
3131 Meade Ave., Ste. C
Las Vegas, NV 89102

Professional medical journal. **Freq:** Monthly. **Trim Size:** 10 3/4 x 13 1/2. **Key Personnel:** Robert Steelman, Managing Editor. **Subscription Rates:** $25 individuals; $40 two years. **Remarks:** Accepts advertising. **URL:** http://www.healthcarejournal.com.
Ad Rates: BW: $1,438   **Circ:** Combined 14,000
                4C: $1,963

458 The Southern Nevada Real Estate Journal
Ingram Communications Group
3131 Meade Ave., Ste. C
Las Vegas, NV 89102

Trade journal for local real estate industry executives and professionals. **Freq:** Monthly. **Trim Size:** 10 3/4 x 13 1/2. **Subscription Rates:** $25 individuals; $40 two years. **Remarks:** Accepts advertising. **URL:** http://www.realestatejournal.com.
Ad Rates: BW: $1,438   **Circ:** Combined 11,000
                4C: $1,963

459 The Southern Nevada Small Business Journal
Ingram Communications Group
3131 Meade Ave., Ste. C
Las Vegas, NV 89102

Trade journal covering small business issues. **Freq:** Monthly. **Trim Size:** 10 3/4 x 13 1/2. **Key Personnel:** Gerald Ingram, Editor and Publisher, publisher@snsbj.com; Kristine McKenzie, Managing Editor, edi-tor@snsbj.com. **Subscription Rates:** $25 individuals; $40 two years. **Remarks:** Accepts advertising. **URL:** http://www.snsbj.com.
Ad Rates: BW: $1,438   **Circ:** Combined 15,000
                4C: $1,963

PAHRUMP

460 Mexico Living and Travel Magazine
Mexico Retirement and Travel Assistance (MRTA)
6301 Squaw Valley Rd., Ste. 23   Phone: (775)641-1152
Pahrump, NV 89048-7949   Fax: (775)641-1152

Consumer magazine covering living and travel in Mexico. **Founded:** 1990. **Freq:** Quarterly. **Trim Size:** 8 1/2 x 11. **Key Personnel:** John Bryant, Editor; Jean Bryant, Editor. **Subscription Rates:** $30 U.S. and Canada; $35 elsewhere. **Remarks:** Accepts advertising. **Former name**: MRTA Guadala-jara/Chapala Update.

                                    Circ: Paid 8000

461 Pahrump Valley Times
2160 E. Calvada Blvd., Ste. A
Pahrump, NV 89048
Publication E-mail: pvtimes@excite.com

Community newspaper. **Founded:** 1970. **Freq:** Semiweekly (Wed. and Fri.). **Key Personnel:** Hank Bond, Publisher, hank407@excite.com; Rich Thurlow, Editor-in-Chief; Henry Brean, Managing Editor; Don Pannell, Circulation Mgr.; Connie Coon, Advertising Mgr. **URL:** http://www.pahrumpvalleytimes.com.

NEW HAMPSHIRE

NASHUA

462 The Clubhouse
Boys & Girls Club of Greater Nashua
47 Grand Ave.
Nashua, NH 03060   Phone: (603)883-0523

Newspaper for the local Boys & Girls Club. **Freq:** Quarterly.

463 Portable Design
PennWell Publishing Co.
98 Spit Brook Rd., 4th Fl.   Phone: (603)891-9134
Nashua, NH 03062-2801   Fax: (603)891-0435

Trade magazine covering mobile computing and communications. **Freq:**
Monthly. **Key Personnel:** Alex Mendelsohn, Editor-in-Chief,
alexm@pennwell.com; John R. Carroll, Group Publisher,
bobz@penwell.com; Pauline Panagakos, Managing Editor, pauli-
nep@pennwell.com. **URL:** http://www.portabledesign.com.

464 The Telegraph
PO Box 1008   Phone: (603)882-2741
Nashua, NH 03061   Fax: (603)882-5138
Publication E-mail: webeditor@telegraph-nh.com

Community newspaper. **Freq:** Daily and Sunday. **Key Personnel:** Nick
Pappas, Editor. **Subscription Rates:** $156 individuals. **Remarks:** Advertising
accepted; rates available upon request. **URL:** http://
www.nashuatelegraph.com.

Circ: (Not Reported)

PETERBOROUGH

465 Appleseeds
Cobblestone Publishing Co.
30 Grove St., Ste. C   Phone: (603)924-7209
Peterborough, NH 03458   Fax: (603)924-7380
                                    Free: (800)821-0115
Publisher E-mail: custsvc@cobblestone.mv.com

Educational, consumer magazine for children ages 7-9. **Freq:** 9/year.
Subscription Rates: $26.95 individuals; $36.84 Canada; $34.95 elsewhere.

466 California Chronicles
Cobblestone Publishing Co.
30 Grove St., Ste. C   Phone: (603)924-7209
Peterborough, NH 03458   Fax: (603)924-7380
                                    Free: (800)821-0115
Publisher E-mail: custsvc@cobblestone.mv.com

Consumer magazine covering California history for children ages 9-14. **Freq:**
5/year. **Subscription Rates:** $23.95 individuals; $31.63 Canada; $29.95
elsewhere.

467 Footsteps
Cobblestone Publishing Co.
30 Grove St., Ste. C   Phone: (603)924-7209
Peterborough, NH 03458   Fax: (603)924-7380
                                    Free: (800)821-0115
Publisher E-mail: custsvc@cobblestone.mv.com

Consumer magazine covering African-American history for children ages 9-
14. **Freq:** 5/year. **Subscription Rates:** $23.95 individuals; $31.63 Canada;
$29.95 elsewhere.

SEABROOK

468 Ocean Side Advertiser
PO Box 1346   Phone: (603)474-9357
Seabrook, NH 03874   Fax: (603)474-4189

Community newspaper. **Freq:** Monthly. **Subscription Rates:** Free. **URL:**
http://www.seacoast.com/~oceanads.

WOLFEBORO

469 Rare Coin Review
Bowers & Merena Galleries
PO Box 1224   Phone: (603)569-5095
Wolfeboro, NH 03894   Fax: (603)569-5319
                                    Free: (800)222-5993
Publisher E-mail: bowersmerena@conknet.com

Journal covering rare coins and collecting. **Freq:** Bimonthly. **Subscription
Rates:** $29 individuals; $10 single issue. **Remarks:** Advertising not accepted.
Circ: (Not Reported)

NEW JERSEY

BURLINGTON

📖 **470 Bristol Express**
Metro Media Publishing, Inc.
PO Box 1798
Burlington, NJ 08016-7398
Publisher E-mail: metroemailamerica online, inc.com

Community newspaper. **Founded:** 1995. **Freq:** Monthly. **Print Method:** Offset. **Trim Size:** 11 x 14. **Cols./Page:** 6. **Col. Width:** 9.5 picas. **Col. Depth:** 12 1/2 inches. **Key Personnel:** David R. Vasquez, Editor and Publisher. **Subscription Rates:** Free. **Remarks:** Accepts advertising.
Ad Rates: BW: $787.50   **Circ:** Non-paid ‡5500
4C: $962.50
PCI: $10.50

📖 **471 Burlington Mail**
Metro Media Publishing, Inc.
PO Box 1798
Burlington, NJ 08016-7398
Publisher E-mail: metroemailamerica online, inc.com

Community newspaper. **Founded:** 1996. **Freq:** Monthly. **Print Method:** Offset. **Trim Size:** 11 x 14. **Cols./Page:** 6. **Col. Width:** 9.5 picas. **Col. Depth:** 12 1/2 inches. **Key Personnel:** David R. Vasquez, Editor and Publisher. **Subscription Rates:** Free. **Remarks:** Accepts advertising.
Ad Rates: BW: $787.50   **Circ:** Non-paid ‡7000
4C: $962.50
PCI: $10.50

📖 **472 Croydon Express**
Metro Media Publishing, Inc.
PO Box 1798
Burlington, NJ 08016-7398
Publisher E-mail: metroemailamerica online, inc.com

Community newspaper. **Founded:** 1996. **Freq:** Bimonthly. **Print Method:** Offset. **Trim Size:** 11 x 14. **Cols./Page:** 6. **Col. Width:** 9.5 picas. **Col. Depth:** 12 1/2 inches. **Key Personnel:** David R. Vasquez, Editor and Publisher. **Subscription Rates:** Free. **Remarks:** Accepts advertising.
Ad Rates: BW: $787.50   **Circ:** Non-paid ‡3250
4C: $962.50
PCI: $10.50

📖 **473 Fairless Hills Express**
Metro Media Publishing, Inc.
PO Box 1798
Burlington, NJ 08016-7398
Publisher E-mail: metroemailamerica online, inc.com

Community newspaper. **Founded:** 1997. **Freq:** Monthly. **Print Method:** Offset. **Trim Size:** 11 x 14. **Cols./Page:** 6. **Col. Width:** 9.5 picas. **Col. Depth:** 12 1/2 inches. **Key Personnel:** David R. Vasquez, Editor and Publisher. **Subscription Rates:** Free. **Remarks:** Accepts advertising.
Ad Rates: BW: $787.50   **Circ:** Non-paid ‡5000
4C: $962.50
PCI: $10.50

📖 **474 Mount Holly Mail**
Metro Media Publishing, Inc.
PO Box 1798
Burlington, NJ 08016-7398
Publisher E-mail: metroemailamerica online, inc.com

Community newspaper. **Founded:** 1997. **Freq:** Monthly. **Print Method:** Offset. **Trim Size:** 11 x 14. **Cols./Page:** 6. **Col. Width:** 9.5 picas. **Col. Depth:** 12 1/2 inches. **Key Personnel:** David R. Vasquez, Editor and Publisher. **Subscription Rates:** Free. **Remarks:** Accepts advertising.
Ad Rates: BW: $787.50   **Circ:** Non-paid ‡7000
4C: $962.50
PCI: $10.50

CEDAR KNOLLS

📖 **475 Wireless Business & Technology**
Wireless Publishing Co.
3 Wing Dr., No. 240   Phone: (973)285-1500
Cedar Knolls, NJ 07927-1000   Fax: (973)285-1519
Publication E-mail: pbi@phillips.com

Trade magazine covering the wireless business. **Freq:** Monthly. **Key Personnel:** Ollie Bieniemy, Jr., Publisher; Cindy Loffler Stevens, Sr. Managing Editor. **Subscription Rates:** Free. **URL:** http://www.phillips.com.

JERSEY CITY

📖 **476 Talisman**
Talisman House Publishers
PO Box 3157   Phone: (201)938-0695
Jersey City, NJ 07303-3157   Fax: (201)938-1693

Journal covering contemporary poetry. **Subtitle:** A Journal of Contemporary Poetry and Poetics. **Founded:** 1988. **Freq:** Semiannual. **Print Method:** Offset. **Trim Size:** 5 1/2 x 8 1/2. **Cols./Page:** 1. **Col. Width:** 4 1/2 inches. **Col. Depth:** 7 1/2 inches. **Key Personnel:** Edward Foster, Editor. **ISSN:** 0898-8684. **Subscription Rates:** $14 individuals; $9 single issue. **Remarks:** Accepts advertising.
Ad Rates: BW: $100   **Circ:** Paid 1000

MAHWAH

📖 **477 The American Psychoanalyst**
Lawrence Erlbaum Associates, Inc.
10 Industrial Ave.   Phone: (201)236-9500
Mahwah, NJ 07430-2262   Fax: (201)236-0072
          Free: (800)9-BOOKS-9
Publication E-mail: tapjournals@analyticpress.com
Publisher E-mail: orders@erlbaum.com

Scholarly journal for psychoanalysts. **Freq:** Quarterly. **Key Personnel:** William D. Jeffrey, Editor. **ISSN:** 1052-7958. **Subscription Rates:** $28.50 U.S. and Canada; $48.50 elsewhere; $55 institutions; $75 institutions out of country. **Remarks:** Accepts advertising.
Ad Rates: BW: $480   **Circ:** (Not Reported)

---

478 Applied Developmental Science
Lawrence Erlbaum Associates, Inc.
10 Industrial Ave.
Mahwah, NJ 07430-2262
Phone: (201)236-9500
Fax: (201)236-0072
Free: (800)9-BOOKS-9

Publisher E-mail: orders@erlbaum.com

Professional journal for psychologists. **Freq:** Quarterly. **Trim Size:** 7 x 10. **Key Personnel:** Richard M. Lerner, Editor; Celia B. Fisher, Editor; Richard A. Weinberg, Editor. **ISSN:** 1088-8691. **Subscription Rates:** $38.50 U.S. and Canada; $68.50 elsewhere; $140 institutions; $170 institutions out of country. **Remarks:** Accepts advertising.
Ad Rates: BW: $275   **Circ:** (Not Reported)

479 Applied Neuropsychology
Lawrence Erlbaum Associates, Inc.
10 Industrial Ave.
Mahwah, NJ 07430-2262
Phone: (201)236-9500
Fax: (201)236-0072
Free: (800)9-BOOKS-9

Publisher E-mail: orders@erlbaum.com

Professional journal for neuropsychologists, speech pathologists, and other medical professionals. **Freq:** Quarterly. **Trim Size:** 7 x 10. **Key Personnel:** Barbara P. Uzzell, Editor-in-Chief. **ISSN:** 0908-4282. **Subscription Rates:** $75 U.S. and Canada; $105 elsewhere; $180 institutions; $210 institutions out of country. **Remarks:** Accepts advertising.
Ad Rates: BW: $275   **Circ:** (Not Reported)

480 Children's Services
Lawrence Erlbaum Associates, Inc.
10 Industrial Ave.
Mahwah, NJ 07430-2262
Phone: (201)236-9500
Fax: (201)236-0072
Free: (800)9-BOOKS-9

Publisher E-mail: orders@erlbaum.com

Academic journal covering children's mental health issues for professionals. **Subtitle:** Social Policy, Research, and Practice. **Freq:** Quarterly. **Trim Size:** 5 x 8. **Key Personnel:** Michael C. Roberts, Editor; Brian Wilcox, Assoc. Editor. **ISSN:** 1093-9644. **Subscription Rates:** $35 U.S. and Canada; $50 elsewhere; $125 institutions; $150 institutions out of country. **Remarks:** Accepts advertising.
Ad Rates: BW: $275   **Circ:** (Not Reported)

481 Communication Booknotes Quarterly
Lawrence Erlbaum Associates, Inc.
10 Industrial Ave.
Mahwah, NJ 07430-2262
Phone: (201)236-9500
Fax: (201)236-0072
Free: (800)9-BOOKS-9

Publisher E-mail: orders@erlbaum.com

Professional, academic journal covering mass communication, telecommunication and information. **Freq:** Quarterly. **Trim Size:** 5 x 8. **Key Personnel:** Christopher H. Sterling, Editor. **ISSN:** 1094-8007. **Subscription Rates:** $40 U.S. and Canada; $65 elsewhere; $125 institutions; $150 institutions out of country. **Remarks:** Accepts advertising.
Ad Rates: BW: $275   **Circ:** (Not Reported)

482 Discourse Processes
Lawrence Erlbaum Associates, Inc.
10 Industrial Ave.
Mahwah, NJ 07430-2262
Phone: (201)236-9500
Fax: (201)236-0072
Free: (800)9-BOOKS-9

Publisher E-mail: orders@erlbaum.com

Scholarly journal covering communication, linguistics, language and educational psychology for professionals. **Freq:** Bimonthly. **Trim Size:** 5 x 8. **Key Personnel:** Arthur C. Graesser, Editor. **ISSN:** 0163-853X. **Subscription Rates:** $85 U.S. and Canada; $115 elsewhere; $220 institutions; ·$250 institutions out of country. **Remarks:** Accepts advertising.
Ad Rates: BW: $275   **Circ:** (Not Reported)

483 Family Futures
Lawrence Erlbaum Associates, Inc.
10 Industrial Ave.
Mahwah, NJ 07430-2262
Phone: (201)236-9500
Fax: (201)236-0072
Free: (800)9-BOOKS-9

Publisher E-mail: orders@erlbaum.com

Professional journal covering family issues for practitioners in professions

serving children, youth, and families; policymakers; and policy activists in the general public. **Freq:** Quarterly. **Trim Size:** 7 x 10. **Key Personnel:** Gary B. Melton, Editor; Brian L. Wilcox, Editor; James Garbarino, Editor; Maureen Donnelly, Managing Editor. **ISSN:** 1088-8713. **Subscription Rates:** $27.50 U.S. and Canada; $57.50 elsewhere; $80 institutions; $110 institutions out of country. **Remarks:** Accepts advertising.
Ad Rates: BW: $700   **Circ:** (Not Reported)

484 Gestalt Review
Lawrence Erlbaum Associates, Inc.
10 Industrial Ave.
Mahwah, NJ 07430-2262
Phone: (201)236-9500
Fax: (201)236-0072
Free: (800)9-BOOKS-9

Publication E-mail: tapjournals@analyticpress.com
Publisher E-mail: orders@erlbaum.com

Scholarly journal for Gestalt and non-Gestalt practitioners and theorists. **Freq:** Quarterly. **Trim Size:** 5 x 8. **Key Personnel:** Joseph Melnick, Editor. **ISSN:** 1084-8657. **Subscription Rates:** $42.50 U.S. and Canada; $62.50 elsewhere; $110 institutions; $130 institutions out of country. **Remarks:** Accepts advertising.
Ad Rates: BW: $265   **Circ:** (Not Reported)

485 International Journal of Cognitive Ergonomics
Lawrence Erlbaum Associates, Inc.
10 Industrial Ave.
Mahwah, NJ 07430-2262
Phone: (201)236-9500
Fax: (201)236-0072
Free: (800)9-BOOKS-9

Publisher E-mail: orders@erlbaum.com

Scholarly journal covering cognitive ergonomics for researchers, cognitive psychologists, air traffic controllers, and the insurance and information technology industries. **Freq:** Quarterly. **Trim Size:** 6 x 9. **Key Personnel:** Richard John Koubek, Editor; Gavriel Salvendy, Editor. **ISSN:** 1088-6362. **Subscription Rates:** $45 U.S. and Canada; $75 elsewhere; $150 institutions; $180 institutions out of country. **Remarks:** Accepts advertising.
Ad Rates: BW: $275   **Circ:** (Not Reported)

486 Journal of Applied Animal Welfare Science
Lawrence Erlbaum Associates, Inc.
10 Industrial Ave.
Mahwah, NJ 07430-2262
Phone: (201)236-9500
Fax: (201)236-0072
Free: (800)9-BOOKS-9

Publisher E-mail: orders@erlbaum.com

Scholarly journal covering animal welfare science for professionals. **Freq:** Quarterly. **Trim Size:** 5 x 8. **Key Personnel:** Stephen Zawistowski, Editor; Kenneth J. Shapiro, Editor. **ISSN:** 1088-8705. **Subscription Rates:** $35 U.S. and Canada; $60 elsewhere; $125 institutions; $150 institutions out of country. **Remarks:** Accepts advertising.
Ad Rates: BW: $375   **Circ:** (Not Reported)

487 Journal of Education for Students Placed at Risk
Lawrence Erlbaum Associates, Inc.
10 Industrial Ave.
Mahwah, NJ 07430-2262
Phone: (201)236-9500
Fax: (201)236-0072
Free: (800)9-BOOKS-9

Publisher E-mail: orders@erlbaum.com

Professional journal for educators and policy makers involved with improving the education of students placed at risk. **Freq:** Quarterly. **Trim Size:** 5 x 8. **Key Personnel:** Samuel C. Stringfield, Editor; John H. Hollifield, Editor; Faustine Jones-Wilson, Assoc. Editor; Amanda Datnow, Assoc. Editor. **ISSN:** 1082-4669. **Subscription Rates:** $35 U.S. and Canada; $65 elsewhere; $135 institutions; $165 institutions out of country. **Remarks:** Accepts advertising.
Ad Rates: BW: $300   **Circ:** (Not Reported)

488 Journal of Organizational Computing and Electronic Commerce
Lawrence Erlbaum Associates, Inc.
10 Industrial Ave.
Mahwah, NJ 07430-2262
Phone: (201)236-9500
Fax: (201)236-0072
Free: (800)9-BOOKS-9

Publisher E-mail: orders@erlbaum.com

Scholarly journal covering electronic commerce worldwide. **Subtitle:** An Official Publication of the Association for Information Systems. **Freq:** Quarterly. **Trim Size:** 6 x 9. **Key Personnel:** Andrew B. Whinston, Editor-in-Chief; Lynda M. Applegate, Editor; Clyde W. Holsapple, Editor; Ravi

Kalakota, Editor; Franz J. Radermacher, Editor. **ISSN:** 1054-1721. **Subscription Rates:** $55 U.S. and Canada; $85 elsewhere; $195 institutions; $225 institutions out of country. **Remarks:** Accepts advertising. **Online:** Online Computer Library Center.

Ad Rates: BW: $275   Circ: (Not Reported)

489 Measurement in Physical Education and Exercise Science
Lawrence Erlbaum Associates, Inc.
10 Industrial Ave.   Phone: (201)236-9500
Mahwah, NJ 07430-2262   Fax: (201)236-0072
                                                Free: (800)9-BOOKS-9

Publisher E-mail: orders@erlbaum.com

Scholarly journal for researchers, methodologists, and practitioners interested in measurement in physical education and exercise science. **Freq:** Quarterly. **Trim Size:** 5 x 8. **Key Personnel:** Ted A. Baumgartner, Editor; James Morrow, Assoc. Editor; Margaret Safrit, Assoc. Editor. **ISSN:** 1091-367X. **Subscription Rates:** $45 U.S. and Canada; $75 elsewhere; $125 institutions; $155 institutions out of country. **Remarks:** Accepts advertising.

Ad Rates: BW: $275   Circ: (Not Reported)

490 Mind, Culture, and Activity
Lawrence Erlbaum Associates, Inc.
10 Industrial Ave.   Phone: (201)236-9500
Mahwah, NJ 07430-2262   Fax: (201)236-0072
                                                Free: (800)9-BOOKS-9

Publisher E-mail: orders@erlbaum.com

Scholarly journal covering the human mind for anthropologists, cognitive scientists, educators, linguists, psychologists, and sociologists. **Freq:** Quarterly. **Trim Size:** 5 x 8. **Key Personnel:** Michael Cole, Editor; Yrjo Engestrom, Editor; Susan Leigh Star, Editor; James V. Wertsch, Editor. **ISSN:** 1074-9039. **Subscription Rates:** $30 U.S. and Canada; $60 elsewhere; $95 institutions; $125 institutions out of country. **Remarks:** Accepts advertising.

Ad Rates: BW: $300   Circ: (Not Reported)

491 Neural Computing Surveys
Lawrence Erlbaum Associates, Inc.
10 Industrial Ave.   Phone: (201)236-9500
Mahwah, NJ 07430-2262   Fax: (201)236-0072
                                                Free: (800)9-BOOKS-9

Publisher E-mail: orders@erlbaum.com

Scholarly journal for professionals and researchers in computer science and neural networks. **Freq:** Quarterly. **Key Personnel:** Arun Jagota, Editor. **ISSN:** 1093-7609. **Subscription Rates:** $100 U.S. and Canada; $125 elsewhere; $175 institutions; $200 institutions out of country. **URL:** http://www.icsi.berkeley.edu/~jagota/NCS.

492 Personality and Social Psychology Review
Lawrence Erlbaum Associates, Inc.
10 Industrial Ave.   Phone: (201)236-9500
Mahwah, NJ 07430-2262   Fax: (201)236-0072
                                                Free: (800)9-BOOKS-9

Publisher E-mail: orders@erlbaum.com

Scholarly journal for social, personality and organizational psychologists and sociologists. **Freq:** Quarterly. **Trim Size:** 7 x 10. **Key Personnel:** Marilynn B. Brewer, Editor; Nancy Cantor, Assoc. Editor; Norbert L. Kerr, Assoc. Editor. **ISSN:** 1088-8683. **Subscription Rates:** $50 U.S. and Canada; $80 elsewhere; $170 institutions; $200 institutions out of country. **Remarks:** Accepts advertising.

Ad Rates: BW: $375   Circ: (Not Reported)

493 Scientific Studies of Reading
Lawrence Erlbaum Associates, Inc.
10 Industrial Ave.   Phone: (201)236-9500
Mahwah, NJ 07430-2262   Fax: (201)236-0072
                                                Free: (800)9-BOOKS-9

Publisher E-mail: orders@erlbaum.com

Scholarly journal covering the science of reading. **Subtitle:** The Official Journal of the Society for the Scientific Study of Reading. **Freq:** Quarterly. **Trim Size:** 5 x 8. **Key Personnel:** Joanna P. Williams, Editor. **ISSN:** 1088-

8438. **Subscription Rates:** $45 U.S. and Canada; $75 elsewhere; $130 institutions; $160 institutions out of country. **Remarks:** Accepts advertising.
Ad Rates: BW: $275   Circ: (Not Reported)

494 Transportation Human Factors
Lawrence Erlbaum Associates, Inc.
10 Industrial Ave.   Phone: (201)236-9500
Mahwah, NJ 07430-2262   Fax: (201)236-0072
                                                Free: (800)9-BOOKS-9

Publisher E-mail: orders@erlbaum.com

Scholarly journal covering transportation and human factors for researchers and professionals. **Freq:** Quarterly. **Key Personnel:** Barry H. Kantowitz, Editor. **ISSN:** 1093-7609. **Subscription Rates:** $45 U.S. and Canada; $70 elsewhere; $140 institutions; $165 institutions out of country.

MAPLEWOOD

495 Classical Singer Magazine
New York Opera Newsletter
PO Box 278   Phone: (973)387-9549
Maplewood, NJ 07040   Fax: (973)378-2372
Publisher E-mail: TNYON@aol.com

Professional magazine covering auditions and information for classical singers. **Founded:** Dec. 1, 1987. **Freq:** Monthly. **Trim Size:** 8 1/2 x 11. **Key Personnel:** C. J. Williamson, Editor. **ISSN:** 1043-2361. **Subscription Rates:** $48 individuals; $84 two years; $54 Canada; $72 two years other countries. **Remarks:** Accepts advertising.

                                                Circ: Combined 4000

MONTVALE

496 CLR/Clinical Laboratory Reference
Medical Economics Co.
5 Paragon Dr.   Phone: (201)358-7500
Montvale, NJ 07645-1725   Fax: (201)358-7260
                                                Free: (800)223-0581

Publisher E-mail: customer.service@medec.com

Professional periodical for clinical laboratory workers. **Freq:** Annual (July). **Subscription Rates:** $32 individuals; $38 out of country.

497 FirstLine
Medical Economics Co.
5 Paragon Dr.   Phone: (201)358-7500
Montvale, NJ 07645-1725   Fax: (201)358-7260
                                                Free: (800)223-0581

Publisher E-mail: customer.service@medec.com

Professional journal covering staff training issues for veterinary hospital workers. **Freq:** Bimonthly. **ISSN:** 1095-0613. **Subscription Rates:** $21 individuals; $37.50 Canada and Mexico; $41.50 elsewhere.

498 Journal of the American Academy of Physician Assistants (JAAPA)
Medical Economics Co.
5 Paragon Dr.   Phone: (201)358-7500
Montvale, NJ 07645-1725   Fax: (201)358-7260
                                                Free: (800)223-0581

Publisher E-mail: customer.service@medec.com

Professional journal for physician assistants. **Freq:** Monthly. **ISSN:** 0893-7400. **Subscription Rates:** $50 individuals; $75 out of country.

499 Nursing Opportunities
Medical Economics Co.
5 Paragon Dr.   Phone: (201)358-7500
Montvale, NJ 07645-1725   Fax: (201)358-7260
                                                Free: (800)223-0581

Publisher E-mail: customer.service@medec.com

Professional magazine covering employment for nurses. **Freq:** Annual (December).

📖 500 Office Nurse
Medical Economics Co.
5 Paragon Dr.   Phone: (201)358-7500
Montvale, NJ 07645-1725   Fax: (201)358-7260
                                       Free: (800)223-0581

Publisher E-mail: customer.service@medec.com

Professional journal for office nurses. **Freq:** 10/year. **Subscription Rates:** $25.97 individuals; $31.97 Canada and Mexico; $37.97 elsewhere.

📖 501 Strategic Medicine
Medical Economics Co.
5 Paragon Dr.   Phone: (201)358-7500
Montvale, NJ 07645-1725   Fax: (201)358-7260
                                       Free: (800)223-0581

Publisher E-mail: customer.service@medec.com

Professional journal for primary care practitioners. **Founded:** 1998. **Freq:** Monthly. **Subscription Rates:** $49.99 individuals; $89 out of country.

MORRIS PLAINS

📖 502 Broadband Systems & Design
Cahners Business Information
301 Gibraltar Dr.   Phone: (973)292-5100
Morris Plains, NJ 07950   Fax: (973)539-3476

Trade magazine covering broadband technology. **Freq:** Weekly. **Key Personnel:** Terry McCoy, Publisher, tmccoy@gordon.cahners.com; Richard Cunningham, Editorial Dir.; Andrea Frucci, Editor-in-Chief. **URL:** http://www.broadbandmag.com.

MOUNT HOLLY

📖 503 Limousine Digest
Digest Publications
1419 Rte. 38 W.   Phone: (609)267-4400
Mount Holly, NJ 08060   Fax: (609)267-6200

Trade magazine for limousine owners/operators, van/bus fleet operators, and other ground transportation professionals in the U.S. **Key Personnel:** Chris Weiss, Publisher; Neil Weiss, Editor. **Subscription Rates:** $19.95 individuals.

NUTLEY

📖 504 Glen Ridge Voice
Orechio Publications and TV
90 Centre St.   Phone: (973)667-2100
Nutley, NJ 07110   Fax: (973)667-3904

Community newspaper. **Freq:** Weekly (Thurs.). **Key Personnel:** Michael Lawson, Publisher; Pam Langan, Editor; Nicole Canfora, Editor. **Subscription Rates:** $24 individuals. **Remarks:** Accepts advertising.
                                       Circ: Paid 710

PALISADES PARK

🎙 505 WMBC-TV -
460 Bergen Blvd., Ste. 355   Phone: (201)944-9622
Palisades Park, NJ 07650   Fax: (201)944-2607

Format: Commercial TV; Ethnic. **Owner:** Asian American TV, at above address. **Founded:** 1994. **Operating Hours:** Continuous.

TRENTON

📖 506 New Jersey School Boards Association School Leader
New Jersey School Boards Association
PO Box 909   Phone: (609)695-7600
Trenton, NJ 08605-0909   Fax: (609)695-0413

Consumer magazine covering education. **Freq:** Bimonthly. **Key Personnel:** Josephine Kane, Editor.

WARETOWN

📖 507 Ocean County Journal
PO Box 250
Waretown, NJ 08758   Phone: (609)660-1900

Community newspaper. **Freq:** Monthly. **Subscription Rates:** $18 individuals. **URL:** http://www.oceancounty.net.

NEW MEXICO

ALBUQUERQUE

📖 **508 New Mexico Jewish Link**
9600 Regal Ridge Dr. N.E.
Albuquerque, NM 87111

Phone: (505)797-1094
Fax: (505)797-1095

Jewish community newspaper. **Freq:** Monthly. **Key Personnel:** Susan Abonyi, Advertising Mgr., sabonyi@flash.net. **Remarks:** Accepts advertising. **URL:** http://www.swcp.com/~thelink.
Ad Rates: BW: $780
Circ: Combined 20,000

GALLUP

📖 **509 Paradoxism**
Universty of New Mexico
200 College Rd.
Gallup, NM 87301

Phone: (505)863-7647
Fax: (505)863-7532

Journal covering avant-garde poetry and fiction. **Founded:** 1993. **Freq:** Semiannual. **Print Method:** Offset. **Key Personnel:** Dr. Florentin Smarandache, Editor, smarand@unm.edu. **ISSN:** 1055-761X. **Subscription Rates:** $19.95 single issue. **Remarks:** Accepts advertising. **URL:** http://www.galup.unm.edu/~smarandache. **Former name:** Paradoxist Literary Movement.
Ad Rates: BW: $20
Circ: Combined 1000

LAS CRUCES

📖 **510 The Las Cruces Sun-News**
Mid-States Newspapers, Inc.
256 W. Las Cruces Ave.
Las Cruces, NM 88004

Phone: (505)541-5400
Fax: (505)541-5498

General newspaper. **Freq:** Daily. **Key Personnel:** David McCollum, Publisher; Harold Cousland, Editor; Bobby Duran, Circulation Mgr.; Charles Brunt, Managing Editor. **Subscription Rates:** $90 individuals; $192 out of state.

SILVER CITY

📖 **511 Borderlines**
Interhemispheric Resource Center
Interhemispheric Resource Center
PO Box 2178
Silver City, NM 88062
Publisher E-mail: resourcectr@igc.apc.org

Phone: (505)388-0208
Fax: (505)388-0619

Periodical covering U.S.-Mexico border issues. **Founded:** 1991. **Freq:** Monthly. **Key Personnel:** George Kourous, Editor, irc_ jorge@zianet.com. **Subscription Rates:** $12 individuals; $20 institutions; $2.50 single issue. **Remarks:** Advertising not accepted. **URL:** http://www.zianet.com/irc1/bordline.
Circ: Combined 350

📖 **512 Foreign Policy in Focus**
Interhemispheric Resource Center
Interhemispheric Resource Center
PO Box 2178
Silver City, NM 88062
Publisher E-mail: resourcectr@igc.apc.org

Phone: (505)388-0208
Fax: (505)388-0619

Periodical covering U.S. foreign policy. **Founded:** 1996. **Freq:** Weekly. **Key Personnel:** Tom Barry, Editor; Martha Honey, Editor, ipsps@igc.apc.org. **Subscription Rates:** $60 individuals; $2.50 single issue. **Remarks:** Advertising not accepted. **URL:** http://www.foreignpolicy-infocus.org.
Circ: Paid 800
Non-paid 250

📖 **513 Interhemispheric Resource Center Bulletin**
Interhemispheric Resource Center
Interhemispheric Resource Center
PO Box 2178
Silver City, NM 88062
Publisher E-mail: resourcectr@igc.apc.org

Phone: (505)388-0208
Fax: (505)388-0619

Periodical covering research news of the Interhemispheric Resource Center. **Freq:** Quarterly. **Key Personnel:** Tom Barry, Editor. **ISSN:** 0891-2688. **Subscription Rates:** $5 individuals. **URL:** http://www.zianet.com/irc1.
Circ: Combined 800

NEW YORK

ARMONK

514 Journal of Endovascular Surgery
Futura Publishing Co., Inc.
135 Bedford Rd.
Armonk, NY 10504-0418

Phone: (914)273-1014
Fax: (914)273-1015
Free: (800)877-8761

Medical journal covering endovascular surgery for professionals. **Freq:** Quarterly. **Trim Size:** 8 1/4 x 10 7/8. **Key Personnel:** Edward B. Diethrich, MD, Editor-in-Chief; Thomas J. Fogarty, MD, Editor-in-Chief. **Subscription Rates:** $85 individuals; $127.50 libraries; $30 single issue. **Remarks:** Accepts advertising.

Ad Rates: BW: $800
                      4C: $1,735

Circ: (Not Reported)

515 Noninvasive Electrocardiology
Futura Publishing Co., Inc.
135 Bedford Rd.
Armonk, NY 10504-0418

Phone: (914)273-1014
Fax: (914)273-1015
Free: (800)877-8761

Medical journal covering noninvasive electrocardiology for professionals. **Freq:** Quarterly. **Trim Size:** 8 1/4 x 10 7/8. **Key Personnel:** Arthur J. Moss, MD, Editor-in-Chief; Shlomo Stern, MD, Editor-in-Chief. **Subscription Rates:** $80 individuals; $120 libraries; $30 single issue. **Remarks:** Accepts advertising.

Ad Rates: BW: $765
                      4C: $1,695

Circ: (Not Reported)

BINGHAMTON

516 Journal of Technology in Human Services
The Haworth Press, Inc.
10 Alice St.
Binghamton, NY 13904-1580

Free: (800)HAWORTH

Publisher E-mail: getinfo@haworthpressinc.com

Professional journal covering computer applications in the human services. **Founded:** 1985. **Freq:** Quarterly. **Trim Size:** 6 x 8. **Key Personnel:** Dick Schoech, Ph.D., Editor. **ISSN:** 0740-445X. **Subscription Rates:** $45 individuals; $90 institutions; $200 libraries. **Remarks:** Accepts advertising. **URL:** http://www.uta.edu/cussn/cussn.html. **Former name:** Computers in Human Services.

Circ: Combined 750

BRONX

517 Nueva Luz
En Foco, Inc.
32 E. Kingsbridge Rd.
Bronx, NY 10468

Phone: (718)584-7718

Publisher E-mail: enfocoinc@aol.com

Journal covering photography by people of Latino, Asian, African, and Native American heritage. **Founded:** 1984. **Freq:** Triennial. **Print Method:** Offset. **Trim Size:** 9 x 12. **Key Personnel:** Charles Biasiny-Rivera, Editor. **ISSN:** 0887-5855. **Subscription Rates:** $25 individuals; $5 single issue. **Remarks:** Accepts advertising.

Ad Rates: BW: $1,000

Circ: Combined 3,500

518 Riverdale Review
Parkchester Publishing Co., Inc.
170 W. 233rd St.
Bronx, NY 10463

Phone: (718)543-5200
Fax: (718)543-4206

Community newspaper. **Founded:** 1993. **Freq:** Weekly (Wed.). **Key Personnel:** Andrew Wolf, Publisher. **Subscription Rates:** Free.

Circ: Combined ♦19,100

BRONXVILLE

519 Curio
Curio Magazine, Inc.
81 Pondfield Rd., Ste. 264
Bronxville, NY 10708

Phone: (914)961-8649
Fax: (914)779-4033

Consumer magazine covering arts and entertainment. **Founded:** May 1996. **Freq:** Quarterly. **Trim Size:** 8 3/8 x 10 1/2. **Key Personnel:** Mickey Z., Editor; M. Teresa Lawrence, Publisher and Advertising Mgr. **ISSN:** 1086-2196. **Remarks:** Accepts advertising.

Ad Rates: BW: $1800
                      4C: $2200

Circ: Paid 50,000

BROOKLYN

520 Kurdish Life
Kurdish Library
345 Park Pl.
Brooklyn, NY 11238

Phone: (718)783-7930
Fax: (718)398-4365

Publisher E-mail: kurdishlib@aol.com

Scholarly journal covering Kurdish and Middle East issues within U.S. foreign policy. **Freq:** Quarterly. **Trim Size:** 8 1/2 x 11. **Cols./Page:** 2. **Key Personnel:** Dr. Vera Beaudin Saeedpour, Director. **Subscription Rates:** $30 individuals; $8 single issue.

BUFFALO

521 Artvoice
500 Franklin St.
Buffalo, NY 14202

Phone: (716)881-6124

Community newspaper. **Freq:** Biweekly. **Subscription Rates:** Free.

Circ: Non-paid **35,747**

COMMACK

522 Nova Journal of Theoretical Physics
Nova Science Publishers, Inc.
6080 Jericho Turnpike, Ste. 207
Commack, NY 11725

Phone: (516)499-3103
Fax: (516)499-3146

Publisher E-mail: novascience@earthlink.net

Scholarly journal covering theoretical physics. **Freq:** Quarterly. **Subscription Rates:** $400 individuals. **URL:** http://www.nexusworld.com/nova.

EAST ROCHESTER

📖 **523 The Shopping Bag**
201 Main St.
East Rochester, NY 14445-1799   Phone: (716)385-1974

Shopping guide. **Freq:** Weekly (Wed.). **Subscription Rates:** Free.
Circ: Non-paid **261,269**

FLUSHING

📖 **524 Chosun Daily**
35-11 Farrington St.   Phone: (718)463-1400
Flushing, NY 11354   Fax: (718)359-2067

Korean language newspaper. **Founded:** 1983. **Freq:** Daily. **Key Personnel:**
Jung Soon Park, Contact. **Remarks:** Accepts advertising.
Ad Rates: BW: $1,500   Circ: (Not Reported)

📖 **525 KTV (Korean American Network News)**
Korean American Network News
130-30 31st Ave., 7th Fl.   Phone: (718)358-3535
Flushing, NY 11354   Fax: (718)358-3428

Korean language community newspaper. **Founded:** 1987. **Freq:** Weekly. **Key
Personnel:** Sun Lim, Contact. **Subscription Rates:** Free; $100 by mail.
Remarks: Accepts advertising.
Ad Rates: BW: $1,000   Circ: Combined 10,000

FREEVILLE

📖 **526 The Suburban Shopper**
Freeville Publishing Co., Inc.
9 Main St.
PO Box 210   Phone: (607)844-9119
Freeville, NY 13068   Fax: (607)844-3381

Shopping guide. **Founded:** 1949. **Freq:** Weekly (Tues.). **Key Personnel:**
Sidney C. Jones, Publisher. **Subscription Rates:** Free.
Circ: Non-paid ♦ **23,767**

GARDEN CITY

📖 **527 CNS Focus**
Cargo Network Services
300 Garden City Plaza, Ste. 312   Phone: (516)747-3312
Garden City, NY 11530-3325   Fax: (516)747-3431

Trade magazine covering shipping. **Freq:** Quarterly. **Key Personnel:**
Anthony F. Calabrese, Editor. **Remarks:** Accepts advertising. **URL:** http://
www.cnsc.net.
Circ: Non-paid 7,000

📖 **528 Inter@ctive Week**
Inter@ctive Enterprises/Ziff Davis
100 Quentin Roosevelt Blvd., No. 508   Phone: (516)229-3700
Garden City, NY 11530   Fax: (516)229-3707

Trade magazine covering the interactive and online industries. **Freq:** Weekly.
Key Personnel: Al Perlman, Publisher, laperlman@zd.com; Tom Steinert-
Threlkeld, Editor-in-Chief, tomhyphen@onramp.net; George Vernadakis,
Editor, gvernada@zd.com. **URL:** http://www.interactive-week.com.

HAMBURG

📖 **529 Kids Courier**
H & K Publications, Inc.
50 Buffalo St.   Phone: (716)649-4413
Hamburg, NY 14075-5002   Fax: (716)649-6374

Children's newspaper for children in grades 1-5 delivered in the classroom.
Freq: Monthly Sept. through June. **Print Method:** Web offset. **Trim Size:** 11
3/8 x 14 7/8. **Key Personnel:** C. F. Kluckhohn, Editor and Publisher, phone
(716)649-4413, cfk@kidscourier.com; Judy Beckwith, Marketing Dir.,
jab@kidscourier.com; Rick Manzone, National Sales Rep., phone (716)649-

4413, ram@kidscourier.com. **Subscription Rates:** Free to qualified subscribers. **Remarks:** Accepts advertising.
Circ: Non-paid 243,500

HUNTINGTON

📖 **530 Workforce Diversity for Engineering and IT Professionals**
Equal Opportunity Publications, Inc.
1160 E. Jericho Tpke., Ste. 200   Phone: (516)421-9421
Huntington, NY 11743   Fax: (516)421-0359
Publisher E-mail: info@eop.com

Professional magazine for the high-tech industry. **Founded:** 1994. **Freq:**
Quarterly. **Key Personnel:** John Miller, Pres./Pub.; Tamara Flaum, VP, Sales
& Mktg., phone (516)421-9438. **URL:** http://www.eop.com.
Circ: Combined ●**15,046**

ISLAND PARK

📖 **531 The Island-Ear**
The Island-Ear, Inc.
PO Box 309   Phone: (516)889-6045
Island Park, NY 11558   Fax: (516)889-5513

Community entertainment newspaper. **Founded:** 1978. **Freq:** Biweekly.
Print Method: Web offset. **Trim Size:** 10 3/4 x 13 3/4. **Key Personnel:** Arie
Nadboy, Publisher; Dan Kline, Editor. **ISSN:** 1041-3812. **Subscription
Rates:** $40 individuals. **Remarks:** Accepts advertising. **URL:** http://
www.islandear.com.
Ad Rates: BW: $1230   Circ: Controlled ‡27,020
          4C: $1705

JACKSON HEIGHTS

📖 **532 Editor's Choice**
Spirit That Moves Us Press
PO Box 720820   Phone: (718)426-8788
Jackson Heights, NY 11372-0820   Fax: (718)426-7246

Literary anthology covering fiction, poetry, and essays. **Founded:** Dec. 1980.
Freq: Irregular. **Print Method:** Offset. **Trim Size:** 5 1/2 x 8 1/2. **Key
Personnel:** Morty Sklar, Editor-in-Chief, msklar@mindspring.com. **ISSN:**
1060-2658. **Subscription Rates:** $16 individuals paper; $22 individuals cloth.
Remarks: Advertising not accepted.
Circ: Paid 3000

📖 **533 The Spirit That Moves Us**
Spirit That Moves Us Press
PO Box 720820   Phone: (718)426-8788
Jackson Heights, NY 11372-0820   Fax: (718)426-7246

Literary magazine covering fiction, poetry, essays, and art. **Founded:** Sept.
1975. **Freq:** Irregular. **Print Method:** Offset. **Trim Size:** 5 1/2 x 8 1/2. **Key
Personnel:** Morty Sklar, Editor-in-Chief, msklar@mindspring.com. **ISSN:**
0364-4014. **Subscription Rates:** $16 individuals paper; $22 individuals cloth.
Remarks: Advertising not accepted.
Circ: (Not Reported)

KINGSTON

📖 **534 Woodstock Times**
Ulster Publishing
322 Wall St.   Phone: (914)334-8200
Kingston, NY 12402   Fax: (914)334-8202
Publication E-mail: news@woodstocktimes.com

Community newspaper. **Freq:** Weekly. **Key Personnel:** Geddy Sveikauskas,
Publisher, geddy@woodstocktimes.com. **Subscription Rates:** $35 individu-
als; $40 out of area. **Remarks:** Advertising accepted; rates available upon
request. **URL:** http://www.woodstocktimes.com.
Circ: (Not Reported)

LIBERTY

535 Catskill Shopper-Eastern Sullivan Edition
Catskill Shopper
PO Box 389
Liberty, NY 12754   Phone: (914)292-0500

Shopping guide. **Freq:** Weekly (Fri.). **Subscription Rates:** Free.
Circ: 19,343

LONG ISLAND CITY

536 The Sae Gae Times
38-42 9th St.   Phone: (718)361-2600
Long Island City, NY 11101   Fax: (718)361-2487

Korean language community and business newspaper. **Founded:** 1981. **Freq:**
Mon.-Sat. **Key Personnel:** Young Seok Han, Contact. **Subscription Rates:**
$120 individuals. **Remarks:** Accepts advertising.
Ad Rates: BW: $1,400   **Circ:** Combined 20,000

MINEOLA

537 The Long Island Voice
Long Island Voice, Inc.
393 Jericho Turnpike   Phone: (516)877-7373
Mineola, NY 11501-1205   Fax: (516)877-0986

Community newspaper. **Freq:** Weekly (Wed.). **Key Personnel:** Dave Parker,
Publisher; John Mancini, Editor-in-Chief; Ward Harkavy, Managing Editor;
Greg Hoy, Production Mgr.; Judy Miszner, VP, Sales & Mktg. **URL:** http://
www.livoice.com.

NEW YORK

538 American Chinese Herald
Sino-US Promotion Council for Economy-Science-Culture
396 Broadway, Ste. 901   Phone: (212)941-1288
New York, NY 10013   Fax: (212)941-1896

Newspaper covering issues for Chinese-American professionals. **Freq:**
Weekly. **Subscription Rates:** Free. **Remarks:** Accepts advertising.
Ad Rates: BW: $1280   **Circ:** Non-paid 35,000
               4C: $938

539 ANS Bulletin
American Name Society
17 Lexington Ave.
PO Box G-1224   Phone: (212)387-1597
New York, NY 10010   Fax: (212)387-1591

Scholarly journal covering genealogy and languages. **Founded:** 1953. **Freq:**
Quarterly. **Key Personnel:** Wayne H. Finke, Contact, wayne_
finke@baruch.cuny.edu. **ISSN:** 0027-7738. **Remarks:** Advertising not accepted.
Circ: Paid 740

540 Archaeology's Dig
Archaeological Institute of America
135 William St.   Phone: (212)732-5154
New York, NY 10038   Fax: (212)732-5707

Consumer magazine covering archaeology for children. **Freq:** Bimonthly.
Key Personnel: Stephen Hanks, Editor-in-Chief. **Subscription Rates:** $19.99
individuals; $34.99 out of country. **URL:** http://dig.archaeology.org/.

541 Asahi Shimbun
845 3rd Ave.   Phone: (212)317-3000
New York, NY 10022   Fax: (212)317-3025

Japanese language general newspaper. **Founded:** 1986. **Freq:** Daily. **Key
Personnel:** Takao Toneyama, General Mgr. **Subscription Rates:** $936
individuals. **Remarks:** Accepts advertising.
Ad Rates: BW: $4,800   **Circ:** Combined 12,000

542 Brand Marketing
Fairchild Publications, Inc.
7 W. 34th St.
New York, NY 10001   Phone: (212)630-4000

Trade newspaper for brand managers, sales and marketing executives and
others in the industry. **Freq:** Monthly. **Remarks:** Advertising accepted; rates
available upon request. **URL:** http://www.brandmarket.com.
Circ: (Not Reported)

543 Challenge New York
Progressive Labor Party
105 W. 28th St., Rm. 301
New York, NY 10001-6103

Political newspaper. **Subtitle:** The Revolutionary Communist Newspaper.
Founded: 1962. **Freq:** Weekly. **Col. Width:** 2 inches. **Key Personnel:** Luis
Castro, Editor-in-Chief. **ISSN:** 0009-1049. **Remarks:** Advertising not accept-
ed. **URL:** http://www.plp.org.
Circ: (Not Reported)

544 China Press
15 Mercer St.   Phone: (212)274-8282
New York, NY 10013   Fax: (212)274-0686

Chinese language general newspaper. **Founded:** 1990. **Freq:** Mon.-Sat. **Key
Personnel:** D.K. Yang, Contact. **Subscription Rates:** $115 individuals.
Remarks: Accepts advertising.
Ad Rates: BW: $864   **Circ:** Combined 120,000
               4C: $1,670

545 Columbia Human Rights Law Review
Columbia Law School
435 W. 116th St.
New York, NY 10027-7201   Phone: (212)854-6044

Scholarly journal covering human rights and law worldwide. **Founded:** 1969.
Freq: Triennial. **ISSN:** 0090-7944. **Subscription Rates:** $40 individuals; $45
institutions; $15 single issue. **Remarks:** Advertising not accepted. **Online:**
LEXIS-NEXIS; Westlaw.
Circ: Paid 650

546 Columbia Journal of Asian Law
Columbia University
435 W. 116th St.
Box C-10   Phone: (212)854-5510
New York, NY 10027   Fax: (212)854-7946

Scholarly journal covering law in Asia for practitioners and scholars.
Founded: 1987. **Freq:** Semiannual. **Key Personnel:** Min Ding, Editor-in-
Chief; Noah Brumfield, Exec. Editor. **ISSN:** 1094-8449. **Subscription Rates:**
$35 individuals; $25 single issue. **Remarks:** Advertising not accepted.
Online: Westlaw. **Former name:** Journal of Chinese Law.
Circ: (Not Reported)

547 Columbia Journal of Environmental Law
Columbia University
Mail Code 3513   Phone: (212)854-1606
New York, NY 10027   Fax: (212)854-7946
Publisher E-mail: jrnenv@law.columbia.edu

Scholarly journal covering environmental law. **Founded:** 1974. **Freq:**
Semiannual. **ISSN:** 0090-7944. **Subscription Rates:** $35 individuals; $20
single issue. **Remarks:** Accepts advertising.
Ad Rates: BW: $100   **Circ:** (Not Reported)

548 Computer Telephony
Miller Freeman, Inc.
1 Penn Plaza, 10th Fl.   Phone: (212)714-1300
New York, NY 10119-1198   Fax: (212)643-5612

Trade magazine covering computer and telephone integration. **Freq:** Monthly.
Key Personnel: Carole Lubin, Publisher, carole@paoffice.mhs.compu; Rick
Luhman, Editor-in-Chief, rick@computertelephony.com; Richard Grigonis,

Ad Rates: GLR = general line rate; BW = one-time black & white page rate; 4C = one-time four color page rate; SAU = standard advertising unit rate;
CNU = Canadian newspaper advertising unit rate; PCI = per column inch rate.
Circulation: ★ = ABC; △ = BPA; ◆ = CAC; ● = CCAB; ❑ = VAC; ⊕ = PO Statement; ‡ = Publisher's Report; Boldface figures = sworn; Light figures = estimated.
Entry type: ▯ = Print; ▮ = Broadcast.

81

Technical Editor, rgrigonis@computertelephony.com. **URL:** http://www.computertelephony.com.

◻ 549 Cong Thuong
PO Box 1975
New York, NY 10013

Vietnamese-language newspaper. **Subtitle:** New York Vietnam Business News. **Freq:** Biweekly. **Trim Size:** 10 x 13. **Subscription Rates:** Free. **Remarks:** Accepts advertising.
Ad Rates:　BW: $400　　　　　　　　　Circ: (Not Reported)

◻ 550 Contemporary Dialysis & Nephrology
Ashlee Publishing Co., Inc.
18 E. 41st St.　　　　　　　　　　Phone: (212)682-7681
New York, NY 10017　　　　　　　　Fax: (212)697-8331

Professional medical magazine for the renal care community. **Freq:** Monthly. **Print Method:** Offset. **Trim Size:** 8 1/4 x 10 7/8. **Subscription Rates:** $42 individuals; $77 two years; $47 Canada and Mexico; $67 elsewhere. **Remarks:** Accepts advertising. **URL:** http://www.ashlee.com/dialysis.
Ad Rates:　BW: $2,798　　　　　　　Circ: (Not Reported)
　　　　　　4C: $3,648

◻ 551 Country Living Gardener
Hearst Business Communications
1790 Broadway, Ste. 6　　　　　　Phone: (212)969-7544
New York, NY 10019-1412　　　　　Fax: (212)969-7563

Consumer magazine covering gardening, crafts, food, entertaining, health and travel. **Founded:** 1994. **Freq:** Bimonthly. **Key Personnel:** Diana Gold Murphy, Editor; Anne Holton, VP/Publisher.
　　　　　　　　　　　　　　　　Circ: Combined 500,000

◻ 552 Dispute Resolution Times
American Arbitration Association
140 W. 51st St.　　　　　　　　　Phone: (212)484-4000
New York, NY 10020-1203　　　　　Fax: (212)541-4041

Professional magazine of the American Arbitration Association.

◻ 553 Executive Technology
Fairchild Publications, Inc.
7 W. 34th St.
New York, NY 10001　　　　　　　Phone: (212)630-4000

Trade magazine covering business and information technology for executives. **Key Personnel:** Marc Millstein, Group Editor, phone (212)630-3760, millstem@fairchildpub.com; Denise Power, Group Man. Editor, phone (212)630-3769, powerd@fairchildpub.com. **URL:** http://www.executivetechnology.com.

◻ 554 Fenestration
Ashlee Publishing Co., Inc.
18 E. 41st St.　　　　　　　　　　Phone: (212)682-7681
New York, NY 10017　　　　　　　　Fax: (212)697-8331

Trade magazine covering fenestration product manufacturing for production and marketing executives, and technical personnel. **Freq:** 9/year. **Trim Size:** 8 x 10 3/4. **Remarks:** Accepts advertising. **URL:** http://www.ashlee.com/fenestration.
Ad Rates:　BW: $1,625　　　　　　　Circ: (Not Reported)
　　　　　　4C: $2,475

◻ 555 Footwear News (FN)
Fairchild Publications, Inc.
7 W. 34th St.
New York, NY 10001　　　　　　　Phone: (212)630-4000

Newspaper covering retailing and merchandising of footwear, accessories, and leather industries. **Founded:** Oct. 6, 1945. **Freq:** Weekly (Mon.). **Print Method:** Offset. Uses mats. **Trim Size:** 11 1/2 x 15. **Cols./Page:** 5. **Col. Width:** 11 picas. **Col. Depth:** 13 7/8 inches. **Key Personnel:** Mark Sullivan, Vice President, phone (212)630-4865, fax (212)630-4879; Jack Powers, Associate Publisher-Advertising, phone (212)630-7825, fax (617)356-7836; Dick Silverman, Associate Publisher-Editorial, phone (212)630-3781, fax (212)630-3796; Donna Heiderstadt, Editor-in-Chief, phone (212)630-3798,

fax (212)630-3796. **ISSN:** 0162-914X. **Subscription Rates:** $48; $75 two years; $100 other countries; $175 two years, other countries.
Ad Rates:　BW: $7,210　　　　　　　Circ: Paid 14,174
　　　　　　4C: $8,830　　　　　　　Non-paid 1,8001

◻ 556 Glass Digest
Ashlee Publishing Co., Inc.
18 E. 41st St.　　　　　　　　　　Phone: (212)682-7681
New York, NY 10017　　　　　　　　Fax: (212)697-8331
Publication E-mail: glassdgst@aol.com

Trade magazine covering flat glass architectural and automotive replacement glass markets. **Freq:** Monthly. **Print Method:** Web offset. **Trim Size:** 8 x 10 3/4. **Subscription Rates:** $40 U.S., Canada, and Mexico; $50 elsewhere; $50 two years U.S., Canada, and Mexico. **Remarks:** Accepts advertising. **URL:** http://www.ashlee.com/glassdigest.
Ad Rates:　BW: $1,800　　　　　　　Circ: (Not Reported)
　　　　　　4C: $3,200

◻ 557 Glass Industry
Ashlee Publishing Co., Inc.
18 E. 41st St.　　　　　　　　　　Phone: (212)682-7681
New York, NY 10017　　　　　　　　Fax: (212)697-8331

Trade magazine covering flat, container, fiber and pressed/blown glass management and in-plant personnel worldwide. **Freq:** Monthly. **Print Method:** Web offset. **Trim Size:** 8 x 10 3/4. **Subscription Rates:** $50 individuals; $60 two years; $50 Canada and Mexico; $60 elsewhere. **Remarks:** Accepts advertising. **URL:** http://www.ashlee.com/glassindustry/.
Ad Rates:　BW: $1,750　　　　　　　Circ: (Not Reported)
　　　　　　4C: $2,750

◻ 558 Home Furnishings News (HFN)
Fairchild Publications, Inc.
7 W. 34th St.
New York, NY 10001　　　　　　　Phone: (212)630-4000

Trade magazine for the home products industry, including furniture, housewares, textiles, electronics and computers. **Founded:** 1929. **Freq:** Weekly. **URL:** http://www.hfnmag.com.

◻ 559 I.F.A.R. Journal
International Foundation for Art Research
500 5th Ave., Ste. 1234　　　　　Phone: (212)391-6234
New York, NY 10110　　　　　　　Fax: (212)391-8794

Professional journal covering art, stolen art, and art authenticity. **Founded:** Apr. 1, 1998. **Freq:** Quarterly. **Print Method:** Offset. **Trim Size:** 8 1/2 x 11. **Cols./Page:** 3. **Key Personnel:** Sharon Flescher, Exec. Director and Editor-in-Chief; Kathleen Ferguson, Editor, kferg@ifar.org. **ISSN:** 1098-1195. **Subscription Rates:** $65 individuals; $16.25 single issue. **Remarks:** Accepts advertising. **URL:** http://www.ifar.org. **Former name:** I.F.A.R. Reports.
　　　　　　　　　　　　　　　　Circ: (Not Reported)

◻ 560 Internet User
Ziff-Davis Inc.
28 E. 28th St.　　　　　　　　　Phone: (212)503-3500
New York, NY 10016　　　　　　　Fax: (212)503-5799

Consumer magazine covering Internet buying. **Freq:** Quarterly. **Key Personnel:** Michael J. Miller, Editor-in-Chief; Don Willmott, Editor; Monica Sirignano, Managing Editor. **URL:** http://www.internetuser.com.
　　　　　　　　　　　　　　　　Circ: Combined 220,000

◻ 561 Jane
Fairchild Publications
7 W. 34th St.　　　　　　　　　　Phone: (212)630-4784
New York, NY 10003　　　　　　　Fax: (212)630-4786
　　　　　　　　　　　　　　　　Free: (800)247-2160

Consumer magazine covering fashion for women. **Freq:** Monthly. **Key Personnel:** Jane Pratt, Editor-in-Chief; Andrea Rosengarten, Exec./Man. Editor. **Subscription Rates:** $2.95 single issue; $3.95 single issue Canada.

▫ **562 The Japanese Daily Sun-Nikkan San**
845 3rd Ave.   Phone: (212)317-3000
New York, NY 10022   Fax: (212)317-3025

Japanese language general newspaper. **Freq:** Daily. **Key Personnel:** Takao Toneyama, General Mgr. **Remarks:** Accepts advertising.
Ad Rates: BW: $4800   **Circ:** (Not Reported)

▫ **563 Journal of Object-Oriented Programming**
SIGS Publications, Inc.
71 W. 23rd St., 3rd Fl.
New York, NY 10010-4102   Phone: (212)242-7447
Publication E-mail: subscriptions@sigs.com
Publisher E-mail: info@sigs.com

Trade magazine covering research, applications, and technical data on object-oriented languages. **Freq:** 9/year. **Key Personnel:** Richard Wiener, Editor; Richard P. Friedman, Publisher. **Subscription Rates:** $71 individuals. **URL:** http://www.sigs.com.
                                          Circ: Combined 24,000

▫ **564 Maxim**
Dennis Publishing
1040 Avenue of the Americas, 23rd Fl.
New York, NY 10018   Phone: (212)302-2626

Consumer magazine covering lifestyle, fashion and entertainment. **Freq:** 10/year. **Key Personnel:** Mike Soutar, Editor-in-Chief; James Kaminsky, Editor; Stephen Perrine, Editor; James Heidenry, Managing Editor; Brian Robinson, Advertising Mgr. **URL:** http://www.maximmag.com.

▫ **565 Ming Pao Daily News**
Ming Pao Enterprise Corporation Ltd.
43-31 33rd St., No. 2F   Phone: (718)786-2888
New York, NY 10001   Fax: (718)433-3858

Chinese language general newspaper. **Freq:** Daily. **Key Personnel:** Peter Man, General Mgr. **Subscription Rates:** $160 individuals. **Remarks:** Advertising accepted; rates available upon request.
                                          Circ: Combined 38,500

▫ **566 Mobile Networks and Applications**
Association for Computing Machinery
1515 Broadway, 17th Fl.   Phone: (212)869-7440
New York, NY 10036-5701   Fax: (212)944-1318
Publication E-mail: orders@acm.org

Technical magazine covering mobile computing. **Freq:** Quarterly. **Key Personnel:** Mark Mandelbaum, Publications Dir. **Subscription Rates:** $42 individuals. **URL:** http://www.acm.org.

▫ **567 Mode**
Mode Magazine
22 E. 49th St.
New York, NY 10017
Publication E-mail: info@modemag.com

Consumer magazine covering fashion and issues for plus size women. **Freq:** Monthly. **URL:** http://www.modemag.com.

▫ **568 NetWorker**
Association for Computing Machinery
1515 Broadway, 17th Fl.   Phone: (212)869-7440
New York, NY 10036-5701   Fax: (212)944-1318
Publication E-mail: editor@networker.org

Trade magazine covering network computer technology. **Freq:** Bimonthly. **Key Personnel:** Steven Cherry, Exec. Editor; Dan Rosenbaum, Editor; Jennifer Bruer, Managing Editor. **URL:** http://www.networker.org.

▫ **569 Nihon Keizai Shimbun**
1325 Avenue of the Americas   Phone: (212)261-6220
New York, NY 10019   Fax: (212)261-6208

Japanese language business newspaper for the Japanese business community

in North America. **Founded:** 1987. **Freq:** Daily. **Key Personnel:** Miho Fujimura, Sales Rep. **Subscription Rates:** $90 individuals. **Remarks:** Accepts advertising.
Ad Rates: BW: $9,000   **Circ:** Combined 16,000

▫ **570 Object Magazine**
SIGS Publications, Inc.
71 W. 23rd St., 3rd Fl.
New York, NY 10010-4102   Phone: (212)242-7447
Publication E-mail: subscriptions@sigs.com
Publisher E-mail: info@sigs.com

Trade magazine covering management and implementation of object oriented technology. **Freq:** Monthly. **Key Personnel:** Richard P. Friedman, Publisher; John Williams, Editor, jwilliams@sigs.com; Seth J. Bookey, Managing Editor, sbookey@sigs.com. **Subscription Rates:** $49 individuals. **URL:** http://www.objectmagazine.com.
                                          Circ: Combined 20,000

▫ **571 OCS News**
5 E. 44th St.   Phone: (212)599-4509
New York, NY 10017   Fax: (212)599-4528

Japanese language community newspaper. **Founded:** 1975. **Freq:** Biweekly. **Key Personnel:** Nao Hoshino, Contact. **Subscription Rates:** $30 individuals. **Remarks:** Accepts advertising.
Ad Rates: BW: $3,040   **Circ:** Combined 19,000

▫ **572 Outyouth**
Lesbian and Gay Community Services Center, Youth Enrichment
   Program
208 W. 13th St.
New York, NY 10011

Periodical covering poetry, fiction, essays, and reports for the lesbian and gay youth community. **Founded:** Apr. 1992. **Freq:** Quarterly. **Key Personnel:** Barbara Bickart, Editor. **Subscription Rates:** Free. **Remarks:** Advertising not accepted.
                                          Circ: (Not Reported)

▫ **573 Plaza Tsushin**
31 W. 21st St., 4th Fl.   Phone: (212)807-6570
New York, NY 10010   Fax: (212)807-6635

Newspaper covering diet, nutrition, Japanese culture and lifestyle in English and Japanese. **Founded:** 1992. **Freq:** Monthly. **Key Personnel:** Miharu Wada, Sales Rep. **Subscription Rates:** Free. **Remarks:** Accepts advertising.
Ad Rates: BW: $1,500   **Circ:** Combined 20,000
                4C: $2,500

▫ **574 Political Affairs**
Political Affairs Publishers, Inc.
235 W. 23rd St., 7th Fl.   Phone: (212)989-4994
New York, NY 10011-2313   Fax: (212)229-1713

Scholarly journal covering politics. **Freq:** Monthly except Sept./Oct. **Key Personnel:** Joseph Sims, Editor-in-Chief. **ISSN:** 0032-3128. **Subscription Rates:** $18 individuals; $32 two years; $27 institutions; $48.50 two years institutions.

▫ **575 Salon News**
Fairchild Publications, Inc.
7 W. 34th St.
New York, NY 10001   Phone: (212)630-4000

Trade newspaper for the salon and beauty industry. **Freq:** Monthly. **Subscription Rates:** Free to qualified subscribers. **URL:** http://www.salonnews.com.
                                          Circ: Combined 75,000

576 Small Business Computing & Communications
Curtco Freedom Group
156 W. 156th St., 3rd Fl.   Phone: (212)547-6300
New York, NY 10019   Fax: (212)333-5560
    Free: (800)537-4638

Trade magazine covering computing and communication technologies for small businesses. **Freq:** Monthly. **Key Personnel:** Cathy Grayson Brower, Editor-in-Chief, cathyb@curtco.com; Kristin Dunlap Godsey, Exec. Editor, kristing@curtco.com; Lissa Mulvihill, Managing Editor, lissam@curtco.com. **Subscription Rates:** $19.97 individuals. **URL:** http://www.smalloffice.com.

577 Stone
Ashlee Publishing Co., Inc.
18 E. 41st St.   Phone: (212)682-7681
New York, NY 10017   Fax: (212)697-8331

Trade magazine for specifiers, fabricators, and suppliers of dimensional stone. **Print Method:** Web offset. **Trim Size:** 8 1/4 x 10 7/8. **Subscription Rates:** $50 individuals; $90 two years; $55 Canada and Mexico; $60 elsewhere. **Remarks:** Accepts advertising. **URL:** http://www.ashlee.com/stone.
Ad Rates: BW: $1,650   **Circ:** (Not Reported)
       4C: $2,300

578 Supermarket News
Fairchild Publications, Inc.
7 W. 34th St.
New York, NY 10001   Phone: (212)630-4000

Magazine focusing on the supermarket and grocery trade.
       Circ: Paid ★43,036

579 talk
250 W. 55th St.
New York, NY 10019

Consumer magazine covering entertainment, films, publishing, writers, and others. **Freq:** Monthly. **Key Personnel:** Tina Brown, Editor-in-Chief. **Subscription Rates:** $2.95 single issue.

580 tele.com
McGraw-Hill, Inc.
1221 Avenue of the Americas
New York, NY 10020   Phone: (212)512-4635
Publication E-mail: tdcnet@teledotcom.com

Trade magazine covering information for network service providers. **Freq:** Monthly. **Key Personnel:** Karen Lynch, Editor-in-Chief, klynch@teledotcom.com; Dennis Mendyk, Sr. Managing Editor, dmendyk@teledotcom.com; Carl Weinschenk, Exec. Technical Editor, cweinsch@teledotcom.com. **Subscription Rates:** $75 individuals. **URL:** http://www.teledotcom.com.

581 Tile & Decorative Surfaces
Ashlee Publishing Co., Inc.
18 E. 41st St.   Phone: (212)682-7681
New York, NY 10017   Fax: (212)697-8331

Trade magazine for the tile and hard surfaces industry. **Trim Size:** 8 1/4 x 10 7/8. **Subscription Rates:** $50 individuals; $90 two years; $55 Canada and Mexico; $60 elsewhere. **Remarks:** Accepts advertising. **URL:** http://www.ashlee.com/tile.
Ad Rates: BW: $2,000   **Circ:** (Not Reported)
       4C: $2,900

582 Time Digital
Time Inc.
Time-Life Bldg., Rockefeller Center
1271 Avenue of the Americas
New York, NY 10020   Phone: (212)522-1212
    Fax: (212)522-0315

Trade magazine covering computer and personal technology. **Freq:** Monthly. **Key Personnel:** Richard A. Raskopf, Publisher; Joshua C. Ramo, Editor.

583 The United Journal
83-85 White St.   Phone: (212)513-1440
New York, NY 10013   Fax: (212)693-1392

Chinese language general newspaper. **Founded:** 1952. **Freq:** Daily. **Key**

Personnel: Edward Lee, Contact. **Subscription Rates:** $108 individuals; $228 out of country. **Remarks:** Accepts advertising.
Ad Rates: BW: $1,400   **Circ:** Combined 25,000

584 U.S. Frontline News
330 Madison Ave., 2nd Fl.   Phone: (212)922-9090
New York, NY 10017   Fax: (212)922-9119

Japanese language consumer business magazine. **Freq:** Monthly. **Key Personnel:** Takeo Ui, Contact. **Subscription Rates:** $39 individuals; $7.50 single issue. **Remarks:** Accepts advertising. **URL:** http://www.ginga.com.
Ad Rates: BW: $3,000   **Circ:** Combined 29,000

585 Unix Developer
SIGS Publications, Inc.
71 W. 23rd St., 3rd Fl.
New York, NY 10010-4102   Phone: (212)242-7447
Publication E-mail: subscriptions@sigs.com
Publisher E-mail: info@sigs.com

Trade magazine for Unix developers. **Freq:** 10/year. **Key Personnel:** Richard P. Friedman, Publisher; Charles F. Bowman, Editor-in-Chief, cfb@panix.com. **Subscription Rates:** Free. **URL:** http://www.sigs.com.

586 The Villager
80 8th Ave., Ste. 200
New York, NY 10011   Phone: (212)229-1890
Publication E-mail: vilpaper@aol.com

Community newspaper. **Key Personnel:** Elizabeth Margaritis Butson, Publisher; Robert N. Sellar, Sr. VP, Marketing; Colin Gregory, Retail Ad. Mgr.; Nancy Flowers, Circ. Dir.; Thomas G. Butson, Editor. **Subscription Rates:** $21 individuals; $35 two years. **URL:** http://www.thevillager.com.

587 Wicked Mystic
532 La Guardia Pl., No. 371
New York, NY 10012   Phone: (718)638-1533

Consumer magazine covering horror fiction. **Subtitle:** The Most Extreme Fiction Being Published Today. **Founded:** 1990. **Freq:** Quarterly. **Key Personnel:** Andre Scheluchin, Editor, scheluchin@wickedmystic.com. **Remarks:** Accepts advertising. **URL:** http://www.wickedmystic.com.
       Circ: Controlled 10,000

588 Wireless & Mobility
Ziff-Davis Inc.
28 E. 28th St.   Phone: (212)503-3500
New York, NY 10016   Fax: (212)503-5799

Trade magazine covering wireless technology and products. **Freq:** Monthly. **Key Personnel:** Jack Killion, Pub./Exec. Editor; Shari Valenz, Editor. **URL:** http://www.wirelessmag.com.

589 Women's Wear Daily
Fairchild Publications, Inc.
7 W. 34th St.
New York, NY 10001   Phone: (212)630-4000

Newspaper (tabloid) on women's and children's apparel, textiles, and technology. **Founded:** July 13, 1910. **Freq:** Daily (morn.). **Print Method:** Offset. **Trim Size:** 11 x 14 3/4. **Cols./Page:** 5. **Col. Width:** 24 nonpareils. **Col. Depth:** 195 agate lines. **Key Personnel:** Ed Nardoza, Vice President, phone (212)630-3500; Ralph Erardy, Publisher; Michael Coady, President; Olivia Thompson, Executive V.P. Publishing; Stephanie George, Senior V.P. and Group Publisher. **Subscription Rates:** $1 single issue. **Remarks:** Advertising accepted; rates available upon request.
       Circ: Mon.-Fri. 44,652

590 Year/2000 Journal
Ziff-Davis Inc.
28 E. 28th St.   Phone: (212)503-3500
New York, NY 10016   Fax: (212)503-5799
Publication E-mail: y2kjournal@connect.net

Trade magazine covering products and solutions to the Year 2000 problems. **Freq:** Bimonthly. **Key Personnel:** Robert H. Thomas, Editor and Publisher; Melissa L. Thomas, Assoc. Pub. **Subscription Rates:** $96 individuals. **URL:** http://www.y2kjournal.com.

591　Yomiuri America
666 5th Ave., 5th Fl.
New York, NY 10103
Phone: (212)765-1111
Fax: (212)765-1618

Japanese and English language community newspaper. **Founded:** 1985. **Freq:** Weekly. **Key Personnel:** Akiyoshi Ueda, Advertising Mgr. **Remarks:** Accepts advertising.
Ad Rates:　　BW: $3,700　　　　　　　**Circ:** Combined 19,600
　　　　　　4C: $5,550

592　Yugntrut
Youth for Yiddish, Inc.
200 W. 72nd St., Ste. 40
New York, NY 10023-2824

Literary journal. **Founded:** 1964. **Freq:** Irregular. **Key Personnel:** Elinor Robinson, Editor. **Subscription Rates:** $18 individuals; $25 institutions; $20 Canada and Mexico; $27 institutions Canada and Mexico; $22 individuals elsewhere. **Remarks:** Advertising not accepted.
Circ: Paid 1000

593　ZD Internet Magazine
Ziff-Davis Inc.
28 E. 28th St.
New York, NY 10016
Phone: (212)503-3500
Fax: (212)503-5799

Consumer magazine for Internet users. **Freq:** Monthly. **Key Personnel:** Angela Young, Publisher, ayoung@zd.com; Melanie McMullen, Editor-in-Chief, mmcmullen@zd.com; Chris Zender, Managing Editor, czender@zd.com. **Subscription Rates:** $25 individuals. **URL:** http://www.zdimag.com.

NEWARK

594　Lyons Shopping Guide
AD Group WC, Inc.
613 S. Main St.
Newark, NY 14513
Phone: (315)331-6956

Shopping guide. **Freq:** Weekly (Wed.). **Subscription Rates:** Free.
Circ: Non-paid **6003**

595　Newark Pennysaver
AD Group WC, Inc.
613 S. Main St.
Newark, NY 14513
Phone: (315)331-6956

Shopping guide. **Freq:** Weekly (Tues.). **Subscription Rates:** Free.
Circ: Non-paid **7003**

596　Sodus Pennysaver
AD Group WC, Inc.
613 S. Main St.
Newark, NY 14513
Phone: (315)331-6956

Shopping guide. **Freq:** Weekly (Tues.). **Subscription Rates:** Free.
Circ: Non-paid **8440**

PEARL RIVER

597　Java Developer's Journal
Sys-Con Publications, Inc.
39 E. Central Ave.
Pearl River, NY 10965
Phone: (914)735-1900
Fax: (914)735-3922
Free: (800)513-7111

Publication E-mail: 73611.756@compuserve.com

Trade magazine for JAVA programmers. **Freq:** Monthly. **Key Personnel:** Fuat A. Kircaali, Publisher; Scott Davison, Exec. Editor; Gail S. Schultz, Managing Editor. **Subscription Rates:** $79 individuals. **URL:** http://www.javadevelopersjournal.com.

ROCHESTER

598　Rochester Business Journal
55 St. Paul St.
Rochester, NY 14604
Phone: (716)546-8303
Fax: (716)546-3398

Local business newspaper. **Freq:** Weekly. **Subscription Rates:** $68 individuals. **Remarks:** Advertising accepted; rates available upon request. **URL:** http://www.rbj.net.
Circ: Combined 40,000

SAG HARBOR

599　The Sag Harbor Express
PO Box 1620
Sag Harbor, NY 11963

Community newspaper. **Subscription Rates:** $23 individuals; $30 out of area; $42 two years. **URL:** http://www.sagharboronline.com.

SYRACUSE

600　Tree Talks
Central New York Genealogical Society, Inc.
PO Box 104, Colvin Sta.
Syracuse, NY 13205

Local genealogical publication covering court records. **Founded:** 1961. **Freq:** Quarterly. **Remarks:** Advertising not accepted.
Circ: Paid 800

Ad Rates:　GLR = general line rate; BW = one-time black & white page rate; 4C = one-time four color page rate; SAU = standard advertising unit rate;
CNU = Canadian newspaper advertising unit rate; PCI = per column inch rate.
Circulation: ★ = ABC; △ = BPA; ♦ = CAC; ● = CCAB; ❑ = VAC; ⊕ = PO Statement; ‡ = Publisher's Report; Boldface figures = sworn; Light figures = estimated.
Entry type: ▥ = Print; ☎ = Broadcast.

NORTH CAROLINA

ASHEVILLE

📖 **601 Good News**
Asheville Citizen-Times Publishing Co.
14 O'Henry Ave.   Phone: (828)252-5611
Asheville, NC 28801   Fax: (828)252-0774
                                               Free: (800)800-4204

Community newspaper. **Founded:** 1996. **Freq:** Weekly (Wed.). **Subscription Rates:** Free.

                                    Circ: Combined ♦43,000

📖 **602 Mountain Xpress**
Green Line Media, Inc.
PO Box 144   Phone: (828)251-1333
Asheville, NC 28802   Fax: (828)251-1311
Publisher E-mail: publisher@mountainx.com

Community newspaper. **Founded:** 1987. **Freq:** Weekly. **Print Method:** Web offset. **Trim Size:** 10 1/2 x 14. **Cols./Page:** 4. **Col. Width:** 2 7/16 inches. **Col. Depth:** 12 3/4 inches. **Key Personnel:** Jeff Fobes, Editor; Wanda Edney, Advertising Dir.; Owen Goolsby, Circulation Mgr. **Subscription Rates:** $65 individuals. **Remarks:** Accepts advertising. **URL:** xpress@mountainx.com.
Former name: Green Line.
Ad Rates: GLR: $18   Circ: Combined **17,503**

BOONE

📖 **603 Exercise Exchange**
Appalachian State University
221 Duncan Hall   Phone: (828)262-2232
Boone, NC 28608   Fax: (828)262-2128

Scholarly journal covering exercise. **Freq:** Semiannual. **Print Method:** Offset. **Trim Size:** 7 x 10. **Cols./Page:** 1. **Col. Width:** 6 3/4 inches. **Col. Depth:** 8 3/4 inches. **Key Personnel:** Charles R. Duke, Editor, dukecr@appstate.edu. **ISSN:** 0531-531X. **Subscription Rates:** $5 individuals; $9 two years; $6 institutions; $10 institutions two-year. **Remarks:** Advertising not accepted. **Alt. Formats:** Microfilm.

                                    Circ: Combined **550**

CHARLOTTE

📖 **604 Business First**
American City Business Journals
120 West Morehead St., Ste. 400   Phone: (704)973-1000
Charlotte, NC 28202   Fax: (704)973-1001
                                               Free: (800)704-3757

Publication E-mail: columbus@amcity.com
Publisher E-mail: info@amcity.com

Local business newspaper. **Subtitle:** The Greater Columbus Business Authority. **Key Personnel:** Bill McMeekin, Editor, bmcmeekin@amcity.com; Dominic Cappa, Managing Editor, dcappa@amcity.com; Neal Hoffman, Advertising Mgr., nhoffman@amcity.com. **Remarks:** Advertising accepted; rates available upon request. **URL:** http://www.amcity.com/columbus.
                                    Circ: Combined **10,516**

📖 **605 The Catholic News & Herald**
Cathedral Publishing Corp.
1123 S. Church St.   Phone: (704)370-3333
Charlotte, NC 28203-4003   Fax: (704)370-3382
Publication E-mail: catholicnews@charlottediocese.org

Newspaper of the Roman Catholic Diocese of Charlotte, NC. **Founded:** 1991. **Freq:** Weekly. **Print Method:** Web offset. **Trim Size:** 11 1/4 x 15. **Cols./Page:** 4. **Col. Width:** 2.39 inches. **Col. Depth:** 13 1/2 inches. **Key Personnel:** Joann S. Keane, Editor, phone (704)370-3336; Jimmy Restar, Assoc. Editor; Julie Radcliffe, Production Assoc.; Cindi Feerick, Advertising. **Subscription Rates:** $18 individuals. **Remarks:** Accepts advertising. **URL:** http://www.charlottediocese.org.
Ad Rates: BW: $1,312.20   Circ: Paid ⊕**42,000**
                4C: $1,712.20
                PCI: $24.30

📖 **606 La Noticia**
6101 Idlewild Rd., Ste. 328   Phone: (704)568-6966
Charlotte, NC 28212   Fax: (704)568-8936
Publication E-mail: subscriptions@lanoticia.com

Spanish language community newspaper. **Key Personnel:** Hilda Gurdian, Publisher, hgurdian@lanoticia.com; Rosario Herrera, Sales Mgr., rherrera@lanoticia.com. **Subscription Rates:** $52 individuals; $78 out of state. **Remarks:** Advertising accepted; rates available upon request. **URL:** http://www.lanoticia.com.
                                    Circ: (Not Reported)

📖 **607 Q-Notes**
4037 E. Independence Blvd., Ste. 611
Charlotte, NC 28205   Phone: (704)531-9988

Community newspaper for a gay and lesbian audience. **Freq:** Biweekly. **URL:** http://www.q-notes.com.

DURHAM

📖 **608 Carolina Woman**
Carolina Woman, Inc.
PO Box 52687
Durham, NC 27717

Consumer magazine for women in North and South Carolina. **Subtitle:** The Magazine for Women in the Triangle. **Freq:** Monthly. **Key Personnel:** Debra Simon, Editor and Publisher; Jay Johnson, Advertising Dir. **Subscription Rates:** $14.95 individuals; $21.95 two years. **Remarks:** Accepts advertising.
Ad Rates: BW: $1583   Circ: (Not Reported)
                4C: $1833

📖 **609 Comparative Studies of South Asia, Africa, and the Middle East**
Duke University Press
University of Washington
Dept. of English
PO Box 354330   Phone: (919)687-3600
Durham, NC 27708-0660   Fax: (919)688-3524
Publisher E-mail: dukepress@duke.edu

Scholarly journal covering regional studies. **Freq:** Semiannual. **Key Person-**

Ad Rates: GLR = general line rate; BW = one-time black & white page rate; 4C = one-time four color page rate; SAU = standard advertising unit rate; CNU = Canadian newspaper advertising unit rate; PCI = per column inch rate.
Circulation: ★ = ABC; △ = BPA; ♦ = CAC; • = CCAB; ❑ = VAC; ⊕ = PO Statement; ‡ = Publisher's Report; Boldface figures = sworn; Light figures = estimated.
Entry type: 📖 = Print; 🎤 = Broadcast.

87

nel: Vasant Kaiwar, Editor; Sucheta Mazumdar, Editor; Amy Hartzler, Advertising, phone (919)687-3636. **Subscription Rates:** $25 individuals; $50 institutions. **Remarks:** Accepts advertising.
Ad Rates:　BW: $350　　　　　　　　　　　　**Circ:** Paid 450

📖 **610　GLQ**
Duke University Press
University of Washington
Dept. of English
PO Box 354330　　　　　　　　　　Phone: (919)687-3600
Durham, NC 27708-0660　　　　　　　Fax: (919)688-3524
Publisher E-mail: dukepress@duke.edu

Scholarly journal covering lesbian and gay studies. **Subtitle:** A Journal of Lesbian and Gay Studies. **Freq:** Quarterly. **Key Personnel:** Carolyn Dinshaw, Editor; David M. Halperin, Editor; Amy Hartzler, Advertising, phone (919)687-3636. **Subscription Rates:** $35 individuals; $79 institutions. **Remarks:** Accepts advertising.
Ad Rates:　BW: $250　　　　　　　　　**Circ:** Combined 1400

📖 **611　IMRN**
Duke University Press
University of Washington
Dept. of English
PO Box 354330　　　　　　　　　　Phone: (919)687-3600
Durham, NC 27708-0660　　　　　　　Fax: (919)688-3524
Publisher E-mail: dukepress@duke.edu

Scholarly journal for mathematicians and research libraries. **Subtitle:** International Mathematics Research Notices. **Freq:** Irregular. **Key Personnel:** Morris Weisfeld, Editor; Amy Hartzler, Advertising, phone (919)687-3636. **Subscription Rates:** $390 individuals; $780 institutions. **Remarks:** Accepts advertising.
Ad Rates:　BW: $200　　　　　　　　　　**Circ:** Paid 200

📖 **612　Journal of Medieval and Early Modern Studies**
Duke University Press
905 W. Main St., Ste. 18-B　　　　　Phone: (919)687-3600
Durham, NC 27708-0660　　　　　　　Fax: (919)688-3524
　　　　　　　　　　　　　　　　　Free: (888)387-5687

Scholarly journal covering medieval and early modern studies. **Freq:** Triennial. **Key Personnel:** Sarah Beckwith, Editor; Annabel Wharton, Editor; Nancy Kimberly, Advertising, phone (919)687-3653, nancy.kimberly@duke.com. **Subscription Rates:** $35 individuals; $122 institutions; $18 students. **Remarks:** Accepts advertising. **URL:** http://juniper.forest.net/dupress.
Ad Rates:　BW: $250　　　　　　　　　**Circ:** Combined 1100

📖 **613　Social Text**
Duke University Press
University of Washington
Dept. of English
PO Box 354330　　　　　　　　　　Phone: (919)687-3600
Durham, NC 27708-0660　　　　　　　Fax: (919)688-3524
Publisher E-mail: dukepress@duke.edu

Scholarly journal covering social and cultural studies. **Freq:** Quarterly. **Key Personnel:** Bruce Robbins, Editor; Toby Miller, Editor; Amy Hartzler, Advertising, phone (919)687-3636. **Subscription Rates:** $30 individuals; $85 institutions; $15 students. **Remarks:** Accepts advertising.
Ad Rates:　BW: $200　　　　　　　　　**Circ:** Combined 850

📖 **614　Theater**
Duke University Press
905 W. Main St., Ste. 18-B　　　　　Phone: (919)687-3600
Durham, NC 27708-0660　　　　　　　Fax: (919)688-3524
　　　　　　　　　　　　　　　　　Free: (888)387-5687
Publication E-mail: theater.magazine@yale.edu

Yale School of Drama magazine covering modern and contemporary theater. **Freq:** Triennial. **Key Personnel:** Erika Munk, Editor; Jonathan Shandell, Exec. Editor; Erika Rundle, Managing Editor; Amy Strahler, Managing Editor. **Subscription Rates:** $25 individuals; $55 institutions. **Remarks:** Accepts advertising. **URL:** http://www.yale.edu/drama/publications/theater.
Ad Rates:　BW: $250　　　　　　　　　**Circ:** Combined 935

FAYETTEVILLE

📖 **615　Up & Coming Magazine**
F & B Publications, Inc.
PO Box 53461
Fayetteville, NC 28305　　　　　　　Phone: (910)484-6200

Consumer magazine covering local arts, cuisine, and entertainment. **Freq:** Semimonthly (Wed.). **Subscription Rates:** Free; $24 by mail.
　　　　　　　　　　　　　　Circ: Non-paid **24,932**

HIGH POINT

📖 **616　High Points**
Fairchild Publications, Inc.
101 S. Main St., Ste. 408　　　　　Phone: (336)841-3203
High Point, NC 27260　　　　　　　　Fax: (336)841-4831

Trade magazine for furniture retailers. **Founded:** 1993. **Subscription Rates:** Free to qualified subscribers. **URL:** http://www.highpointsmag.com.

LEXINGTON

📖 **617　The Dispatch**
30 E. 1st Ave.
Lexington, NC 27292　　　　　　　　Phone: (336)249-3981

General newspaper. **Founded:** 1882. **Freq:** Mon.-Sat. **Key Personnel:** Betty Barnes, Advertising Dir., phone (336)249-1637, fax (336)249-2944. **Remarks:** Advertising accepted; rates available upon request. **URL:** http://www.the-dispatch.com.
　　　　　　　　　　　　　　　　Circ: (Not Reported)

LUMBERTON

📖 **618　The Robesonian**
Community Newspaper Holdings, Inc.
121 W 5th St.　　　　　　　　　　Phone: (910)739-4322
Lumberton, NC 28358　　　　　　　　Fax: (910)739-6553

General newspaper. **Founded:** 1870. **Freq:** Daily (eve.), Sat. and Sun. (morn.). **Key Personnel:** John Bauer, Pub./Gen. Mgr.; Gregg Ratliff, Advertising Dir.; Donnie Douglas, Editor; Worth Graham, Business Mgr.; Ed Knight, Circulation Mgr. **Subscription Rates:** $111.30 individuals; $185.50 out of area; $212 out of state. **URL:** http://www.cnhi.com/robesonian.
　　　　　　　　　　　　　　　　Circ: Combined 15,500

NAGS HEAD

📖 **619　Outer Banks Sentinel**
PO Box 546　　　　　　　　　　　Phone: (252)480-2234
Nags Head, NC 27959　　　　　　　　Fax: (252)480-1146

Community newspaper. **Freq:** Weekly. **Subscription Rates:** $22.25 individuals. **URL:** http://outer-banks.nc.us/sentinel.

SOUTHERN PINES

📖 **620　The Pilot**
145 W. Pennsylvania Ave.
Southern Pines, NC 28387
Publication E-mail: editor@thepilot.com

Community newspaper. **Key Personnel:** Dennis Lenart, Circ. Dir.; Tom Bryant, Advertising Dir.; Mary Marchman, Publisher; Steve Bouser, Editor. **URL:** http://www.thepilot.com. **Feature Editors:** Hunter Chase, *Sports*; Clark Cox, *News*; Faye Dasen, *Features*.

NORTH DAKOTA

DICKINSON

🎙 **621 KLTO-FM - 99.1**
PO Box 1478   Phone: (701)227-1876
Dickinson, ND 58601   Fax: (701)227-1959

Format: Hot Country. **Networks:** ABC. **Founded:** Nov. 1996. **Operating Hours:** 5 a.m.-12 a.m. **Key Personnel:** Ray David, Pres./Gen. Mgr. **Wattage:** 51,000. **Ad Rates:** $8 for 15 seconds; $12 for 30 seconds.

FARGO

📖 **622 Impact Assessment and Project Appraisal**
International Association for Impact Assessment
PO Box 5256
Fargo, ND 58105
Publication E-mail: rhamm@ndsuext.nodak.edu

Professional journal covering environmental, social, and technological impact assessment for an international audience. **Subtitle:** Journal of the International Association for Impact Assessment. **Freq:** Quarterly. **Key Personnel:** Daniel Bronstein, Editor. **Subscription Rates:** $175 individuals. **URL:** http://IAIA.ext.nodak.edu/IAIA.

OHIO

AKRON

623 West Side Leader
Leader Publications
1815 W. Market St., Ste. 300
Akron, OH 44313

Phone: (330)865-4410
Fax: (330)865-4419

Community newspaper. **Freq:** Weekly (Thurs.). **Remarks:** Accepts advertising. **URL:** http://www.akron.com.
Ad Rates: PCI: $16.50   **Circ:** Combined 41,000

CANTON

624 WOFN-FM - 88.7
109 Miles Ave. SW
Canton, OH 44710

Phone: (918)455-5693
Fax: (918)455-0411

E-mail: mail@oasisnetwork.org

Format: Religious; Southern Gospel. **Owner:** Stark Educational Media, Inc., PO Box 1924, Tulsa, OK 74101. **Founded:** 1999. **Operating Hours:** Continuous. **Key Personnel:** David Warren, Program Dir. **URL:** http://www.oasisnetwork.org.

CINCINNATI

625 Spaniels in the Field
Chiridion Wild Wings, Inc.
10714 Escondido Dr.
Cincinnati, OH 45249

Phone: (513)489-2727
Fax: (513)489-4105

Publication E-mail: artspaniel@aol.com
Publisher E-mail: chiridion@aol.com

Consumer magazine covering spaniel dogs. **Freq:** Monthly. **Key Personnel:** Harry Henriques, Publisher; Sandy Henriques, Assoc. Publisher; Art Rodger, Managing Editor. **ISSN:** 1043-5034. **Subscription Rates:** $34 individuals; $36 Canada; $51 elsewhere; $10 single issue. **Remarks:** Accepts advertising. **URL:** http://www.spanielsinthefield.com.
Ad Rates: BW: $250   **Circ:** Combined ⊕1802
                4C: $600

CLEVELAND

626 WVMN-FM - 90.1
9756 Barr Rd.
Cleveland, OH 44141

Phone: (440)526-1111
Fax: (440)526-1319

E-mail: wcrf@moody.edu

Format: Religious. **Networks:** Sun Radio; Moody Broadcasting. **Owner:** Moody Bible Institute of Chicago, Inc., 820 N. LaSalle Dr., Chicago, IL 60610. **Founded:** Nov. 23, 1958. **Operating Hours:** Continuous. **Key Personnel:** Dick Lee, Manager; Paul Carter, Asst. Mgr.; Doug Hainer, Chief Engineer; Gary Bittner, Music Dir. **Wattage:** 5,000. **Ad Rates:** Noncommercial. **URL:** http://www.wcrf.mbn.org.

COLUMBUS

627 Columbus Alive
Columbus Alive, Inc.
17 Brickel St.
Columbus, OH 43215

Phone: (614)221-2449

Community newspaper. **Freq:** Weekly (Thurs.). **Subscription Rates:** Free.
Circ: Combined **24,805**

628 Newsreel
Newsreel, Inc.
5 E. Long St., Rm. 907
Columbus, OH 43215

Phone: (614)469-0700
Fax: (614)469-7077

Audio magazine by and for the visually handicapped. **Founded:** 1958. **Freq:** Monthly. **Key Personnel:** Irwin Hott, Editor. **Subscription Rates:** $30 individuals; $50 sponsorship available. **Remarks:** Advertising not accepted. **Alt. Formats:** Audio tape.
Circ: Combined 1000

ELYRIA

629 Over the Back Fence
Back Fence Publishing, Inc.
5311 Meadow Lane Ct., Ste. 3
Elyria, OH 44035
Publication E-mail: backfencepub@centuryinter.net

Consumer magazine covering local issues, poetry, fiction, and entertainment. **Freq:** Quarterly. **Key Personnel:** Connie L. Smart, Publisher; Kelly Boyer Sagert, Managing Editor; Kelli Moss, Associate Publisher. **Subscription Rates:** $9.97 individuals; $18.94 two years; $2.95 single issue. **Remarks:** Advertising accepted; rates available upon request.
Circ: (Not Reported)

GRAND RAPIDS

630 Equipment Echoes
Historical Construction Equipment Association
PO Box 328
Grand Rapids, OH 43522

Phone: (419)832-4232
Fax: (419)832-4034

Trade magazine covering history and construction. **Founded:** 1986. **Freq:** Quarterly. **Subscription Rates:** $18 individuals; $5 single issue. **Remarks:** Accepts advertising.
Circ: (Not Reported)

LAKEWOOD

631 Hubbell Family Historical Society Annual
Hubbell Family Historical Society
c/o John A. Hubbell, Editor
1662 Mars Ave.
Lakewood, OH 44107

Phone: (216)521-9027
Fax: (216)521-9028

Periodical covering the activities of The Hubbell Family Historical Society. **Founded:** 1983. **Freq:** Annual. **Key Personnel:** John A. Hubbell, Editor.

Ad Rates: GLR = general line rate; BW = one-time black & white page rate; 4C = one-time four color page rate; SAU = standard advertising unit rate;
CNU = Canadian newspaper advertising unit rate; PCI = per column inch rate.
Circulation: ★ = ABC; △ = BPA; ♦ = CAC; ● = CCAB; ❑ = VAC; ⊕ = PO Statement; ‡ = Publisher's Report; Boldface figures = sworn; Light figures = estimated.
Entry type: ❑ = Print; ♨ = Broadcast.

91

Subscription Rates: Free to qualified subscribers. Remarks: Advertising not accepted.

Circ: (Not Reported)

PIKETON

632 WXZQ-FM - 100.1
PO Box 894
Piketon, OH 45661-0894

Phone: (740)947-0059
Fax: (740)947-4600

Format: Adult Contemporary; Contemporary Hit Radio (CHR). Owner: Piketon Communications, at above address. Founded: Dec. 1, 1997. Operating Hours: Continuous. Key Personnel: Gerald Davis, General Mgr.; Gina Baldwin, Sales Mgr.; Debbie Davis, Traffic Mgr. Wattage: 6,000. Ad Rates: $7-9 for 30 seconds; $9-11 for 60 seconds.

SIDNEY

633 Miamisburg Sun
Amos Press, Inc.
911 Vandemark Rd.
PO Box 150
Sidney, OH 45365-0150

Phone: (937)498-0800
Fax: (937)498-0812
Free: (800)673-8311

Community newspaper. Freq: Weekly (Thurs.). Key Personnel: Cheryl Mahoney, News; Dick Schneider, Circulation Mgr.; Jacqueline Helter, Advertising Mgr. Subscription Rates: Free. URL: http://www.sndnew.com/publications/msun.html.

SOLON

634 Environmental Technology
Adams Business Media
29100 Aurora Rd., Ste. 200
Solon, OH 44139-1855

Phone: (440)248-1125
Fax: (440)248-0187

Trade journal for environmental professionals. Print Method: Web offset. Trim Size: 8 x 10 3/4. Key Personnel: Daniel J. Corcoran, Group Publisher; Rinda E. Vas, Editor/Assoc. Pub., rvas@environetcenter.com; Michael A. Giannone, Editor-in-Chief; Diane E. Davis, Business Mgr.; Nanette R. Eiloo, Prod. Dir. Remarks: Accepts advertising. URL: http://www.environet.net/et/.
Ad Rates: BW: $5,943
4C: $7,203

Circ: Combined •65,500

635 Quality in Manufacturing
Adams Business Media
29100 Aurora Rd., Ste. 200
Solon, OH 44139-1855

Phone: (440)248-1125
Fax: (440)248-0187

Professional magazine covering parts manufacturing in various industries. Freq: Bimonthly. Print Method: Web offset. Trim Size: 11 x 14 1/2. Key Personnel: Daniel Corcoran, Group Publisher, dcorcoran@qualityinmfg.com; Christine Taylor, Assoc. Pub./Editor-in-Chief, ctaylor@qualityinmfg.com; Diane Davis, Business Mgr., ddavis@qualityinmfg.com; Stephanie Fellenstein, Managing Editor, sfellenstein@qualityinmfg.com; Diane Dobies, Prod./Customer Svc. Mgr., ddobies@qualityinmfg.com. Remarks: Accepts advertising. URL: http://www.qualityindustry.com/.
Ad Rates: BW: $9,750
4C: $11,310

Circ: (Not Reported)

TIPP CITY

636 Troy Advocate
Suburban Newspapers
1455 W. Main St.
Tipp City, OH 45371

Phone: (937)667-8512
Fax: (937)667-8987

Community newspaper. Key Personnel: Marilyn McConahay, Editor, phone (937)667-2214; Julie Binkley, Circulation Mgr., phone (937)335-8320; Ron Uecker, Advertising Mgr. Subscription Rates: $26 individuals; $35 by mail. URL: http://www.sndnews.com/publications/advocate.html.

TROY

637 Miami Valley Sunday News
TDN, Inc.
224 S. Market St.
Troy, OH 45373-3300

Phone: (513)335-5634
Fax: (513)335-3552

Publication E-mail: editorial@tdnpublishing.com

Community newspaper. Freq: Weekly (Sun.). URL: http://www.tdn-net.com/tdnpublishing/miami_ sunday.html.

Circ: Combined 32,000

WAPAKONETA

638 Wapakoneta Daily News
8 Willipie St.
PO Box 389
Wapakoneta, OH 45895

Phone: (419)738-2120
Fax: (419)738-5352

General newspaper. Freq: Daily. Key Personnel: Dianna J. Epperly, Publisher, depperly@wapakwdn.com; J. Swygart, Editor, jswygart@wapakwdn.com; Diana Spencer, Advertising Dir., dspencer@wapakwdn.com; Terry Stahler, Circulation Mgr., phone (419)738-2128. URL: http://www.wapakdailynews.com. Feature Editors: Joe Menden, Sports.

WAUSEON

639 The Barnes Family Quarterly
Professional Business Services
450 Potter St.
Wauseon, OH 43567

Phone: (419)335-6485

Periodical covering Barnes family genealogy. Founded: 1984. Key Personnel: Howard V. Fausey, Advertising Mgr. Subscription Rates: $12 individuals.

WINTERSVILLE

640 WCDK-FM - 106.3
116 Bantam Ridge Rd.
Wintersville, OH 43952

Phone: (614)266-2700
Fax: (614)266-6648

Format: Hot Country. Networks: Jones Satellite. Owner: The McGraw Group, c/o Charlie Devine, 22 Randolph Ave., Elkins, WV 26241. Founded: 1991. Operating Hours: Continuous. Key Personnel: Charlie Devine, VP, Sales; Todd Elliott, VP, Operations.

OKLAHOMA

BROKEN ARROW

🎤 641 KMSI-FM - 88.1
11717 S. 129 E. Ave.　　　　　　　　Phone: (405)794-5674
Broken Arrow, OK 74011　　　　　　　Fax: (918)455-0411
E-mail: mail@oasisnetwork.org

Format: Religious; Gospel. **Owner:** Creative Educational Media Corp., Inc., PO Box 1924, Tulsa, OK 74101, (918)455-5693. **Founded:** 1989. **Operating Hours:** Continuous. **Key Personnel:** David Warren, Program Dir., phone (918)455-5693; David Dick, Station Mgr. **Wattage:** 30,000. **URL:** http://www.oasisnetwork.org.

MOORE

📖 642 Moore American
South Metro Publications
PO Box 6739
Moore, OK 73153　　　　　　　　　Phone: (405)794-5555

Community newspaper. **Freq:** Weekly. **Subscription Rates:** Free.
　　　　　　　　　　　　　　　Circ: Combined **3530**

📖 643 South OKC Leader
South Metro Publications
PO Box 6739
Moore, OK 73153　　　　　　　　　Phone: (405)794-5555

Community newspaper. **Freq:** Weekly. **Subscription Rates:** Free.
　　　　　　　　　　　　　　　Circ: Combined **15,756**

OKLAHOMA

📖 644 Oklahoma City Trader
3732 S.E. 24th
Oklahoma, OK 73115

Shopping guide. **URL:** http://okctrader.com.

OKMULGEE

📖 645 Okmulgee Daily Times
114 E. 7th St.　　　　　　　　　　Phone: (918)756-3600
Okmulgee, OK 74447　　　　　　　　Fax: (918)756-8197
Publication E-mail: drtimes@galstar.com

Community newspaper. **Freq:** Daily (morn.) (except Mon.). **Key Personnel:** Jerry W. Quinn, Publisher, jwquinn@galstar.com; Herman L. Brown, Editor, odteditor@okmulgeetimes.com; Jo Collins, Asst. Editor; Phyllis Argyle, Circulation Mgr., drtimes@galstar.com; Donna Craddock, Advertising Dir., odtadmgr@okmulgeetimes.com. **URL:** http://www.okmulgeetimes.com. **Feature Editors:** Daryl Holloman, *Sports*, phone (918)756-3675, odtsports@okmulgeetimes.com; Christie Jackson, *Lifestyle*, phone (918)756-3681, odtlifestyles@okmulgeetimes.com.

TAHLEQUAH

📖 646 The Northeastern
Northeastern State University
Tahlequah, OK 74464-2399
Publication E-mail: tne@cherokee.nsuok.edu

College newspaper. **Freq:** Weekly August 1 through May 31. **Key Personnel:** Anita Hylton, Editor; Gregg Simmons, Editor; Tony Lytle, Advertising Mgr. **Subscription Rates:** Free to qualified subscribers. **Remarks:** Accepts advertising. **Feature Editors:** Robert Williams, *Entertainment*; Justin Zaun, *Sports*.
　　　　　　　　　　　　　　　Circ: (Not Reported)

📖 647 Tahlequah Daily Press
Indian Nations Communications, Inc.
106 W. 2nd St.
Tahlequah, OK 74465

Daily newspaper. **Key Personnel:** Brad Sugg, Publisher and General Mgr.; Kim Poindexter, Managing Editor; Pam Hutton, Advertising Mgr.; Tom Dunavin, Circulation Mgr.; Barbara Fritts, Business Mgr. **Subscription Rates:** $79.80 individuals; $118.80 out of area; $136.80 out of state. **Remarks:** Accepts advertising.
　　　　　　　　　　　　　　　Circ: (Not Reported)

📖 648 The Tahlequah Times Journal
Sentinel Communications Corp.
PO Box 1839
Tahlequah, OK 74465-1839　　　　　Phone: (918)458-0816

Community newspaper. **Key Personnel:** David Rennie, Owner and General Mgr.; Cathye Rennie, Owner; Cathye C. Rennie, Publisher.

TULSA

📖 649 Urban Tulsa
Renegade Publishing, Inc.
2318 E. Admiral Blvd.　　　　　　　Phone: (918)592-5550
Tulsa, OK 74110　　　　　　　　　　Fax: (918)592-5970
Publication E-mail: urbantul@urbantulsa.com

Community newspaper. **Freq:** Weekly. **Key Personnel:** Keith Skrzypcazk, Editor and Publisher; Jan Carmichael, Advertising Dir.; Andrea Colpitts, Business Mgr. **Subscription Rates:** $24 individuals; $42 two years. **URL:** http://www.urbantulsa.com.

🎤 650 KDKR-FM - 91.3
PO Box 1924　　　　　　　　　　　Phone: (918)455-5693
Tulsa, OK 74101　　　　　　　　　　Fax: (918)455-0411
E-mail: mail@oasisnetwork.org

Format: Religious; Southern Gospel. **Owner:** Creative Educational Media Corp., Inc., at above address. **Founded:** 1998. **Operating Hours:** Continuous. **Key Personnel:** David Warren, Program Dir. **URL:** http://www.oasisnetwork.org.

🎙 **651 KOZO-FM - 89.7**
PO Box 1924
Tulsa, OK 74101
E-mail: mail@oasisnetwork.org

Format: Religious; Southern Gospel. **Owner:** Creative Educational Media Corp., Inc., at above address. **Founded:** 1998. **Operating Hours:** Continuous. **Key Personnel:** David Warren, Program Dir., phone (918)455-0411; Rick Beasley, Station Mgr. **Wattage:** 20,000. **URL:** http://www.oasisnetwork.org.

OREGON

PORT ORFORD

652 Port Orford Today
The Downtown Fun Zone
832 Hwy. 101
PO Box 49
Port Orford, OR 97465   Phone: (541)332-6565
Publisher E-mail: funzone@harborside.com

Community newspaper. **Freq:** Weekly (Thurs.). **Subscription Rates:** Free.
Remarks: Accepts advertising. **URL:** http://www.harborside.com/fundzone/
dfz-pot.htm.
Ad Rates: BW: $65   **Circ:** (Not Reported)
          PCI: $5

ROSEBURG

653 Umpqua Trapper
Douglas County Historical Society
733 W. Ballf St.
Roseburg, OR 97470

Journal covering local history. **Founded:** 1965. **Freq:** Quarterly. **Print
Method:** Offset. **Subscription Rates:** $10 individuals; $2.50 single issue.
Remarks: Advertising not accepted.
                                   Circ: Paid 340

SCAPPOOSE

654 The South County Spotlight
Bridge Publications, Inc.
PO Box C   Phone: (503)543-6387
Scappoose, OR 97056   Fax: (503)543-6380

Community newspaper. **Freq:** Weekly (Wed.). **Key Personnel:** Dallas
Bentley, Advertising Dir. **Subscription Rates:** $15 individuals; $17 out of
area. **Remarks:** Accepts advertising. **URL:** http://www.columbia-center.org/
newsspot.
Ad Rates: PCI: $7.35   **Circ:** Paid 4,370

PENNSYLVANIA

BETHLEHEM

🎙 **655 WDIY-FM - 88.1**
301 Broadway, 3rd Fl.
Bethlehem, PA 18015

Format: Public Radio. **Operating Hours:** Continuous. **Ad Rates:** Noncommercial. **URL:** http://www.wdiyfm.org/.

ELKINS PARK

📖 **656 Sunday Topic Korean News**
1925 W. Cheltenham Ave., No. J-K
Elkins Park, PA 19027

Phone: (215)885-4230
Fax: (215)885-1777

Korean language community newspaper. **Freq:** Weekly. **Key Personnel:** Jae Yeol Shin, Contact. **Subscription Rates:** $30 individuals. **Remarks:** Accepts advertising.
Ad Rates: BW: $700   **Circ:** Combined 15,000

FORT WASHINGTON

📖 **657 The Colonial**
Montgomery Publishing Co.
290 Commerce Dr.
Fort Washington, PA 19034

Phone: (215)542-0200
Fax: (215)643-1257

Community newspaper. **Founded:** 1992. **Freq:** Weekly (Thurs.). **Key Personnel:** Art Howe, Publisher. **Subscription Rates:** $15 individuals; $20 out of area; $25 out of state.

Circ: Combined ♦2599

📖 **658 Glenside News**
Montgomery Publishing Co.
290 Commerce Dr.
Fort Washington, PA 19034

Phone: (215)542-0200
Fax: (215)643-1257

Community newspaper. **Founded:** 1923. **Freq:** Weekly (Wed.). **Key Personnel:** Art Howe, Publisher. **Subscription Rates:** $31.20 individuals; $36 out of area; $42 out of state.

Circ: Combined ♦2983

📖 **659 Main Line Life**
Montgomery Publishing Co.
290 Commerce Dr.
Fort Washington, PA 19034

Phone: (215)542-0200
Fax: (215)643-1257

Community newspaper. **Founded:** 1995. **Freq:** Weekly (Wed.). **Key Personnel:** Art Howe, Publisher. **Subscription Rates:** $26 by mail; $32 out of state.
Circ: Combined ♦11,500

📖 **660 Montgomery Life**
Montgomery Publishing Co.
290 Commerce Dr.
Fort Washington, PA 19034

Phone: (215)542-0200
Fax: (215)643-1257

Community newspaper. **Founded:** 1998. **Freq:** Weekly (Thurs.). **Key Personnel:** Art Howe, Publisher. **Subscription Rates:** $14 individuals; $18 out of area; $24 out of state.

Circ: Combined ♦2,500

📖 **661 The Springfield Reporter**
Montgomery Publishing Co.
290 Commerce Dr.
Fort Washington, PA 19034

Phone: (215)542-0200
Fax: (215)643-1257

Community newspaper. **Founded:** 1872. **Freq:** Weekly (Wed.). **Key Personnel:** Art Howe, Publisher. **Subscription Rates:** $18 individuals; $20 out of area; $24 out of state.

Circ: Combined ♦2,712

📖 **662 Times Chronicle**
Montgomery Publishing Co.
290 Commerce Dr.
Fort Washington, PA 19034

Phone: (215)542-0200
Fax: (215)643-1257

Community newspaper. **Founded:** 1894. **Freq:** Weekly (Wed.). **Key Personnel:** Art Howe, Publisher. **Subscription Rates:** $31.20 individuals; $36 out of area; $42 out of state.

Circ: Combined ♦6,433

📖 **663 Willow Grove Guide**
Montgomery Publishing Co.
290 Commerce Dr.
Fort Washington, PA 19034

Phone: (215)542-0200
Fax: (215)643-1257

Community newspaper. **Founded:** 1925. **Freq:** Weekly (Wed.). **Key Personnel:** Art Howe, Publisher. **Subscription Rates:** $31.20 individuals; $36 out of area; $42 out of state.

Circ: Combined ♦1,594

LEBANON

📖 **664 Weekender Cover Story**
Kapp Advertising Service, Inc.
PO Box 840
Lebanon, PA 17042

Phone: (717)273-8127
Fax: (717)273-0420

Publisher E-mail: kapp@nbn.net

Shopping guide. **Founded:** 1994. **Freq:** Sat. and Sun. **Key Personnel:** Joanne M. Walkinshaw, Circulation Mgr. **Subscription Rates:** Free.
Circ: Combined ♦45,929

PHILADELPHIA

📖 **665 Academic Physician & Scientist**
Lippincott Williams & Wilkins
530 Walnut St.
Philadelphia, PA 19106

Phone: (215)238-4200
Fax: (215)238-4227
Free: (800)777-2295

Professional magazine covering news and employment listings for those in academic medicine. **Subtitle:** The Comprehensive Single Source for Positions in Academic Medicine. **Freq:** Bimonthly. **Key Personnel:** Fay Jarosh Ellis, Editor. **ISSN:** 1039-1139. **Subscription Rates:** Free to qualified subscribers. **URL:** http://www.acphysci.com.

666 AWHONN Lifelines
Lippincott Williams & Wilkins
530 Walnut St.
Philadelphia, PA 19106

Phone: (215)238-4200
Fax: (215)238-4227
Free: (800)777-2295

Professional journal covering practice management resources and industry trends in women's health. **Subtitle:** An AWHONN Publication. **Freq:** Bimonthly. **Key Personnel:** Barbara Peterson Sinclar, MN, Editor-in-Chief. **ISSN:** 1019-5923.

667 Cancer Case Presentations
Lippincott Williams & Wilkins
530 Walnut St.
Philadelphia, PA 19106

Phone: (215)238-4200
Fax: (215)238-4227
Free: (800)777-2295

Professional journal covering cancer care. **Subtitle:** The Tumor Board. **Freq:** Bimonthly. **Key Personnel:** David P. Winchester, M.D., Editor; Glenn D. Steele, M.D., Editor. **ISSN:** 1090-7491.

668 Dong-A Daily
500 E. Luzerne St.
Philadelphia, PA 19124

Phone: (215)423-6220
Fax: (215)423-1672

Korean language general newspaper. **Founded:** 1980. **Freq:** Mon.-Sat. **Key Personnel:** Bo Hyun Lim, Contact. **Subscription Rates:** $156 individuals. **Remarks:** Accepts advertising.
Ad Rates: BW: $1,000   **Circ:** Combined 23,000
           4C: $3,360
           PCI: $21

669 Home Care Manager
Lippincott Williams & Wilkins
530 Walnut St.
Philadelphia, PA 19106

Phone: (215)238-4200
Fax: (215)238-4227
Free: (800)777-2295

Professional journal for home care managers. **Freq:** Bimonthly. **Key Personnel:** Carolyn J. Humphrey, RN, Editor. **ISSN:** 1094-0375.

670 Home Healthcare Nurse Manager
Lippincott Williams & Wilkins
530 Walnut St.
Philadelphia, PA 19106

Phone: (215)238-4200
Fax: (215)238-4227
Free: (800)777-2295

Professional journal for homecare managers. **Founded:** 1996. **Freq:** Bimonthly. **Print Method:** Sheetfed offset. **Trim Size:** 7 7/8 x 10 7/8. **Key Personnel:** Carolyn J. Humphrey, RN, MS, Editor-in-Chief; Sandra Kasko, Associate Publisher; Michele Kampe, Advertising Mgr., phone (212)886-1386. **Subscription Rates:** $55 individuals; $85 institutions. **Remarks:** Accepts advertising.
Ad Rates: BW: $765   **Circ:** (Not Reported)
           4C: $1,720

671 Journal of Child and Family Nursing
Lippincott Williams & Wilkins
530 Walnut St.
Philadelphia, PA 19106

Phone: (215)238-4200
Fax: (215)238-4227
Free: (800)777-2295

Professional journal covering pediatric nursing. **Founded:** 1998. **Freq:** Bimonthly. **Print Method:** Sheetfed offset. **Trim Size:** 8 1/8 x 11. **Key Personnel:** Marion E. Broome, Ph.D, Editor-in-Chief; Lisa Marshall, Publisher; Michele Kampe, Advertising Mgr., phone (212)886-1386. **Subscription Rates:** $54 individuals; $88 institutions. **Remarks:** Accepts advertising.
Ad Rates: BW: $765   **Circ:** (Not Reported)
           4C: $1720

672 Journal of Vascular and Interventional Radiology
Lippincott Williams & Wilkins
530 Walnut St.
Philadelphia, PA 19106

Phone: (215)238-4200
Fax: (215)238-4227
Free: (800)777-2295

Professional journal covering vascular and interventional radiology. **Subtitle:** Official Journal of the Society of Cardiovascular & Interventional Radiology.

Freq: Bimonthly. **Key Personnel:** Daniel Picus, M.D., Editor. **ISSN:** 1051-0443.

673 Lippincott's Primary Care Practices
Lippincott Williams & Wilkins
530 Walnut St.
Philadelphia, PA 19106

Phone: (215)238-4200
Fax: (215)238-4227
Free: (800)777-2295

Professional journal covering primary medical care. **Freq:** Bimonthly. **Key Personnel:** Sandra M. Nettina, RN, Editor. **ISSN:** 1088-5471.

674 Outcomes Management for Nursing Practice
Lippincott Williams & Wilkins
530 Walnut St.
Philadelphia, PA 19106

Phone: (215)238-4200
Fax: (215)238-4227
Free: (800)777-2295

Professional journal covering nursing. **Freq:** Quarterly. **Key Personnel:** Marilyn H. Oermann, Ph.D., Editor; Diane Huber, Ph.D., Associate Editor. **ISSN:** 1093-1783.

675 Physical Therapy Case Reports
Lippincott Williams & Wilkins
530 Walnut St.
Philadelphia, PA 19106

Phone: (215)238-4200
Fax: (215)238-4227
Free: (800)777-2295

Professional journal covering physical therapy. **Founded:** Jan. 1998. **Freq:** Bimonthly. **Key Personnel:** Darlene K. Sekerak, Ph.D., Editor. **ISSN:** 1094-0367.

676 Primary Care Case Reviews
Lippincott Williams & Wilkins
530 Walnut St.
Philadelphia, PA 19106

Phone: (215)238-4200
Fax: (215)238-4227
Free: (800)777-2295

Professional journal for primary care physicians. **Subtitle:** Cost-Effective, Evidence-Based Diagnosis and Management. **Freq:** Quarterly. **Key Personnel:** Robert W. Schrier, M.D., Editor-in-Chief. **ISSN:** 1096-8954.

677 Sports Chiropractic & Rehabilitation
Lippincott Williams & Wilkins
530 Walnut St.
Philadelphia, PA 19106

Phone: (215)238-4200
Fax: (215)238-4227
Free: (800)777-2295

Professional journal covering physical therapy. **Founded:** 1987. **Freq:** Quarterly. **Print Method:** Sheetfed offset. **Trim Size:** 8 1/8 x 10 7/8. **Key Personnel:** Dana J. Lawrence, DC, Editor-in-Chief; Sandra Kasko, Associate Publisher; James L. Nagle, Advertising Dir. **Subscription Rates:** $96 individuals; $140 institutions. **Remarks:** Accepts advertising.
Ad Rates: BW: $585   **Circ:** Paid 2121
           4C: $1485

678 Techniques in Hand and Upper Extremity Surgery
Lippincott Williams & Wilkins
530 Walnut St.
Philadelphia, PA 19106

Phone: (215)238-4200
Fax: (215)238-4227
Free: (800)777-2295

Professional journal covering hand and upper extremity surgery. **Freq:** Quarterly. **Key Personnel:** Andrew J. Weiland, M.D., Editor-in-Chief. **ISSN:** 1089-3393.

679 University of Pennsylvania Journal of International Economic Law
University of Pennsylvania
3400 Chestnut St.
Philadelphia, PA 19104-6204

Professional legal journal. **Founded:** Jan. 1978. **Freq:** Quarterly. **Remarks:** Advertising not accepted. **Online:** LEXIS-NEXIS; Westlaw. **Former name:** Journal of International Business Law.

                                         Circ: Paid ‡650

PITTSBURGH

680 Boundary 2
Duke University Press
c/o Paul A. Bove
Univ. of Pittsburgh
Dept. of English
526 Cathedral of Learning, 5th Ave. &
  Bigelow
Pittsburgh, PA 15260
Publisher E-mail: dukepress@duke.edu

Scholarly journal covering literature and culture worldwide. **Subtitle:** An International Journal of Literature and Culture. **Freq:** Triennial. **Key Personnel:** Paul A. Bove, Editor; Amy Hartzler, Advertising, phone (919)687-3636. **Subscription Rates:** $29 individuals; $84 institutions. **Remarks:** Accepts advertising.
Ad Rates: BW: $200   **Circ:** Paid 850

SPRING MILLS

681 Universal Light Messenger
Light Bridge Publishing
RR 3
Box 242
Spring Mills, PA 16875   Phone: (814)422-8112

New Age newspaper. **Freq:** Monthly. **URL:** http://www.mindspring.com/~ulmpaper.

STATE COLLEGE

682 Voices of Central Pennsylvania
103 E. Beaver Ave., Ste. 11
State College, PA 16801   Phone: (814)234-1699
Publication E-mail: voices@epicom.com

Community newspaper. **Freq:** Monthly. **Key Personnel:** Andrew Churlik, Business Mgr.; Mike Sletson, Advertising. **URL:** http://www.epicom.com/voices. **Feature Editors:** Michael Casper, *Political*; Emily Kuntz, *Lifestyle*.

UNIVERSITY PARK

683 Journal of Wave-Material Interaction
Pennsylvania State University
149 Hammond Bldg.   Phone: (814)863-4210
University Park, PA 16802   Fax: (814)865-3052

Technical engineering journal. **Key Personnel:** V.K. Varadan, Editor. **Subscription Rates:** $130 individuals; $40 single issue.

WILKES BARRE

684 The Expressline
The Times Leader
15 N. Main St.   Phone: (570)829-7100
Wilkes Barre, PA 18711   Fax: (570)831-7362
                                           Free: (800)427-8649

Shopping guide. **Founded:** 1991. **Freq:** Weekly. **Key Personnel:** Mark Contreras, Pres./Pub. **Subscription Rates:** Free.
                                    Circ: Non-paid ◆50,589

YORK

685 The Best from American Canals
American Canal & Transportation Center
809 Rathton Rd.
York, PA 17403   Phone: (717)843-4035

Journal of the American Canal Society. **Subscription Rates:** $9.50 single issue.

RHODE ISLAND

PROVIDENCE

📖 **686 Real Estate Software Guide**
Z-Law Software, Inc
619 Hospital Trust Bldg.   Phone: (401)273-5588
Providence, RI 02903   Fax: (401)421-5334
Publication E-mail: zlaw1@aol.com
Publisher E-mail: catalog@z-law.com

Trade magazine covering real estate software for realtors, investors, property managers, developers, attorneys, and others. **Founded:** Sept. 1, 1995. **Freq:** Quarterly. **Trim Size:** 6 x 11. **Cols./Page:** 1. **Col. Width:** 4 inches. **Col. Depth:** 8 3/4 inches. **Key Personnel:** Gary L. Sherman, Editor. **ISSN:** 1521-5512. **Subscription Rates:** $16 individuals; $4 single issue. **Remarks:** Advertising not accepted. **URL:** http://www.z-law.com.

Circ: Paid 63,000

WAKEFIELD

📖 **687 The Chariho Times**
Southern Rhode Island Newspapers
187 Main St.
PO Box 232   Phone: (401)789-9744
Wakefield, RI 02880   Fax: (401)783-1550

Community newspaper. **Founded:** 1993. **Freq:** Weekly (Thurs.). **Key Personnel:** Michael O'Sullivan, Publisher. **Subscription Rates:** $24 individuals; $32 out of state; $18 students prepaid.

Circ: Combined ♦**2,278**

📖 **688 The Coventry Courier**
Southern Rhode Island Newspapers
187 Main St.
PO Box 232   Phone: (401)789-9744
Wakefield, RI 02880   Fax: (401)783-1550

Community newspaper. **Founded:** 1996. **Freq:** Weekly. **Key Personnel:** Michael O'Sullivan, Publisher. **Subscription Rates:** $30 individuals; $40 out of state; $24 students prepaid.

Circ: Combined ♦**1665**

📖 **689 South County Independent**
South County Newspapers, Inc.
202 Church St.   Phone: (401)789-6000
Wakefield, RI 02879-2912   Fax: (401)792-9176

Community newspaper. **Founded:** 1997. **Freq:** Weekly (Thurs.). **Key Personnel:** Fredrick J. Wilson III, Publisher.

Circ: Combined ♦**6865**

SOUTH CAROLINA

COLUMBIA

690 Point
18 Bluff Rd.
PO Box 8325
Columbia, SC 29202
Publisher E-mail: scpoint@mindspring.com

Phone: (803)808-3384
Fax: (803)808-3781
Free: (800)849-1803

Community newspaper. **Freq:** Monthly. **Key Personnel:** Brett Bursey, Publisher; Becci Robbins, Editor. **Subscription Rates:** $26 individuals. **URL:** http://www.mingspring.com/~scpoint/point.

HILTON HEAD ISLAND

691 TennisPro
U.S. Professional Tennis Registry
PO Box 4739
Hilton Head Island, SC 29938

Phone: (803)785-7244
Fax: (803)686-2033
Free: (800)421-6289

Publisher E-mail: usptr@hargray.com

Professional magazine for USPTR members covering tennis. **Founded:** 1981. **Freq:** Bimonthly. **Trim Size:** 8 1/2 x 11. **Key Personnel:** Jeff Dalpiaz, Editor. **Subscription Rates:** Free to qualified subscribers. **Remarks:** Accepts advertising.

Circ: Combined 15,000

KINGSTREE

692 The News
Kingstree Communications, Inc.
107 E. Mill St.
Kingstree, SC 29556
Publication E-mail: thenews@ftc-i.net

Phone: (843)354-7454
Fax: (843)354-6530

Community newspaper. **Freq:** Weekly (Wed.). **Key Personnel:** Vickey Nexsen Boyd, Publisher; Tami K. Rodgers, Advertising Mgr.; Susan Morris, Adv. Sales. **Subscription Rates:** $16 individuals; $19 out of area; $25 out of state. **URL:** http://www.kingstreenews.com. **Feature Editors:** Linda Brown, *News*.

ORANGEBURG

693 WSPX-FM - 94.5
PO Box 1546
Orangeburg, SC 29115
E-mail: bbinc@oburg.net

Phone: (803)536-1710
Fax: (803)531-1089

Format: Sports. **Networks:** ESPN Radio. **Owner:** Boswell Broadcasting, Inc., at above address. **Founded:** Oct. 1997. **Operating Hours:** Continuous. **Key Personnel:** Chuck Boswell, President. **Wattage:** 6,000. **URL:** http://www.boswellbroadcasting.com.

SOUTH DAKOTA

PIERRE

📖 **694 Pierre Capital Journal**
333 W. Dakota
PO Box 878
Pierre, SD 57501   Phone: (605)224-7301

Community newspaper. **Founded:** 1881. **Freq:** Daily. **Key Personnel:** Dana Hess, Editor, news@capjournal.com; Terry Hipple, Publisher, publisher@capjournal.com; Lois Ries, Advertising Mgr., sales@capjournalc.com.

TENNESSEE

CLEVELAND

📖 **695 Bradley News Weekly**
The Bradley County Weekly Inc.
149 Inman St. SE
Cleveland, TN 37320

Phone: (423)472-2882
Fax: (423)339-2135

Community newspaper. **Founded:** 1991. **Freq:** Weekly (Wed.). **Key Personnel:** Susan Shelton, Publisher. **Subscription Rates:** Free.

Circ: Combined ♦**21,988**

COOKEVILLE

📖 **696 The Putnam Pit**
PO Box 1483
Cookeville, TN 38503-1483

Free: (800)971-9227

Publication E-mail: putnampit@reporters.net

Alternative political newspaper. **Key Personnel:** Geoff Davidian, Editor and Publisher; Chris Davidian, Managing Editor. **ISSN:** 1091-9171. **Subscription Rates:** $30 individuals. **URL:** http://www.putnampit.com.

JACKSON

🎙 **697 WIGH-FM - 88.7**
PO Box 3488
Jackson, TN 38303-3488

Phone: (901)427-8000
Fax: (901)427-0730
Free: (800)890-8465

Format: Educational. **Owner:** Guiding Hands for the Blind, Inc., at above address. **Operating Hours:** Continuous. **Key Personnel:** Ernest Harper, Jr., General Mgr., ernestharper@webtv.net. **Wattage:** 15,000. **Ad Rates:** Advertising accepted; rates available upon request.

LA FOLLETTE

📖 **698 La Follette Press**
PO Box 1261
La Follette, TN 37766

Phone: (423)562-8468
Fax: (423)566-7060

General newspaper. **Subscription Rates:** $15.25 individuals; $27.50 out of area. **URL:** http://www.lafollettepress.com.

LIVINGSTON

📖 **699 Overton County News**
415 W. Main St.
PO Box 479
Livingston, TN 38570

Phone: (931)823-6485
Fax: (931)823-6486

Publication E-mail: ocnews@usit.net

Community newspaper. **Freq:** Weekly (Wed.). **Remarks:** Accepts advertising. **URL:** http://www.overtoncountynews.com.

Ad Rates: PCI: $3.80   **Circ:** (Not Reported)

MURFREESBORO

📖 **700 The Sword of the Lord**
Sword of the Lord Publishers
224 Bridge Ave.
PO Box 1099
Murfreesboro, TN 37133

Phone: (615)893-6700
Fax: (615)895-7447

Publisher E-mail: 102657.3622@compuserve.com

Religious publication for Christians. **Subtitle:** America's Foremost Revival Publication. **Freq:** Biweekly. **Key Personnel:** Dr. Shelton Smith, Editor. **Subscription Rates:** $15 individuals; $18 out of country.

UNION CITY

🎙 **701 WWUC-FM - 105.7**
PO Box 100
Union City, TN 38281
E-mail: sales@realrockradio.com

Format: Classic Rock. **Networks:** ABC; Westwood One Radio. **Owner:** Twin States Broadcasting, Inc., at above address. **Founded:** Mar. 1994. **Operating Hours:** Continuous. **ADI:** Paducah,KY-Cape Girardeau,MO-Marion,IL. **Key Personnel:** Rodney K. Taylor, Pres./General Mgr., quakefm@hotmail.com; Robin G. Francis, Program Dir., programming@realrockradio.com; Don Wilson, Music Dir., drwilson@usit.net; Kathy Jo Roberts, Sales Mgr., sales@realrockradio.com. **Wattage:** 6000. **Ad Rates:** $6.50-12.50 for 30 seconds; $8.50-14.50 for 60 seconds. **URL:** http://www.realrockradio.com.

TEXAS

AUSTIN

702 The American Journal of Criminal Law
University of Texas School of Law Publications
727 E. Dean Keeton St.   Phone: (512)232-1149
Austin, TX 78705   Fax: (512)471-6988
Publication E-mail: publications@mail.law.utexas.edu

Professional journal covering news of interest to legal scholars and practitioners worldwide. **Founded:** 1972. **Freq:** Annual. **Print Method:** Web offset. **Trim Size:** 6 3/4 x 10. **ISSN:** 0092-2315. **Subscription Rates:** $25 individuals; $28 out of country. **URL:** http://tarlton.law.utexas.edu/journals/ajcl/index.htm.

Circ: Combined 600

703 Moderna
Hispanic Publishing Corp.
98 San Jacinto Blvd., Ste. 1150
Austin, TX 78701   Phone: (512)476-5599
                                         Fax: (512)320-1942

Consumer magazine for a Hispanic audience. **URL:** http://www.hisp.com/moderna.

704 Nerve Cowboy
Liquid Paper Press
PO Box 4973
Austin, TX 78765

Journal of contemporary poetry and short fiction. **Freq:** Semiannual. **Trim Size:** 7 x 8. **Key Personnel:** Joseph Shields, Editor; Jerry Hagins, Editor. **ISSN:** 1088-713X. **Subscription Rates:** $7 individuals; $4 single issue. **Remarks:** Accepts advertising.
Ad Rates: BW: $50   **Circ:** Combined 250

705 Texas Environmental Law Journal
University of Texas School of Law Publications
727 E. Dean Keeton St.   Phone: (512)232-1149
Austin, TX 78705   Fax: (512)471-6988

Professional journal covering environmental law. **Freq:** Quarterly. **ISSN:** 0163-545X.

706 Texas Forum on Civil Liberties and Civil Rights
University of Texas School of Law Publications
727 E. Dean Keeton St.   Phone: (512)232-1149
Austin, TX 78705   Fax: (512)471-6988
Publication E-mail: tfclcr@mail.law.utexas.edu

Professional journal covering civil rights in the U.S. **Founded:** 1992. **Freq:** Annual. **Print Method:** Web offset. **Trim Size:** 6 3/4 x 10. **ISSN:** 1085-942X. **Subscription Rates:** $25 individuals; $28 out of country. **URL:** http://www.utexas.edu/students/tfclcr.

Circ: Combined 400

707 Texas Hispanic Journal of Law and Policy
University of Texas School of Law Publications
727 E. Dean Keeton St.   Phone: (512)232-1149
Austin, TX 78705   Fax: (512)471-6988
Publication E-mail: thjlp@mail.law.utexas.edu

Professional journal covering Hispanic concerns and the law. **Founded:** 1994. **Freq:** Annual. **Print Method:** Web offset. **Trim Size:** 6 3/4 x 10. **ISSN:** 1075-8461. **Subscription Rates:** $25 individuals; $28 out of country. **URL:** http://www.utexas.edu/students/thjlp.

Circ: Combined 250

708 Texas Intellectual Property Law Journal
University of Texas School of Law Publications
727 E. Dean Keeton St.   Phone: (512)232-1149
Austin, TX 78705   Fax: (512)471-6988
Publication E-mail: tiplj@mail.law.utexas.edu

Professional journal covering developments in the areas of patent, copyright, trademark, unfair competition, and trade secret law. **Founded:** 1993. **Freq:** Annual. **Print Method:** Web offset. **Trim Size:** 6 3/4 x 10. **ISSN:** 1068-1000. **Subscription Rates:** $25 individuals; $28 out of country. **URL:** http://www.utexas.edu/law/journals/tiplj/index.htm.

Circ: Combined 1700

709 Texas Journal of Business Law
University of Texas School of Law Publications
727 E. Dean Keeton St.   Phone: (512)232-1149
Austin, TX 78705   Fax: (512)471-6988

Professional journal covering business law. **URL:** http://www.obeliskcom.com/blaw/tjbl.html.

710 Texas Journal of Women and the Law
University of Texas School of Law Publications
727 E. Dean Keeton St.   Phone: (512)232-1149
Austin, TX 78705   Fax: (512)471-6988
Publication E-mail: tjwl@mail.law.utexas.edu

Professional journal covering law and women for legal scholars and practitioners. **Founded:** 1990. **Freq:** Annual. **Print Method:** Web offset. **Trim Size:** 6 3/4 x 10. **ISSN:** 1058-5427. **Subscription Rates:** $25 individuals; $28 out of country. **URL:** http://tarlton.law.utexas.edu/journals/tjwl/.

Circ: Combined 250

711 Texas Law Review Manual on Usage and Style
University of Texas School of Law Publications
727 E. Dean Keeton St.   Phone: (512)232-1149
Austin, TX 78705   Fax: (512)471-6988
Publication E-mail: publications@mail.law.utexas.edu

Professional journal covering usage and style in law. **Subscription Rates:** $4 single issue.

712 Texas Law Review Texas Rules of Form
University of Texas School of Law Publications
727 E. Dean Keeton St.   Phone: (512)232-1149
Austin, TX 78705   Fax: (512)471-6988
Publication E-mail: publications@mail.law.utexas.edu

Professional journal covering law. **Subscription Rates:** $4.25 single issue.

Ad Rates: GLR = general line rate; BW = one-time black & white page rate; 4C = one-time four color page rate; SAU = standard advertising unit rate; CNU = Canadian newspaper advertising unit rate; PCI = per column inch rate.
Circulation: ★ = ABC; △ = BPA; ♦ = CAC; • = CCAB; ❏ = VAC; ⊕ = PO Statement; ‡ = Publisher's Report; Boldface figures = sworn; Light figures = estimated.
Entry type: ⌑ = Print; ♣ = Broadcast.

109

713 Texas Review of Law and Politics
University of Texas School of Law Publications
727 E. Dean Keeton St.   Phone: (512)232-1149
Austin, TX 78705   Fax: (512)471-6988
Publication E-mail: editors@trolp.org

Professional journal covering law and politics. **Founded:** 1996. **Freq:** Annual. **Print Method:** Web offset. **Trim Size:** 6 3/4 x 10. **ISSN:** 1098-4577. **Subscription Rates:** $25 individuals; $28 out of country. **URL:** http://www.trolp.org.

Circ: Combined 800

BRYAN

714 Texas Shore Magazine
Sea Grant Program
1716 Briarcreat, Ste. 603   Phone: (409)862-3767
Bryan, TX 77802   Fax: (409)862-3786

Consumer magazine covering the marine environment in Texas. **Founded:** 1985. **Freq:** Quarterly. **Print Method:** Offset. **Trim Size:** 8 1/2 x 11. **Col. Width:** 3 1/4 inches. **Col. Depth:** 10 3/4 inches. **Key Personnel:** Jim Hiney, Editor, bohiney@unix.tamu.edu. **ISSN:** 0747-0959. **Subscription Rates:** Free; $7.55 out of state. **Remarks:** Advertising not accepted. **URL:** http://texas-sea-grant.tamu.edu.

Circ: Combined 5,500

715 KBMA-FM - 99.5
103 N. Main St.   Phone: (409)779-5262
Bryan, TX 77803   Fax: (409)779-0225

Format: Ethnic. **Owner:** Mexican-American Community Entertainment B/C Group, 1451 South Oaks Dr., College Station, TX 77845, (409)690-1367. **Founded:** Oct. 7, 1991. **Operating Hours:** Continuous. **Key Personnel:** Gloria Torres, Operations Mgr., gt.kbma@myriad.net. **Wattage:** 3,000. **Ad Rates:** $12 for 15 seconds; $5-15 for 30 seconds; $7-18 for 60 seconds.

CORPUS CHRISTI

716 KFGG-FM - 88.7
PO Box 1177   Phone: (512)289-0887
Corpus Christi, TX 78403   Fax: (512)289-7719
E-mail: kfgg@swbell.net

Format: Religious. **Networks:** USA Radio. **Owner:** Roloff Evangelistic Enterprises Inc., at above address. **Founded:** Mar. 1992. **Operating Hours:** Continuous. **Key Personnel:** Albert Cox, Station Mgr. **Wattage:** 5,000. **URL:** http://www.kfgg.cjb.net.

DUNCANVILLE

717 Cedar Hill Today
Today Newspapers, Inc.
606 Oriole Blvd., Ste. 101
PO Box 381029   Phone: (214)775-2371
Duncanville, TX 75138   Fax: (214)298-6369

Community newspaper. **Freq:** Weekly (Thurs.). **Key Personnel:** Jon Whitcomb, Circulation Mgr. **Subscription Rates:** $23.50 individuals; $32.50 out of area.

Circ: Combined 2,523

718 Desoto Today
Today Newspapers, Inc.
606 Oriole Blvd., Ste. 101
PO Box 381029   Phone: (214)775-2371
Duncanville, TX 75138   Fax: (214)298-6369

Community newspaper. **Freq:** Weekly (Thurs.). **Key Personnel:** Jon Whitcomb, Circulation Mgr. **Subscription Rates:** $23.50 individuals; $32.50 out of area.

Circ: Combined 3,595

719 Duncanville Today
Today Newspapers, Inc.
606 Oriole Blvd., Ste. 101
PO Box 381029   Phone: (214)775-2371
Duncanville, TX 75138   Fax: (214)298-6369

Community newspaper. **Freq:** Weekly (Thurs.). **Key Personnel:** Jon Whitcomb, Circulation Mgr. **Subscription Rates:** $23.50 individuals; $32.50 out of area.

Circ: Combined 4,835

720 Lancaster Today
Today Newspapers, Inc.
606 Oriole Blvd., Ste. 101
PO Box 381029   Phone: (214)775-2371
Duncanville, TX 75138   Fax: (214)298-6369

Community newspaper. **Freq:** Weekly (Thurs.). **Key Personnel:** Jon Whitcomb, Circulation Mgr. **Subscription Rates:** $20.50 individuals; $32.50 out of area.

Circ: Combined 2,657

EL PASO

721 Discovering Archaeology
Leach Publishing Group Ltd.
1205 N. Oregon   Phone: (917)533-8503
El Paso, TX 79902   Fax: (917)544-9276
                                          Free: (877)347-2724
Publication E-mail: editor@discoveringarchaeology.com

Professional journal covering archaeology. **Freq:** Bimonthly. **Key Personnel:** Jeff. D. Leach, Pub./Editor-in-Chief; Robert Locke, Exec. Editor; Johanna Hunziker, Managing Editor; Melinda Wallace Melton, Advertising Dir. **ISSN:** 1521-9496. **Subscription Rates:** $19.95 individuals; $4.95 single issue; $29.95 out of country. **URL:** http://www.discoveringarchaeology.com.

722 KCOS-TV - 13
PO Box 68650   Phone: (915)747-6500
El Paso, TX 79968-9991   Fax: (915)747-6605

Format: Commercial TV. **Networks:** Public Broadcasting Service (PBS). **Owner:** El Paso Public Television Foundation, at above address. **Founded:** Aug. 18, 1978. **Operating Hours:** Continuous. **Key Personnel:** Craig A. Brush, President/General Mgr., craig_ brush@kcos.pbs.com; Bobbie Hakin, VP, Business Affairs; David Echaniz, VP, Engineering; Kayla Marks, VP, Marketing. **Wattage:** 25,000. **URL:** http://www.kcostv.org.

FLORESVILLE

723 Wilson County News
1012 C St.
PO Box 115   Phone: (830)216-4519
Floresville, TX 78114   Fax: (830)393-3219

Community newspaper. **Freq:** Weekly. **Key Personnel:** Elaine Kolodziej, Publisher; Marty Kufus, Editor; Cathy Green, Production Mgr.; Ashlee Ring, Bus. Editor/Sales; Kristen Kolodziej, Circ. **Remarks:** Accepts advertising. **URL:** http://www.wcn-online.com.
Ad Rates: BW: $716.10   Circ: Combined 9,500
              PCI: $7.25

FORT WORTH

724 Linden Lane Magazine
Linden Lane Press
PO Box 331964   Phone: (817)346-8384
Fort Worth, TX 76163   Fax: (817)346-8384

Literary magazine covering Latin American literature in the US in Spanish and English. **Founded:** Mar. 1982. **Freq:** Quarterly. **Trim Size:** 11 x 17. **Cols./Page:** 4. **Key Personnel:** Belkis Cuza, Editor and Publisher. **ISSN:** 0736-1084. **Subscription Rates:** $12 individuals; $22 institutions; $3 single issue. **Remarks:** Accepts advertising.
Ad Rates: BW: $500   Circ: Paid 2000
              4C: $1000

GARLAND

725 Vietnam Weekly News
3306 W. Walnut St., Ste. 400
Garland, TX 75042

Phone: (214)272-4898
Fax: (214)272-4657

Vietnamese language community newspaper. **Founded:** 1987. **Freq:** Weekly.
Key Personnel: Loc Tran, Contact. **Remarks:** Accepts advertising.
Ad Rates: BW: $500   **Circ:** Combined **12,000**

HOUSTON

726 African-American News & Issues
Malonson Company, Inc.
6130 Wheatley St.
Houston, TX 77091

Phone: (713)692-1892

Community newspaper for an African-American audience. **Freq:** Semimonthly. **Subscription Rates:** Free.

Circ: Combined **175,750**

727 La Voz De Houston Newspaper
La Voz Publishing Corp.
6101 S.W. Fwy., Ste. 127
Houston, TX 77057

Phone: (713)664-4404
Fax: (713)664-4414

Spanish newspaper. **Founded:** 1979. **Freq:** Weekly. **Print Method:** Offset.
Trim Size: 13 1/2 x 22. **Cols./Page:** 6. **Col. Width:** 13 inches. **Col. Depth:**
21 inches. **Key Personnel:** Olga Ordoniz, President. **Subscription Rates:** $25
individuals. **Remarks:** Accepts advertising.
Ad Rates: GLR: $1.35   **Circ:** Non-paid **75,000**
          BW: $3,528
          4C: $4,128
          PCI: $28

728 Ngay Nay
3121 San Jacinto
Houston, TX 77004

Phone: (713)526-5352
Fax: (713)526-8637

Vietnamese language community newspaper. **Freq:** Biweekly. **Key Personnel:** Huong Pham, Contact. **Subscription Rates:** $30 individuals. **Remarks:**
Accepts advertising.
Ad Rates: BW: $500   **Circ:** Combined **30,000**

729 The Philippine Observer
Ernie Azucena
2600 Southwest Fwy., Ste. 415
Houston, TX 77098

Phone: (713)524-6929
Fax: (713)524-4991

Community newspaper for Filipino-Americans. **Freq:** Bimonthly. **Key
Personnel:** Ernie Azucena, Publisher. **Subscription Rates:** Free; $30 by mail.
Remarks: Accepts advertising.
Ad Rates: BW: $350   **Circ:** Combined **10,000**

KILLEEN

730 Killeen Daily Herald
Frank Mayborn Enterprises
1809 Florence Rd.
PO Box 1300
Killeen, TX 76541
Publication E-mail: kdh.adv@vvm.com

Phone: (254)634-2125
Fax: (254)634-2125
Free: (800)460-1809

General newspaper. **Founded:** 1890. **Freq:** Daily (morn.). **Subscription
Rates:** $99 individuals; $110 by mail. **Remarks:** Advertising accepted; rates
available upon request. **URL:** http://www.kdhnews.com.

Circ: (Not Reported)

LAREDO

731 KHOY-FM -
1901 Corpus Christi St.
Laredo, TX 78043-3308

Phone: (956)722-4167

Format: Religious. **Owner:** Catholic Telecommunication, at above address.
Operating Hours: Continuous. **Key Personnel:** Jose Angel Jimenez,
Program Dir.; Bennett McBride, Station Dir. **URL:** http://www.goccn.org/
khoy/.

LEWISVILLE

732 The Colony Leader
Scripps Community Newspapers
100 Lakeland Plaza, Ste. 100
Lewisville, TX 75067

Phone: (972)436-3566

Community newspaper. **Freq:** Weekly (Fri.). **Subscription Rates:** $12
individuals; $36 by mail.

Circ: Combined **10,278**

733 VM Update
Xephon
1301 W. Hwy. 407, Ste. 201-450
Lewisville, TX 75067
Publisher E-mail: info@xephon.com

Phone: (940)455-7050
Fax: (940)455-2492

Professional journal covering computers and data processing. **Freq:** Monthly.
Subscription Rates: $265 individuals; $500 two years. **Remarks:** Advertising not accepted.

Circ: (Not Reported)

LUFKIN

734 Nacogdoches Daily Sentinel
Cox Newspapers
PO Box 1089
Lufkin, TX 75902-1089

Phone: (409)632-6631
Fax: (409)632-6655

Daily newspaper. **Freq:** Mon.-Sun. **Subscription Rates:** $111 individuals;
$120 by mail.

ONALASKA

735 Adams Addenda II
Adams Addenda Association
218 Kickapoo Forest
Onalaska, TX 77360
Publisher E-mail: adad@syslink.mcs.com

Periodical covering Adams genealogy. **Founded:** 1997. **Freq:** Semiannual.
Key Personnel: Florence Marshall, President; Eugene Adams, Treasurer.
URL: http://www.qpt.com/~ad-ad/index.html.

PALESTINE

736 The Clarion
Meaux Walsh Publishing, Inc.
228 Wall Dr.
Palestine, TX 75801
Publication E-mail: tclarion@flash.net

Community newspaper. **Subscription Rates:** $18 individuals; $36 by mail.
URL: http://www.flash.net/~tclarion.

ROUND TOP

📖 **737 The Round Top Register**
PO Box 225
Round Top, TX 78954

Phone: (409)249-5550

Community newspaper. **Subscription Rates:** Free. **URL:** http://www.roundtop.com/.

SAN ANTONIO

🎤 **738 KPAC-FM - 88.3**
8401 Datapoint Dr., Ste. 800
San Antonio, TX 78229-5903

Phone: (210)614-8977
Free: (800)622-8977

Format: Public Radio; Classical. **Owner:** Texas Public Radio, at above address. **Operating Hours:** Continuous. **Key Personnel:** Penny Dennis, Programming, penny@tpr.org. **Ad Rates:** Noncommercial; underwriting available. **URL:** http://www.tpr.org.

WILLS POINT

📖 **739 Van Zandt News**
Van Zandt Newpapers, L.L.C.
PO Box 60
Wills Point, TX 75169
Publication E-mail: vznews@aol.com

Phone: (903)873-2525
Fax: (903)873-4321

Community newspaper. **Freq:** Weekly (Sun.). **Key Personnel:** Linda Brown, Editor; Linda Nielsen, General Mgr.; David Barber, Advertising. **Subscription Rates:** $16 individuals; $17 out of area; $20 out of state. **URL:** http://www.vanzandtnews.com.

UTAH

SALT LAKE CITY

📖 **740 The Pillar**
Pillar Publishing
PO Box 57744
Salt Lake City, UT 84157-0744
Publication E-mail: pillarslc@aol.com

Phone: (801)265-0066
Fax: (801)261-2923

Newspaper serving the gay and lesbian community. **Freq:** Monthly. **Key Personnel:** Todd Dayley, Editor and Publisher; Randolph Prawitt, Prod. Ed. **Subscription Rates:** $25 individuals. **URL:** http://members.aol.com/pillarslc.

VERMONT

DORSET

📖 **741 The Opera Quarterly**
Duke University Press
c/o Christopher Hatch
RR 2, Box 1590
Dorset, VT 05251
Publisher E-mail: dukepress@duke.edu

Scholarly journal covering opera. **Freq:** Quarterly. **Key Personnel:** E. Thomas Glasow, Editor; Amy Hartzler, Advertising, phone (919)687-3636. **Subscription Rates:** $38 individuals; $100 institutions. **Remarks:** Accepts advertising.
Ad Rates: BW: $500   **Circ:** Combined 3800

VIRGINIA

ALEXANDRIA

📖 **742 Alexandria Gazette Packet**
Connection Publishing, Inc.
1610 King St.
Alexandria, VA 22314   Phone: (703)549-3155

Community newspaper. **Freq:** Weekly (Thurs.). **Print Method:** Offset. **Key Personnel:** Peter C. Labovitz, Pres./Pub. **Remarks:** Accepts advertising.
Circ: Combined ♦**19,835**

📖 **743 Flight Safety Digest**
Flight Safety Foundation, Inc.
601 Madison St., Ste. 300   Phone: (703)739-6700
Alexandria, VA 22314-1756   Fax: (703)739-6708
Publisher E-mail: fsf@radix.net

Trade magazine covering aviation safety. **Key Personnel:** Roger Rozelle, Editor.

📖 **744 Mt. Vernon Gazette**
Connection Publishing, Inc.
1610 King St.
Alexandria, VA 22314   Phone: (703)549-3155

Community newspaper. **Freq:** Weekly (Thurs.). **Key Personnel:** Peter C. Labovitz, President. **Subscription Rates:** Free.
Circ: Combined ♦**15,498**

📖 **745 Prince William Journal**
The Journal Newspapers
6408 Edsall Rd.   Phone: (703)560-4000
Alexandria, VA 22312   Fax: (703)846-8505
Free: (800)531-1223

Community newspaper. **Freq:** Daily. **Subscription Rates:** $40 individuals.
Circ: Combined **10,599**

ARLINGTON

📖 **746 The Hospice Professional**
National Hospice Organization
1901 N. Moore St., Ste. 901   Phone: (703)243-5400
Arlington, VA 22209   Fax: (703)525-5762
Free: (800)658-8898
Publication E-mail: drsnho@cais.com

Professional magazine for hospice workers. **Freq:** Quarterly. **Remarks:** Accepts advertising. **URL:** http://www.nho.org.
Circ: (Not Reported)

📖 **747 R.E. Magazine**
National Rural Electric Cooperative Association
4301 Wilson Blvd.   Phone: (703)907-5500
Arlington, VA 22203   Fax: (703)907-5521

Trade magazine of the National Rural Electric Cooperative Association. **Freq:** Monthly. **Trim Size:** 8 1/8 x 10 7/8. **Cols./Page:** 2. **Key Personnel:** Frank

Gallant, Editor; Andrea Smith, Advertising Mgr.; Val Parks, Circulation Mgr. **Remarks:** Accepts advertising.
Circ: (Not Reported)

ASHBURN

📖 **748 Loudoun Easterner**
Creative Publications of Virginia, Inc.
20735 Ashburn Rd.   Phone: (703)858-5300
Ashburn, VA 20147   Fax: (703)858-7651
Publication E-mail: editor@easterner.com

Community newspaper. **Remarks:** Advertising accepted; rates available upon request. **URL:** http://www.easterner.com.
Circ: (Not Reported)

BLACKSBURG

🎤 **749 WVTW-FM - 88.5**
315 Burruss Hall   Phone: (540)989-8900
Blacksburg, VA 24061   Fax: (540)776-2727
Free: (800)856-8900
E-mail: wvtf@vt.edu

Format: Classical; Full Service; News; Talk. **Networks:** National Public Radio (NPR). **Owner:** Virginia Tech Foundation, Inc., at above address. **Founded:** Sept. 1998. **Operating Hours:** Continuous. **ADI:** Charlottesville, VA. **Key Personnel:** Steve Mills, General Mgr.; Paxton Durham, Chief Engineer; Glenn Gleixner, Development Dir.; Rick Mattioni, News Dir. **Wattage:** 120. **Ad Rates:** Advertising accepted; rates available upon request. **URL:** http://www.wvtf.org.

FAIRFAX

📖 **750 Communications Industries Report**
International Communications Industries Association
11242 Waples Mill Rd., Ste. 200   Phone: (703)273-7200
Fairfax, VA 22030   Fax: (703)278-8082
Free: (800)659-7469
Publisher E-mail: icia@iciahq.org

Newspaper covering information for the video, multimedia, telecommunications, interactive, and computer industries. **Key Personnel:** Dick Larsen, Managing Editor, dlarsen@atwood.com. **URL:** http://www.icia.org.

📖 **751 ITEA Journal of Test and Evaluation**
International Test and Evaluation Association (ITEA)
4400 Fair Lakes Ct.   Phone: (703)631-6220
Fairfax, VA 22033-3899   Fax: (703)631-6221
Publisher E-mail: itea@itea.org

Professional magazine covering testing. **Founded:** 1985. **Freq:** Quarterly. **Subscription Rates:** $40 individuals; $15 single issue. **Remarks:** Accepts advertising.
Circ: Combined 2,575

GLOUCESTER

📖 **752 Intermarket Review**
International Institute for Economic Research
PO Box 624   Phone: (804)696-0415
Gloucester, VA 23061   Fax: (804)694-0028
Publication E-mail: info@pring.com

Professional journal covering financial markets worldwide for investment brokers and others. **Freq:** Monthly. **Key Personnel:** Lisa H. Pring, Managing Editor. **ISSN:** 1096-1747. **Subscription Rates:** $265 individuals. **URL:** http://www.pring.com.

LORTON

📖 **753 Hoa Thinh Don Viet Bao**
8394-C2 Terminal Rd.   Phone: (703)339-9852
Lorton, VA 22079   Fax: (703)339-9857

Vietnamese language community newspaper. **Founded:** 1984. **Freq:** Weekly. **Key Personnel:** Suong Truong, Contact. **Subscription Rates:** Free. **Remarks:** Accepts advertising.
Ad Rates: BW: $260   **Circ:** Combined 6,000

LYNCHBURG

📖 **754 The News Advance**
Media General, Inc.
101 Wyndale Dr.
PO Box 10129   Phone: (804)385-5555
Lynchburg, VA 24506   Fax: (804)385-5538
Publisher E-mail: tppost@widomaker.com

Community newspaper. **URL:** http://www.newsadvance.com.

MCLEAN

📖 **755 Korean Weekly**
6719 Curran St., 3rd Fl.   Phone: (703)556-0349
McLean, VA 22101   Fax: (703)556-0352

Korean and English language community newspaper. **Founded:** 1991. **Freq:** Weekly. **Key Personnel:** Hyun Song, Contact. **Subscription Rates:** Free; $45 by mail. **Remarks:** Accepts advertising.
Ad Rates: BW: $450   **Circ:** Combined 12,000

RESTON

📖 **756 U.S. Geological Survey, Mineral Industry Surveys-Commodities: Barite**
U.S. Geological Survey
989 National Center   Phone: (703)648-4750
Reston, VA 20192   Fax: (703)648-7757

Journal covering geology.

RICHMOND

📖 **757 American Painting Contractor**
Douglas Publications, Inc.
2807 N. Parham Rd., Ste. 200   Phone: (804)762-9600
Richmond, VA 23294   Fax: (804)217-8999
Publisher E-mail: amdouglas3@aol.com

Professional magazine for painting contractors. **Key Personnel:** Andrew Dwyer, Editor, phone (314)863-8979, fax (314)863-8786, ajdwyer1@aol.com; John J. McDevitt, Pub./Advertising Sales, phone (201)634-0479, fax (201)634-0490, jmcdevitt@aol.com. **Remarks:** Accepts advertising. **URL:** http://www.douglaspublications.com/apc.html.
Ad Rates: BW: $3,245   **Circ:** (Not Reported)
4C: $4,500

📖 **758 Flooring Magazine**
Douglas Publications, Inc.
2807 N. Parham Rd., Ste. 200   Phone: (804)762-9600
Richmond, VA 23294   Fax: (804)217-8999
Publisher E-mail: amdouglas3@aol.com

Trade magazine for the floor covering industry. **Key Personnel:** Dave Foster, Senior Editor, phone (706)625-3528, fax (706)625-0928, dfoster@floorradio.com; Roland Boucher, Publisher, phone (678)363-9730, fax (678)363-9731, rolandb1@aol.com. **Subscription Rates:** $37 individuals; $67 two years; $45 Canada; $97 elsewhere. **Remarks:** Accepts advertising. **URL:** http://www.douglaspublications.com/flooring.html.
Ad Rates: BW: $6,063   **Circ:** Combined •20,000
4C: $8,118

📖 **759 Lifting & Transportation International**
Douglas Publications, Inc.
2807 N. Parham Rd., Ste. 200   Phone: (804)762-9600
Richmond, VA 23294   Fax: (804)217-8999
Publisher E-mail: amdouglas3@aol.com

Trade magazine covering the major lifting and hauling industry. **Key Personnel:** Andrew Dwyer, Editor, phone (314)863-8979, fax (314)863-8786, ajdwyer1@aol.com; Carolyn Ward, Advertising Mgr., phone (704)664-2750, fax (704)664-6642, carolynw11@aol.com. **Subscription Rates:** $65 individuals; $98 two years; $98 Canada; $145 elsewhere. **Remarks:** Accepts advertising. **URL:** http://www.douglaspublications.com/lti.html.
                                              Circ: Combined ‡16,325

📖 **760 Robotics World**
Douglas Publications, Inc.
2807 N. Parham Rd., Ste. 200   Phone: (804)762-9600
Richmond, VA 23294   Fax: (804)217-8999
Publisher E-mail: amdouglas3@aol.com

Professional magazine covering flexible automation and intelligent machines. **Key Personnel:** Guy Potok, Senior Editor, phone (810)493-6657, fax (810)463-4966, gpotok@tir.com; Carolyn Ward, Advertising Mgr., phone (704)664-2750, fax (704)664-6642, carolynw11@aol.com; Alan Douglas, Publisher, phone (804)762-9600, fax (804)217-8999, amdouglas2@aol.com. **Subscription Rates:** $42 individuals; $67 two years; $57 Canada; $82 elsewhere. **Remarks:** Accepts advertising. **URL:** http://www.douglaspublications.com/robotics.html.
Ad Rates: BW: $5,010   **Circ:** Combined ‡26,050
4C: $6,275

ROANOKE

📻 **761 WVTR-FM - 91.9**
4235 Electric Rd. SW, Ste. 105   Phone: (540)989-8900
Roanoke, VA 24014   Fax: (540)776-2727
                                              Free: (800)856-8900

E-mail: wvtf@vt.edu

Format: Classical; Full Service; News; Talk. **Networks:** National Public Radio (NPR). **Owner:** Virginia Tech Foundation, Inc., at above address. **Founded:** Nov. 1991. **Operating Hours:** Continuous. **ADI:** Charlottesville, VA. **Key Personnel:** Steve Mills, General Mgr.; Paxton Durham, Chief Engineer; Glenn Gleixner, Development Dir.; Rick Mattioni, News Dir. **Wattage:** 4,400. **Ad Rates:** Advertising accepted; rates available upon request. **URL:** http://www.wvtf.org.

VIENNA

📖 **762 Foundation Update**
Newspaper Association of America Foundation
The Newspaper Center
1921 Gallows Rd., Ste. 600   Phone: (703)902-1726
Vienna, VA 22182-3900   Fax: (703)902-1735

Trade magazine covering the newspaper industry. **Trim Size:** 8 1/2 x 11. **Key Personnel:** John Sturm, President and Chief Exec. Officer, phone (703)902-1601, sturj@naa.org; Toni F. Laws, Senior VP, phone (703)902-1725, lawst@naa.org; Ronn Levine, Communications Specialist/Update Editor, phone (703)902-1731, levir@naa.org.

WASHINGTON

BREMERTON

📖 **763 North Kitsap Neighbors**
Scripps Howard Company
545 Fifth St.   Phone: (360)377-3711
Bremerton, WA 98337-0053   Fax: (360)377-9237

Community newspaper. **Founded:** 1996. **Freq:** Weekly (Wed.). **Key Personnel:** Curtis Huber, Circ. Dir. **Subscription Rates:** Free.
Circ: Combined ♦**12,899**

📖 **764 South Kitsap Neighbors**
Scripps Howard Company
545 Fifth St.   Phone: (360)377-3711
Bremerton, WA 98337-0053   Fax: (360)377-9237

Community newspaper. **Founded:** 1996. **Freq:** Weekly (Wed.). **Key Personnel:** Curtis Huber, Circ. Dir. **Subscription Rates:** Free. **Remarks:** Accepts advertising.
Circ: Combined ♦**22,565**

PULLMAN

📖 **765 Frontiers**
Washington State University Press
PO Box 645910   Phone: (509)335-3518
Pullman, WA 99164-5910   Fax: (509)335-8568
                                                       Free: (800)354-7360

Publisher E-mail: wsupress@wsu.edu

Scholarly journal covering women studies. **Subtitle:** A Journal of Women Studies. **Freq:** Triennial. **Key Personnel:** Susan Armitage, Editor. **ISSN:** 0160-9009. **Subscription Rates:** $24 individuals; $45 institutions; $33 out of country; $54 institutions out of country.

SEATTLE

📖 **766 American Jones Building & Maintenance**
PO Box 9569
Seattle, WA 98109

Literary magazine covering poetry and fiction. **Freq:** Quarterly. **Subscription Rates:** $12 individuals.

📖 **767 Internet Voyager**
KFH Publications
3530 Bagley Ave. N.   Phone: (206)547-4950
Seattle, WA 98103   Fax: (206)545-6591
                                                       Free: (800)897-8230

Trade magazine covering Internet news. **Freq:** Bimonthly. **Key Personnel:** Stan Kehl, Publisher, stankehl@cuix.pscu.com; Donald L. Nicholas, Editor-in-Chief, dln@bluedolphin.com; John Shaw, Editor, john-show@cuix.pscu.com. **Subscription Rates:** $29 individuals. **URL:** http://www.internetvoyager.com.

📖 **768 Linux Journal**
SSC
PO Box 55549   Phone: (206)782-7733
Seattle, WA 98155-0549   Fax: (206)782-7191
Publication E-mail: linux@ssc.com

Trade magazine for Linux users. **Freq:** Monthly. **Key Personnel:** Phil Hughes, Publisher, phil@ssc.com; Marjorie Richardson, Editor, ljeditor@ssc.com; Belinda Frazier, Assoc. Prod., bbf@ssc.com. **Subscription Rates:** $22 individuals. **URL:** http://www.ssc.com/lj.
Circ: Combined 30,000

📖 **769 Northwest Parent Connection**
Northwest Parent Publishing
1530 Westlake Ave. N., Ste. 600
Seattle, WA 98109

Consumer magazine covering parenting. **Freq:** Monthly. **Subscription Rates:** $15 individuals; $25 two years. **Remarks:** Advertising accepted; rates available upon request. **URL:** http://www.nwparent.com.
Circ: (Not Reported)

WOODINVILLE

📖 **770 The Northlake News**
Northwest NEWS
13342 N.E. 175th St.
PO Box 587   Phone: (425)483-0606
Woodinville, WA 98072   Fax: (425)486-7593

Community newspaper. **URL:** http://www.nwnews.com.

📖 **771 Valley View**
Northwest News
PO Box 587   Phone: (425)483-0606
Woodinville, WA 98072   Fax: (425)486-7593

Community newspaper. **URL:** http://www.nwnews.com.

WEST VIRGINIA

ELKINS

🎙 **772 WVUC-FM - 93.1**
228 Randolph Ave.
Elkins, WV 26241

Phone: (304)367-9882
Fax: (304)472-1528

Format: Country. **Simulcasts:** WBRB-FM. **Owner:** The McGraw Group, at above address. **Founded:** 1995. **Operating Hours:** Continuous. **Key Personnel:** Charlie Devine, VP, Sales; Todd Elliott, VP, Operations. **Wattage:** 6,000.

WISCONSIN

ALGOMA

📖 **773 Kewaunee County Sunday Chronicle**
Brown County Publishing
602 Third St.
PO Box 68
Algoma, WI 54201

Phone: (920)487-2222
Fax: (920)487-3194

Shopping guide. **Founded:** 1873. **Freq:** Weekly (Sun.). **Key Personnel:** Larry Wilken, General Mgr. **Subscription Rates:** Free.

Circ: Non-paid ◆**9565**

APPLETON

📖 **774 The Scene**
Scene Publications
300 N. Appleton St., Ste. 2
Appleton, WI 54911

Phone: (920)733-5743
Fax: (920)733-5783

Community newspaper. **Key Personnel:** Joseph Amann, General Mgr., joseph@valleyscene.com; Jim Meyer, Editor, jimmeyer@athenet.net. **Subscription Rates:** Free. **URL:** http://www.valleyscene.com.

BELOIT

📖 **775 Magazine of Speculative Poetry**
Box 564
Beloit, WI 53512

Consumer magazine covering science fiction and fantastic poetry. **Founded:** 1984. **Freq:** Semiannual. **Print Method:** Offset. **Key Personnel:** Roger Dutcher, Editor. **Subscription Rates:** $11 individuals; $3.50 single issue. **Remarks:** Advertising not accepted.

Circ: Combined 120

CEDARBURG

📖 **776 The Sunday Post-Ozaukee County**
Lakeshore Newspapers, Inc.
N. 19 W. 6733 Commerce Ct.
PO Box 47
Cedarburg, WI 53012

Phone: (414)375-5100
Fax: (414)375-5107

Publisher E-mail: ngraphic@lakeshorenewspapers.com

Shopping guide. **Founded:** 1991. **Freq:** Weekly (Sun.). **Key Personnel:** Kenneth A. Troedel, Publisher. **Subscription Rates:** Free.

Circ: Combined ◆**24,408**

GREEN BAY

🎙 **777 WGBM-FM - 94.7**
Bel-Mart Centre, Ste. 8B
2733 Manitowoc Rd.
Green Bay, WI 54311

Phone: (920)465-3947
Fax: (920)468-9471
Free: (800)947-WGBM

E-mail: contact@wgbm.com

Format: Country. **Networks:** Jones Satellite. **Owner:** Bay Lakes Valley Broadcasters, Inc., at above address. **Founded:** 1994. **Operating Hours:** Continuous. **ADI:** Green Bay-Appleton (Suring), WI. **Key Personnel:** Phil

Robbins, Pres./General Mgr., phil@wgbm.com; Bill Cole, Program Dir., bill@wgbm.com. **Wattage:** 6,000. **Ad Rates:** $10 for 30 seconds; $14 for 60 seconds. **URL:** http://www.wgbm.com.

HARTLAND

📖 **778 J Desk International**
4612 Vettelson Rd.
Hartland, WI 53029

Phone: (414)367-7674
Fax: (414)367-0196

Publication E-mail: jdesk@execpc.com

Japanese language community newspaper. **Founded:** 1990. **Freq:** Quarterly. **Key Personnel:** Chiyoko Bermant, Publisher; Tozen Akiyama, Editor-in-Chief. **Subscription Rates:** Free. **Remarks:** Accepts advertising.
Ad Rates: BW: $350

Circ: Combined 1,000

📖 **779 Oconomowoc Buyers Guide**
Lake Country Publications
PO Box 200
Hartland, WI 53029

Phone: (414)367-3272
Fax: (414)367-7414

Community newspaper. **Founded:** 1987. **Freq:** Weekly (Mon.). **Key Personnel:** Lori Marchek, Publisher. **Subscription Rates:** Free.

Circ: Non-paid ◆**11,630**

IOLA

📖 **780 Toy Cars & Vehicles**
Krause Publications, Inc.
700 E. State St.
Iola, WI 54990

Phone: (715)445-2214
Fax: (715)445-4087
Free: (800)258-0929

Publisher E-mail: info@krause.com; krause@krause.com

Consumer magazine covering die-cast and model kit hobbies for the toy vehicle enthusiast. **Founded:** Mar. 1998. **Freq:** Monthly. **Print Method:** Offset. **Trim Size:** 10 x 13. **Cols./Page:** 4. **Col. Width:** 2 1/4 inches. **Col. Depth:** 13 inches. **Key Personnel:** Sharon Korbeck, Editor, korbecks@krause.com; Merry Dudley, Assoc. Editor, dudleym@krause.com. **ISSN:** 8750-8737. **Subscription Rates:** $20.98 individuals; $2.99 single issue. **Remarks:** Accepts advertising. **URL:** http://www.krause.com. **Former name:** Model Car Journal.
Ad Rates: BW: $446
           4C: $1,256

Circ: Paid 11,000

📖 **781 Waupaca County News**
Trey Foerster Ink, Inc.
PO Box 235
Iola, WI 54945

Phone: (715)445-3415
Fax: (715)445-3988

Publication E-mail: waupacanews@gglbbs.com

Community newspaper. **Key Personnel:** Trey Foerster, Publisher; Mary Foerster, Publisher. **URL:** http://www.waupacanews.com. **Feature Editors:** Jane Myhra, *News*.

JEFFERSON

782 Jefferson County Advertiser
ADD, Inc.
121 N. Main St.
PO Box 376   Phone: (414)674-2672
Jefferson, WI 53549   Fax: (414)674-6322

Shopping guide. **Founded:** 1969. **Freq:** Weekly. **Key Personnel:** Joyce Lydon, General Mgr. **Subscription Rates:** Free.

               Circ: Non-paid ♦**23,250**

783 Jefferson County Weekender
ADD, Inc.
121 N. Main St.
PO Box 376   Phone: (414)674-2672
Jefferson, WI 53549   Fax: (414)674-6322

Shopping guide. **Founded:** 1990. **Freq:** Weekly (Fri.). **Key Personnel:** Joyce Lydon, General Mgr. **Subscription Rates:** Free.

               Circ: Non-paid ♦**23,250**

MADISON

784 Art's Garbage Gazette
Art Paul Schlosser
523 W. Wilson St., Apt. 203
Madison, WI 53703-3631

Alternative newspaper for a Christian audience. **Key Personnel:** Art Paul Schlosser, Editor. **Subscription Rates:** $2.50 single issue. **Remarks:** Accepts advertising. **URL:** http://members.theglobe.com/mynameisart/default.html.

               Circ: (Not Reported)

MILWAUKEE

785 Aldrichimica Acta
Aldrich Chemical Co.
1001 W. St. Paul Ave.   Phone: (414)273-3850
Milwaukee, WI 53233   Fax: (414)273-4979
                     Free: (800)558-9160

Trade magazine covering chemicals. **Founded:** 1967. **Freq:** Quarterly. **Remarks:** Advertising not accepted.

               Circ: (Not Reported)

786 Philosophy & Theology
Marquette University Press
PO Box 1881   Phone: (414)288-1564
Milwaukee, WI 53201-1881   Fax: (414)288-3300
                     Free: (800)247-6553

Scholarly journal covering philosophy and theology. **Founded:** 1986. **Freq:** Quarterly. **Key Personnel:** Phillip Rossi, Editor; Mary K. Berger, Managing Editor. **Subscription Rates:** $25 individuals; $30 out of country. **Alt. Formats:** Diskette.

787 The Sunday Post
Conley Publishing Group
3397 S. Howell Ave.   Phone: (414)744-6370
Milwaukee, WI 53207   Fax: (414)744-6884

Shopping guide. **Founded:** 1992. **Freq:** Weekly. **Key Personnel:** Skipp Thomson, Publisher. **Subscription Rates:** Free.

               Circ: Non-paid ♦**167,461**

788 KCVS-FM - 90.7
3434 W. Kilbourn Ave.
Milwaukee, WI 53208   Phone: (414)935-3000
E-mail: wvcf@vcyamerica.org

Format: Religious. **Networks:** USA Radio; Voice of Christian Youth America; Ambassador Inspirational Radio. **Owner:** VCY/America, Inc., at above address. **Operating Hours:** Continuous. **Key Personnel:** Vic Eliason, Vice President/General Mgr., vic@vcyamerica.org; Jim Schneider, Program Dir., jims@vcyamerica.org; Andy Eliason, Chief Engineer. **Wattage:** 1,000. **URL:** http://www.vcyamerica.org.

789 WVCF-FM - 90.5
3434 W. Kilbourn Ave.
Milwaukee, WI 53208   Phone: (414)935-3000
E-mail: wvcf@vcyamerica.org

Format: Religious. **Networks:** Voice of Christian Youth America; USA Radio; Ambassador Inspirational Radio. **Owner:** VCY/America, Inc., at above address. **Operating Hours:** Continuous. **ADI:** La Crosse-Eau Claire, WI. **Key Personnel:** Vic Eliason, Vice President/General Mgr., vic@vcyamerica.org; Jim Schneider, Program Dir., jims@vcyamerica.org; Andy Eliason, Chief Engineer. **Wattage:** 980. **URL:** http://www.vcyamerica.org.

790 WVCY-AM - 690
3434 W. Kilbourne Ave.
Milwaukee, WI 53208   Phone: (414)935-3000
E-mail: wvcy@vcyamerica.org

Format: Religious. **Networks:** USA Radio; Voice of Christian Youth America; Ambassador Inspirational Radio. **Owner:** VCY/America, Inc., at above address. **Operating Hours:** Continuous. **Key Personnel:** Vic Eliason, Vice President/General Mgr., vic@vcyamerica.org; Jim Schneider, Program Dir., jims@vcyamerica.org; Andy Eliason, Chief Engineer. **Wattage:** 250. **URL:** http://www.vcyamerica.org.

MONROE

791 Monroe Area Shopping News
Woodward Communications
1909 11th Ave.   Phone: (608)325-2030
PO Box 311   Fax: (608)325-1470
Monroe, WI 53566-0311   Free: (800)272-7653

Shopping guide. **Freq:** Weekly (Wed.). **Subscription Rates:** Free. **Remarks:** Accepts advertising.

               Circ: Non-paid 18,849

OCONOMOWOC

792 Lake Area Sunday
Conley Publishing Company
212 E. Wisconsin Ave.   Phone: (414)567-5511
Oconomowoc, WI 53066   Fax: (414)567-4422

Shopping guide. **Founded:** 1953. **Freq:** Weekly (Sun.). **Key Personnel:** Wayne Toske, Publisher. **Subscription Rates:** Free.

               Circ: Combined ♦**32,313**

PORTAGE

793 Cent Saver Buyer's Guide
Independent Media Group, Inc.
PO Box 470   Phone: (608)742-2111
Portage, WI 53901   Fax: (608)742-8346

Shopping guide. **Freq:** Weekly (Sat.). **Subscription Rates:** Free.

               Circ: Non-paid 12,460

794 Cent Saver Extra
Independent Media Group, Inc.
PO Box 470   Phone: (608)742-2111
Portage, WI 53901   Fax: (608)742-8346

Shopping guide. **Freq:** Weekly (Sat.). **Subscription Rates:** Free.

               Circ: Non-paid 16,500

795 Cent Saver Reminder
Independent Media Group, Inc.
PO Box 470   Phone: (608)742-2111
Portage, WI 53901   Fax: (608)742-8346

Shopping guide. **Freq:** Weekly (Sat.). **Subscription Rates:** Free.

               Circ: Non-paid 22,065

796 Elroy Wonewoc Keystone Tribune
Independent Media Group, Inc.
PO Box 470
Portage, WI 53901

Phone: (608)742-2111
Fax: (608)742-8346

Community newspaper. **Freq:** Semiweekly (Wed. and Sat.). **Subscription Rates:** $35 by mail.

Circ: Combined **1,045**

797 Mauston Star Times
Independent Media Group, Inc.
PO Box 470
Portage, WI 53901

Phone: (608)742-2111
Fax: (608)742-8346

Community newspaper. **Freq:** Semiweekly (Wed. and Sat.). **Subscription Rates:** $37 by mail.

Circ: Combined **3000**

798 Portage Daily Register
Independent Media Group, Inc.
PO Box 470
Portage, WI 53901

Phone: (608)742-2111
Fax: (608)742-8346

Daily newspaper. **Freq:** Daily and Sunday. **Subscription Rates:** $100 individuals; $104.60 by mail.

Circ: Combined **4,490**

799 West Salem Coulee News
Independent Media Group, Inc.
PO Box 470
Portage, WI 53901

Phone: (608)742-2111
Fax: (608)742-8346

Community newspaper. **Freq:** Weekly (Thurs.). **Subscription Rates:** $28 by mail.

Circ: Combined **1,998**

SHAWANO

800 The Shawano Shopper
109 1/2 S. Main St.
Shawano, WI 54166-0476

Phone: (715)526-6188
Fax: (715)526-6420

Shopping guide. **Founded:** 1961. **Freq:** Weekly (Tues.). **Key Personnel:** David Early, Publisher. **Subscription Rates:** Free.

Circ: Non-paid ◆**23,112**

SPOONER

801 Spooner Advocate
509 Front St.
PO Box 338
Spooner, WI 54801
Publication E-mail: advocate@spacestar.net

General newspaper. **Founded:** 1901. **Subscription Rates:** $29 individuals. **URL:** http://www.spooneradvocate.com.

WHITEWATER

802 Good Morning Advertiser
Good Morning Advertiser, Inc.
136 W. Main St.
Whitewater, WI 53190

Phone: (414)473-2711
Fax: (414)473-4575

Shopping guide. **Founded:** 1932. **Freq:** Weekly (Tues.). **Key Personnel:** Julie Mudgett, General Mgr. **Subscription Rates:** Free.

Circ: Combined ◆**18,893**

ALBERTA

CALGARY

803 Business in Calgary
OT Communications, Inc.
237 8th Ave. SE, Ste. 600
Calgary, AB, Canada T2G 5C3   Phone: (403)264-3270
    Fax: (403)234-3276
Publication E-mail: bic@lions.com

Consumer magazine covering business in Calgary. **Founded:** 1990. **Freq:** Monthly. **Subscription Rates:** $30 individuals Canada; $45 elsewhere; $3.50 single issue. **URL:** http://www.businessincalgary.com.
    Circ: Combined ●**32,382**

804 Journal of West African Languages
T. Scruggs
4316 10 St. N. E.
Calgary, AB, Canada T2E 6K3   Phone: (403)250-5411
    Fax: (403)250-2623
Publisher E-mail: tscruggs@cadvision.com

Professional journal covering linguistics and language analysis. **Freq:** Semiannual. **Key Personnel:** Keir Hansford, Editor; Terri Scruggs, Business Mgr., tscruggs@cadvision.com. **Remarks:** Advertising not accepted.
    Circ: (Not Reported)

805 On/Site Review
ThinkDesign Ltd.
2225 15th St. S.E.
Calgary, AB, Canada T2G 3M3
Publication E-mail: info@onsitereview.com

Professional journal covering architecture and design in Canada. **Freq:** Semiannual (March and October). **Key Personnel:** Stephanie White, Editor. **Subscription Rates:** $17.50 Canada; $19.50 elsewhere. **URL:** http://www.onsitereview.com/.

EDMONTON

806 DirectGuide
DirectGuide Publishing Inc.
1109 Toronto Dominion Tower, Edmonton
Centre
10205 - 101 St.   Phone: (403)424-6222
Edmonton, AB, Canada T5J 2Z1   Fax: (403)425-8392
Publication E-mail: feedback@satguide.com

Consumer magazine for satellite dish owners and satellite equipment retailers. **Founded:** 1995. **Freq:** Monthly. **Key Personnel:** S. Vogel, Publisher; J. Goode, Circulation Mgr. **Subscription Rates:** $52 individuals; $96 two years; $5.95 single issue. **URL:** http://www.satguide.com.
    Circ: Paid ●**21,084**

807 Satellite Entertainment Guide
Vogel Satellite T.V. Publishing Inc.
1109 Toronto Dominion Tower, Edmonton
Centre
10205 - 101 St.   Phone: (403)424-6222
Edmonton, AB, Canada T5J 2Z1   Fax: (403)425-8392
Publication E-mail: feedback@satguide.com

Consumer magazine for satellite dish owners and retailers of satellite equipment. **Founded:** 1983. **Freq:** Monthly. **Key Personnel:** S. Vogel, Publisher; J. Goode, Circulation Mgr. **Subscription Rates:** $57 individuals; $105 two years. **URL:** http://www.satguide.com.
    Circ: Combined ●**65,863**

FORT SASKATCHEWAN

808 The Fort Saskatchewan Record
Bowes Publishers Ltd.
10420 98th Ave., No. 155
Fort Saskatchewan, AB, Canada T8L 2N6   Phone: (403)998-7070
    Fax: (403)998-5515

Community newspaper. **Key Personnel:** Jack Kindred, Editor and Publisher; Debby Lorimar, Advertising Mgr.; Frank Salvatore, Sales Rep.; Dixie Gibbon, Circ. **Subscription Rates:** $17.66 individuals; $32.05 two years; $31.57 out of area; $55.64 out of country. **URL:** http://www.bowesnet.com/fortsask. **Feature Editors:** Corey Osmak, *Sports*.

GRANDE PRAIRIE

809 Daily Herald-Tribune
Bowes Publishers Ltd.
10604 100th St., Bag 3000
Grande Prairie, AB, Canada T8V 6V4   Phone: (403)532-1110
    Fax: (403)532-2120
Publication E-mail: dht@bowesnet.com
Publisher E-mail: bowes@agt.net

General newspaper. **Freq:** Daily. **Key Personnel:** Peter Woolsey, Publisher, pwoolsey@bowesnet.com; Fred Rinne, Managing Editor, frinne@bowesnet.com; Doug Hare, Advertising Mgr.; Val Hunt, Circulation Mgr., val@bowes.com. **Subscription Rates:** $89.99 individuals; $131.25 out of area; $295 out of country. **Remarks:** Advertising accepted; rates available upon request. **URL:** http://www.bowesnet.com/dht. **Feature Editors:** Kathryn Engel, *Rural Development*; Scott Fisher, *Sports*; Jeff McCoshen, *City*.
    Circ: (Not Reported)

LLOYDMINSTER

810 Meridian Booster
Meridian Printing Ltd.
5714 44th St.
Lloydminster, AB, Canada T9V 0B6   Phone: (403)875-3362
    Fax: (403)875-3423
Publisher E-mail: booster@telusplanet.net

Community newspaper. **Freq:** Semiweekly (Wed. and Sun.). **Key Personnel:** Tom Tenszen, Publisher; Stuart Elson, Managing Editor; Ron Walsh, Mrkt. Mgr. **Subscription Rates:** $125 Canada; $260 U.S. **URL:** http://www.bowesnet.com/lloydminster.

PEACE RIVER

811 Record-Gazette
Bowes Publishers Ltd.
10009 100 Ave.
PO Box 6870
Peace River, AB, Canada T8S 1S6   Phone: (403)624-2591
    Fax: (403)624-8600
Publication E-mail: rgazette@telusplanet.net

Community newspaper. **Founded:** 1914. **Freq:** Weekly (Tues.). **Key Person-

nel: Erkki Pohjolainen, Editor; Al Guthro, Pub./Adv. Mgr. **Subscription Rates:** $25 individuals; $55 U.S. **URL:** http://www.bowesnet.com/peace.
Circ: Paid 3,900

BRITISH COLUMBIA

ALDERGROVE

812 The Afro News
PO Box 1101
Aldergrove, BC, Canada V4W 2V1
Phone: (604)525-3666
Fax: (604)525-0089
Publication E-mail: roger@walkandroll.com

Black community newspaper. **Subtitle:** The Voice of the Black Community. **Subscription Rates:** $20 individuals. **Remarks:** Accepts advertising. **URL:** http://www.walkandroll.com/afronews.
Ad Rates:　BW: $800
PCI: $12
Circ: (Not Reported)

FORT ST. JOHN

813 Alaska Highway News
Alaska Highway Publications Ltd.
9916 98th St.
Fort St. John, BC, Canada V1J 3T8
Phone: (250)785-5631
Fax: (250)785-3522
Publication E-mail: ahnews@awink.com

Community newspaper. **Key Personnel:** Bruce Lantz, Publisher; Marc Piche, Managing Editor; Sarah Brown, Circ. **Remarks:** Advertising accepted; rates available upon request. **URL:** http://www.sterlingnews.com/alaska.
Circ: (Not Reported)

GOLD RIVER

814 The Record
Box 279
Gold River, BC, Canada V0P 1G0

Community newspaper. **Freq:** Semimonthly (Wed.). **Trim Size:** 10 3/10 x 16. **Subscription Rates:** $30 individuals; $32.10 Canada. **Remarks:** Advertising accepted; rates available upon request. **URL:** http://www.goldrvr.island.net/~record.
Circ: Combined 1,600

NORTH VANCOUVER

815 The Voice Community Magazine
North and West Voice Publishing Ltd.
200-116 E. 3rd St.
North Vancouver, BC, Canada V7L 1E6
Phone: (604)987-5300
Fax: (604)987-5322
Publication E-mail: sales@voicemag.com

Consumer magazine covering local community issues. **Founded:** 1996. **Freq:** Semimonthly. **Key Personnel:** C. Anderson, Publisher; M. Najafi, Circulation Mgr. **Subscription Rates:** Free. **URL:** http://www.voicemag.com. **Former name**: The North & West Voice.
Circ: Non-paid ●72,000

OKANAGAN FALLS

816 Lifestyles Review
South Okanagan Review Ltd.
PO Box 220
Okanagan Falls, BC, Canada V0H 1R0
Phone: (250)497-8880
Fax: (604)497-8860
Publisher E-mail: revpaper@uip.net

Consumer recreation and entertainment guide. **Founded:** 1980. **Freq:** Monthly. **Cols./Page:** 6. **Col. Width:** 1 9/16 inches. **Col. Depth:** 14 inches. **Key Personnel:** Ron Loftus, Publisher; Lyonel Doharty, Editor. **Remarks:** Accepts advertising.
Ad Rates:　BW: $375
4C: $529
PCI: $.43
Circ: (Not Reported)

PENTICTON

817 Penticton Western News-Advertiser
2250 Camrose St.
Penticton, BC, Canada V2A 8R1
Phone: (250)492-0444
Fax: (250)492-9843
Publisher E-mail: western@img.net

Community newspaper. **Freq:** Semiweekly. **Key Personnel:** Juanita Gibney, Pub./General Mgr. **Subscription Rates:** $112 individuals; $152 U.S. **Remarks:** Advertising accepted; rates available upon request. **URL:** http://www.bowesnet.com/penticton.
Circ: (Not Reported)

PRINCE GEORGE

818 The Prince George Free Press
Cariboo Press (1969) Ltd.
200-1515 Second Ave.
Prince George, BC, Canada V2L 3B8
Phone: (250)564-0005
Fax: (250)562-0025
Publication E-mail: editor@freepress.com

Community newspaper. **Founded:** 1994. **Freq:** Semiweekly (Thurs. and Sun.). **Key Personnel:** L. Doerkson, Publisher; K. Hastey, Circulation Mgr. **Subscription Rates:** Free. **URL:** http://pgfreepress.com.
Circ: Combined ●30,549

SURREY

819 The Now Community
Lower Mainland Publishing Ltd.
7889 - 132 St., No. 201
Surrey, BC, Canada V3W 4N2
Phone: (604)572-0064
Fax: (604)572-6438
Publication E-mail: surrey@van.net

Community newspaper. **Founded:** 1984. **Freq:** Semiweekly (Wed. and Sun.). **Key Personnel:** F. Tesky, Publisher; A. Schultz, Circulation Mgr. **Subscription Rates:** Free.
Circ: Combined ●106,145

820 Punjab Guardian
Charhdi Kala Weekly Punjabi Newspaper
7743 128th St., Unit 6
Surrey, BC, Canada V3W 4E6
Phone: (604)590-6397
Fax: (604)591-6397

Community newspaper. **Freq:** Semiweekly. **Cols./Page:** 4. **Col. Width:** 2 1/16 inches. **Col. Depth:** 15 inches. **Subscription Rates:** $90 individuals. **Remarks:** Accepts advertising.
Circ: (Not Reported)

Ad Rates: GLR = general line rate; BW = one-time black & white page rate; 4C = one-time four color page rate; SAU = standard advertising unit rate; CNU = Canadian newspaper advertising unit rate; PCI = per column inch rate.
Circulation: ★ = ABC; △ = BPA; ◆ = CAC; ● = CCAB; ❑ = VAC; ⊕ = PO Statement; ‡ = Publisher's Report; Boldface figures = sworn; Light figures = estimated.
Entry type: ❑ = Print; ❚ = Broadcast.

129

VANCOUVER

821 Raddle Moon
Raddle Moon Press
518-350 E. Second Ave.
Vancouver, BC, Canada V5T 4R8

Journal covering poetry. **Founded:** 1984. **Freq:** Semiannual. **Trim Size:** 6 1/4 x 8. **Key Personnel:** Susan Clark, Editor. **Subscription Rates:** $15 individuals; $20 institutions. **Remarks:** Advertising not accepted.
                                                              Circ: Paid 700

822 CHKG-FM - 96.1
525 W. Broadway, No. A1
Vancouver, BC, Canada V5Z 4K5   Phone: (604)708-1236

Format: Contemporary Hit Radio (CHR); World Beat. **Owner:** Fairchild Radio Vancouver FM, at above address. **Operating Hours:** Continuous. **Key Personnel:** Patrick Wong, Sr. VP/Chief Operating Officer; Linda Lu, Vice President, Bus. Dev.; Mary Lo, PRGD; Cal Koay, Intl. Program Dir.

VICTORIA

823 Fermata
University of Victoria
Box 1700, MS 7902   Phone: (250)721-7902
Victoria, BC, Canada V8W 2Y2   Fax: (250)721-6597

Scholarly journal covering music. **Founded:** 1995. **Freq:** Annual. **Key Personnel:** Lynda Smyth, Editor. **ISSN:** 1201-6624. **Subscription Rates:** $12 Canada. **Remarks:** Advertising not accepted.
                                                              Circ: Combined 100

WHITE ROCK

824 Occupational Therapy NOW
Canadian Association of Occupational Therapists
c/o Westprint Communications
1454 129A St.   Phone: (604)536-4575
White Rock, BC, Canada V4A 3Y7   Fax: (604)536-4570
Publication E-mail: lsheehan@caot.ca
Publisher E-mail: caot@caot.ca

Professional magazine covering issues in occupational therapy in English and French. **Founded:** Jan. 1999. **Freq:** Bimonthly. **Print Method:** Web offset. **Trim Size:** 8 1/2 x 11. **Cols./Page:** 2. **Key Personnel:** Mary Clark Green, Editor; Han Posthuma, Publication Coord., phone (613)523-2268. **ISSN:** 1481-5532. **Subscription Rates:** $30 Canada; $46 individuals U.S.; $55 elsewhere. **Remarks:** Accepts advertising. **URL:** http://www.caot.ca. **Former name**: CAOT National Newsletter.
Ad Rates: BW: $790   **Circ:** Combined 6,500
                  4C: $1,845

MANITOBA

ALTONA

🎙 **825 CILT-FM - 96.7**

PO Box 950
Altona, MB, Canada R0G 0B0

Phone: (204)346-5483
Fax: (204)326-2299

Format: Easy Listening. **Owner:** Golden West Broadcasting Ltd., at above address. **Founded:** 1998. **Operating Hours:** Continuous. **Key Personnel:** E. Hildebrand, President; D. Wiebe, General Mgr.; L. Friesen, Station Mgr. **Wattage:** 50,000.

Ad Rates: GLR = general line rate; BW = one-time black & white page rate; 4C = one-time four color page rate; SAU = standard advertising unit rate; CNU = Canadian newspaper advertising unit rate; PCI = per column inch rate.
Circulation: ★ = ABC; △ = BPA; ♦ = CAC; ● = CCAB; ❑ = VAC; ⊕ = PO Statement; ‡ = Publisher's Report; Boldface figures = sworn; Light figures = estimated.
Entry type: 📖 = Print; 🎙 = Broadcast.

131

NEW BRUNSWICK

FREDERICTON

📖 **826 Atlantic Snowmobile**
Atlantic Snowmobiler Publishing Inc.
527 Beaverbrook Ct., Ste. 510   Phone: (506)444-6489
Fredericton, NB, Canada E3B 1X6   Fax: (506)444-6453

Consumer magazine covering snowmobiles. **Subtitle:** The Magazine for Maritime Snowmobilers. **Founded:** 1993. **Freq:** Quarterly. **Key Personnel:** T. Kehoe, Publisher; R. Kehoe, Circulation Mgr. **Subscription Rates:** $9 individuals; $18 two years; $2.50 single issue.
Circ: Combined •**17,830**

🎙 **827 CBAT-TV -**
1160 Regent
Fredericton, NB, Canada E3B 3Z1   Phone: (506)451-4129
E-mail: nbnow@fredericton.cbc.ca

Format: Commercial TV. **Owner:** at above address. **Operating Hours:** Continuous. **Key Personnel:** Peter Anawati, Network Producer; Elaine Bateman, Producer. **URL:** http://www.discribe.ca/cbc/about.

ST. JOHN

📖 **828 Saint John Times Globe**
New Brunswick Publishing Co.
210 Crown St.
PO Box 2350   Phone: (506)632-8888
St. John, NB, Canada E2L 3V8   Fax: (506)648-2562

General newspaper. **Freq:** Daily. **Key Personnel:** Victor Mlodecki, Publisher, phone (506)632-4448, vmlodecki@dailygleaner.com; Carolyn Ryan, Editor, phone (506)634-2360, ryan.carolyn@nbnet.nb.ca; Tom Badger, Advertising Mgr., phone (506)648-3157, badger.tom@nbpub.com. **URL:** http://www.timesglobe.com. **Feature Editors:** Rob Linke, *Editorials*; Erin Swyer, *City*.

NEWFOUNDLAND

ST. JOHN

📖 **829 The Telegram**
Columbus Dr.
PO Box 5970
St. John, NF, Canada A1C 5X7
Publication E-mail: telegram@thetelegram.com

General newspaper. **Freq:** Daily. **Key Personnel:** Miller Ayre, Publisher, phone (709)748-0800, mayre@thetelegram.com; Jeanette Payne, Mkt. Mgr., phone (709)748-0803, jpayne@thetelegram.com; Bretton Loney, Managing Editor, phone (709)748-0825, bloney@thetelegram.com; Dan Johnson, Sales Mgr., phone (709)748-0846, fax (709)364-9333, djohnson@thetelegram.com. **Subscription Rates:** $195 individuals; $205 by mail. **Remarks:** Advertising accepted; rates available upon request. **URL:** http://www.thetelegram.com.
Circ: (Not Reported)

NORTHWEST TERRITORIES

YELLOWKNIFE

830 Deh Cho Drum
Northern News Services Ltd.
Box 2820
Yellowknife, NT, Canada X1A 2R1
Publisher E-mail: northnews@nnsl.com

Phone: (867)873-4031
Fax: (867)873-8507

Community newspaper. **Freq:** Weekly (Thurs.). **Key Personnel:** J. W. Sigvaldason, General Mgr.; Mike Scott, General Mgr. **Subscription Rates:** $50 individuals; $80 out of country. **URL:** http://www.nnsl.com/ops/pub/dechopromo.html.

Circ: Combined 1,600

831 Inuvik Drum
Northern News Services Ltd.
Box 2820
Yellowknife, NT, Canada X1A 2R1
Publisher E-mail: northnews@nnsl.com

Phone: (867)873-4031
Fax: (867)873-8507

Community newspaper. **Founded:** 1965. **Freq:** Weekly (Thurs.). **Subscription Rates:** $50 individuals; $80 out of country. **URL:** http://www.nnsl.com/frames/nnservices/inuvikpromo.html.

Circ: Combined 1,900

NOVA SCOTIA

HALIFAX

📖 **832 APLA Bulletin**
Atlantic Provinces Library Association (APLA)
Dalhousie University
School of Library and Information Studies   Phone: (902)424-5264
Halifax, NS, Canada B3H 4H8   Fax: (902)542-2128

Periodical for librarians. **Freq:** Bimonthly. **Key Personnel:** John Neilson, Editor, phone (506)453-4752, fax (506)453-4595, neilson@unb.ca; Linda Hansen, phone (506)648-5701, fax (506)648-5788, lhansen@unbsj.ca; Brian McNally, Advertising/News Editor, phone (506)364-2237, fax (506)364-2617, bmcnally@mta.ca. **ISSN:** 0001-2203. **Remarks:** Accepts advertising.
Ad Rates: BW: $200   **Circ:** Paid 350

📖 **833 The Daily News Worldwide**
The Daily News
PO Box 8330, Sta. A
Halifax, NS, Canada B3K 5M1   Phone: (902)468-1222
Publication E-mail: letterstoeditor@hfxnews.southam.ca

General newspaper. **Freq:** Mon.-Sun. **Key Personnel:** Mark Richardson, Pres./Pub., publisher@hfxnews.southam.ca; Bill Turpin, Editor, bturpin@hfxnews.southam.ca. **URL:** http://www.hfxnews.southam.ca.

📖 **834 The Halifax Herald Ltd.**
1650 Argyle St.   Phone: (902)426-1187
Halifax, NS, Canada B3J 2T2   Fax: (902)426-1158
      Free: (800)563-1187

General newspaper. **Key Personnel:** Terry O'Neil, Managing Editor. **URL:** http://www.herald.ns.ca. **Feature Editors:** Mike Flemming, *Sports*; Greg Guy, *Entertainment*; Margaret MacKay, *Living*; Roger Taylor, *Financial/ Business*.

ONTARIO

AJAX

📖 **835 Home Digest**
Home Digest International Ltd.
28 Hearne Crescent
Ajax, ON, Canada L1T 3P5

Phone; (905)686-3093
Fax: (905)686-8680

Consumer magazine covering home and life improvement in Toronto. **Founded:** 1995. **Freq:** Quarterly. **Subscription Rates:** Free.
Circ: Non-paid ●**522,678**

AMHERSTBURG

📖 **836 The Amherstburg Echo**
Bowes Publishers Ltd.
238 Dalhousie St.
Amherstburg, ON, Canada N9V 1W4

Phone: (519)736-2147
Fax: (519)736-8384

Community newspaper. **Founded:** 1874. **Key Personnel:** Alan Glaser, Gen. Mgr./Editor; Alice Maitre, Office Mgr.; Katie Langlois, Sales Rep.; Jillian Hotson, Sales Rep.; Darrie Jibb, Prod. **Remarks:** Advertising accepted; rates available upon request. **URL:** http://www.bowesnet.com/amhertburgecho.
Circ: (Not Reported)

ARNPRIOR

📖 **837 Chronicle Weekender**
Chronicle-Guide Newspapers Ltd.
116 John St.
Arnprior, ON, Canada K7S 2N6

Phone: (613)623-6571
Fax: (613)623-7518

Publisher E-mail: chronicle@igs.net

Community newspaper. **Founded:** 1996. **Freq:** Weekly (Sat.). **Print Method:** Offset. **Key Personnel:** Marjory McBride, Advertising Mgr.; Fred Runge, General Mgr.; Jason Marshall, News Editor; Derek Wells, Publisher. **Subscription Rates:** Free. **Remarks:** Accepts advertising.
Ad Rates: GLR: $.54   **Circ:** Non-paid ●**13,300**
    BW: $904
    4C: $1,812
    PCI: $6.30

📖 **838 West Carleton Review**
Chronicle-Guide Newspapers Ltd.
116 John St.
Arnprior, ON, Canada K7S 2N6

Phone: (613)623-6571
Fax: (613)623-7518

Publisher E-mail: chronicle@igs.net

Community newspaper. **Founded:** 1998. **Freq:** Weekly (Sat.). **Print Method:** Offset. **Key Personnel:** Marjory McBride, Advertising Mgr.; Fred Runge, General Mgr.; Jason Marshall, News Editor; Derek Wells, Publisher. **Subscription Rates:** Free. **Remarks:** Accepts advertising.
Ad Rates: GLR: $.54   **Circ:** Non-paid ●**6,100**
    BW: $904
    4C: $1,812
    PCI: $6.30

BARRIE

📖 **839 Ajax-Pickering News Advertiser**
Metroland Printing, Publishing & Distributing Ltd.
21 Patterson Rd., Unit 26 & 29
Barrie, ON, Canada L4N 7W6

Community newspaper. **Founded:** 1965. **URL:** http://www.durhamnews.net/newsad.html.
Circ: Combined 42,000

📖 **840 The Collingwood Connection**
Metroland Printing, Publishing & Distributing Ltd.
21 Patterson Rd., Unit 26 & 29
Barrie, ON, Canada L4N 7W6

Community newspaper. **Freq:** Semiweekly. **Key Personnel:** Joe Anderson, Publisher; Lesley Leighton, General Mgr.; John Devine, Editor-in-Chief; Julie Chadwick, Sr. Adv. Rep. **URL:** http://www.simcoe.com/info/collingwood.html. **Feature Editors:** Lee Ballantyne, *News*.

📖 **841 The Midland Mirror**
Metroland Printing, Publishing & Distributing Ltd.
21 Patterson Rd., Unit 26 & 29
Barrie, ON, Canada L4N 7W6
Publication E-mail: meditor@interhop.net

Community newspaper. **Freq:** Semiweekly. **Key Personnel:** Joe Anderson, Publisher; Chris Webster, General Mgr.; John Devine, Editor-in-Chief; Lee Ballantyne, Editor. **Remarks:** Accepts advertising. **URL:** http://www.simcoe.com/info/mirror.html.
Circ: Combined 18,200

📖 **842 Orillia Today**
Metroland Printing, Publishing & Distributing Ltd.
21 Patterson Rd., Unit 26 & 29
Barrie, ON, Canada L4N 7W6
Publication E-mail: oeditor@interhop.net

Community newspaper. **Founded:** 1991. **Freq:** Semiweekly (Wed. and Sat.). **Key Personnel:** Joe Anderson, Publisher; Rob LaTorre, General Mgr.; John Devine, Editor-in-Chief; Joan MacDonald, Production Mgr. **Remarks:** Accepts advertising. **URL:** http://www.simcoe.com/info/orillia.html. **Feature Editors:** Lee Ballantyne, *News*.
Circ: Combined 18,500

CREEMORE

📖 **843 Creemore Echo**
Mad and Noisy Valley Corp.
PO Box 180
Creemore, ON, Canada L0M 1G0

Phone: (705)466-9906
Fax: (705)466-9908

Publication E-mail: creemoreecho@georgian.net

Community newspaper. **Founded:** Nov. 5, 1997. **Freq:** Weekly (Wed.). **Print Method:** Web offset. **Key Personnel:** Sylvia Wiggins, Publisher; Julie Fletcher, Editor. **Subscription Rates:** Free; $35 mailed. **Remarks:** Accepts advertising.
Ad Rates: GLR: $.43   **Circ:** Combined 51,000
    4C: $250

DON MILLS

844 National Post
Southam Inc.
1450 Don Mills Rd.
Don Mills, ON, Canada M3B 2X7

Phone: (416)445-6641
Fax: (416)442-2213
Free: (800)387-0273

General newspaper. **Freq:** Daily. **Key Personnel:** Ken Whyte, Editor-in-Chief; Martin Newland, Asst. Deputy Editor. **Subscription Rates:** $12 monthly. **URL:** http://www.nationalpost.com. **Feature Editors:** Mark Stevenson, *Features.*

845 The Northern Miner
Southam Inc.
1450 Don Mills Rd.
Don Mills, ON, Canada M3B 2X7

Phone: (416)445-6641
Fax: (416)442-2214
Free: (800)387-0273

Trade newspaper for the mining industry. **Freq:** Weekly. **Key Personnel:** Vivian Danielson, Editor, phone (416)510-6863, tmm@southam.ca; Brian Warriner, Sales Rep., phone (416)442-2172, bwarriner@southam.ca. **URL:** http://www.northernminer.com.

ETOBICOKE

846 Automotive Parts & Technology
Cardiff Communications Ltd.
130 Belfield Rd.
Etobicoke, ON, Canada M9W 1G1
Publication E-mail: apt@onramp.ca

Phone: (416)614-0955
Fax: (416)614-2781

Trade magazine for the automotive aftermarket and automotive service and repair industry in Canada. **Founded:** 1995. **Freq:** 10/year. **Key Personnel:** W. B. James, Publisher; L. Kantor, Circulation Mgr.
Circ: Combined ●30,109

GANANOQUE

847 PIC Press
1000 Islands Publishers, LTD
79 King St. E.
Gananoque, ON, Canada K7G 1E8
Publication E-mail: editor@picpress.com

Phone: (613)382-2156
Fax: (613)382-3010

Alternative community newspaper. **Freq:** Monthly. **Key Personnel:** Kate Archibald-Cross, Editor; Mikael Eklund, Managing Editor; Jill Smith, Advertising. **Subscription Rates:** Free. **Remarks:** Advertising accepted; rates available upon request. **URL:** http://www.picpress.com. **Feature Editors:** Nicholas Woolley, *News.*
Circ: Non-paid 9,000

HAMILTON

848 Russell
McMaster University Press
c/o Titles, McMaster University Bookstore
McMaster University
Hamilton, ON, Canada L8S 4L6

Scholarly journal covering philosophy and history. **Subtitle:** The Journal of the Bertrand Russell Archives. **Founded:** 1971. **Freq:** Semiannual. **Print Method:** Offset. **Key Personnel:** Dr. Kenneth Blackwell, Editor, blackwk@mcmaster.ca. **ISSN:** 0036-0163. **Subscription Rates:** $16 individuals; $28 institutions. **Remarks:** Accepts advertising.
Circ: Paid 450

KITCHENER

849 Kitchener-Waterloo Record
225 Fairway Rd. S.
Kitchener, ON, Canada N2G 4E5

Phone: (519)894-2231

Community newspaper. **Freq:** Daily. **Key Personnel:** Larry Hooper, Advertising Dir.; Paul Nicholson, Sr. Adv. Mgr.; Carl Vosatka, Sales Mgr.; Gabe Deutschlander, Operations Mgr. **Subscription Rates:** $155.50 individuals;

$164.40 out of area. **Remarks:** Advertising accepted; rates available upon request. **URL:** http://www.therecord.com.
Circ: (Not Reported)

LONDON

850 The Shoreline News
Bowes Publishers Ltd.
1147 Gainsborough Rd.
PO Box 7400
London, ON, Canada N5Y 4X3
Publisher E-mail: natnnews@telusplanet.net

Phone: (519)473-0010
Fax: (519)473-2256
Free: (800)567-3276

Community newspaper. **Key Personnel:** Carol McKnight, General Mgr.; Kathleen Jones, Office Mgr. **Subscription Rates:** $34.30 individuals. **Remarks:** Accepts advertising. **URL:** http://www.bowesnet.com/shoreline.
Circ: Combined 3,200

MISSISSAUGA

851 Manufacturing Automation
Kerrwil Publications Ltd.
395 Matheson Blvd. E.
Mississauga, ON, Canada L4Z 2H2
Publisher E-mail: info@kerrwil.com

Phone: (905)890-1846
Fax: (905)890-3829

Trade magazine for the manufacturing, processing, and industrial automation industry in Canada. **Founded:** 1986. **Freq:** Bimonthly. **Key Personnel:** K. Pirker, Publisher, kpirker@kerrwil.com; J. Bilkey, Circ. Dir. **URL:** http://automationmag.com.
Circ: Combined ●21,721

NEPEAN

852 Monitor
GRL Communications
PO Box 11261, Sta. H
Nepean, ON, Canada K2H 7T9

Phone: (613)596-1358
Fax: (613)820-1461

Consumer magazine covering computers. **Freq:** Monthly. **Remarks:** Accepts advertising. **URL:** http://www.monitor.ca/monitor.
Ad Rates: BW: $556
4C: $806
Circ: (Not Reported)

NEW LISKEARD

853 Temiskaming Speaker
Temiskaming Printing Co. Ltd.
18 Wellington St.
Box 580
New Liskeard, ON, Canada P0J 1P0

Phone: (705)647-6791
Fax: (705)647-9669

Community newspaper. **Founded:** 1906. **Freq:** Weekly (Wed.). **Subscription Rates:** $52 Canada; $68.74 out of area; $145.67 elsewhere. **Remarks:** Accepts advertising. **URL:** http://www.nt.net/~tpc/atts.htm.
Circ: Combined 7,400

OTTAWA

854 The Hill Times
69 Sparks St.
Ottawa, ON, Canada K1P 5A5
Publisher E-mail: hilltimes@achilles.net

Phone: (613)232-5952
Fax: (613)232-9055

Newspaper covering Canadian government. **Subtitle:** Canada's Parliamentary Newspaper. **Freq:** Weekly. **Subscription Rates:** $149 individuals. **Remarks:** Accepts advertising. **URL:** http://www.thehilltimes.ca.
Ad Rates: BW: $3,500
4C: $3,995
Circ: (Not Reported)

PARRY SOUND

855 Sounding Line
Lucid Communication Group
Box 736
Parry Sound, ON, Canada P2A 2Z1
Publication E-mail: bartlett@parrysound.net

Phone: (705)746-6422
Fax: (705)746-6859

Community newspaper. **Freq:** Biweekly. **Subscription Rates:** Free. **URL:** http://www.zeuter.com/parrysd/sndgline.

RENFREW

📖 **856 The Renfrew Mercury Weekender**
Runge Publishing Inc.
35 Opeongo Rd.
PO Box 400   Phone: (613)432-3655
Renfrew, ON, Canada K7V 4A8   Fax: (613)432-6689

Community newspaper. **Subtitle:** The Valley's Leisure Paper. **Founded:** 1996. **Freq:** Weekly (Sat.). **Key Personnel:** D. Walter, Publisher; R. Vincent, Circulation Mgr. **Subscription Rates:** Free.
     Circ: Non-paid ●**14,106**

ST. GEORGE

📖 **857 Brant Life**
RR 1   Phone: (519)448-4001
St. George, ON, Canada N0E 1N0   Fax: (519)448-4411
     Free: (800)215-9574
Publication E-mail: brant@life.ca

Community newspaper. **Key Personnel:** Wendy Priesnitz, Editor. **URL:** http://www.life.ca/brantlife.

SAULT SAINTE MARIE

📖 **858 Post-adoption Helper**
Robin R. Hilborn
185 Panoramic Dr.
Sault Sainte Marie, ON, Canada P6B 6E3   Phone: (705)945-1170
Publisher E-mail: helper@helping.com

Consumer magazine covering issues for adoptive parents. **Freq:** Quarterly. **Key Personnel:** Jennifer Smart, Editor, smartot@age.net. **Subscription Rates:** $28 individuals; $7 single issue.

STRATHROY

📖 **859 The Age Dispatch**
Bowes Publishers Ltd.
8 Front St. E.   Phone: (519)245-2370
Strathroy, ON, Canada N7G 1Y4   Fax: (519)245-1647

Community newspaper. **Freq:** Weekly. **Print Method:** Web offset. **Key Personnel:** Steve Down, Publisher; Dave Cameron, Editor; Aileen Cnockaert, Production Mgr. **Remarks:** Accepts advertising. **URL:** http://www.bowesnet.com/agedispatch.
Ad Rates: PCI: $7.77   **Circ:** Paid 5,400

TORONTO

📖 **860 AutoCAD User**
CAD Communications, Inc.
338-4195 Dundas St. W.   Phone: (416)236-5856
Toronto, ON, Canada M8X 1Y4   Fax: (416)236-5219

Trade magazine for AutoCAD users. **Founded:** 1993. **Freq:** Quarterly. **Print Method:** Web offset. **Trim Size:** 8 1/8 x 10 7/8. **Cols./Page:** 2. **Col. Width:** 3 1/2 inches. **Col. Depth:** 10 inches. **Key Personnel:** Arvid Stonkus, Publisher, cfm@sympatico.ca. **ISSN:** 1198-0869. **Subscription Rates:** $18 individuals. **Remarks:** Accepts advertising.
Ad Rates: BW: $3,000   **Circ:** Controlled ●15,000
     4C: $3,995

📖 **861 Broken Pencil**
PO Box 203, Sta. P
Toronto, ON, Canada M5S 2S7

Consumer magazine covering magazines and culture in Canada and world-wide. **Founded:** 1995. **Freq:** Quarterly. **Key Personnel:** Hal Niedzwiecki,

Editor, hal@brokenpencil.com; Emily Pohl-Meary, Managing Editor, zines@brokenpencil.com. **Subscription Rates:** $12 individuals; $5 single issue. **Remarks:** Accepts advertising.
Ad Rates: BW: $195   **Circ:** Combined 3,000

📖 **862 CARPNews**
Kemur Publishing Co. Ltd.
27 Queen St. E., Ste. 702   Phone: (416)363-5562
Toronto, ON, Canada M5C 2M6   Fax: (416)363-7394
Publication E-mail: dwatson@fifty-plus.net

Consumer magazine of the Canadian Association of Retired Persons. **Founded:** 1985. **Freq:** Bimonthly. **Subscription Rates:** $7.95 individuals; $3.95 single issue. **URL:** http://www.fifty-plus.net.
     Circ: Combined ●**210,244**

📖 **863 Chirp**
Multi-Vision Publishing, Inc.
655 Bay St., Ste. 1100   Phone: (416)595-9944
Toronto, ON, Canada M5G 2K4   Fax: (416)595-7217
Publication E-mail: owlfamily@m-v-p.com

Magazine for children two to six years of age. **Founded:** 1997. **Freq:** 9/year. **Subscription Rates:** $24 individuals; $2.95 single issue. **URL:** http://www.owl.on.ca.
     Circ: Combined ●**30,085**

📖 **864 Confronting Violence in Women's Lives**
Resources for Feminist Research/Documentation Sur La Recherche Feministe
Ontario Institute for Studies in Education
University of Toronto
252 Bloor St. W.   Phone: (416)923-6641
Toronto, ON, Canada M5S 1V6   Fax: (416)926-4725
Publication E-mail: rfrdrf@oise.utoronto.ca
Publisher E-mail: rfrdrf@oise.utoronto.ca

French and English language scholarly journal covering women's issues. **Subtitle:** Contrer La Violence Faite Aux Femmes. **Freq:** Quarterly. **Trim Size:** 6 x 9. **Key Personnel:** Lorraine Gauthier, Editor; Melanie Randall, Editor. **ISSN:** 0707-8412. **Subscription Rates:** $38 Canada; $58 elsewhere; $76 institutions Canada; $94 institutions elsewhere. **URL:** http://www.oise.utoronto.ca/rfr.

📖 **865 Counter Culture**
ARRT Corp.
260 Richmond St. W., No. 200   Phone: (416)596-9464
Toronto, ON, Canada M5V 1W5   Fax: (416)596-9052
Publisher E-mail: dabdat@aol.com

Trade magazine covering items of interest to bartenders and food service professionals. **Subtitle:** The Magazine for Bar and Restaurant Staff. **Founded:** 1998. **Freq:** Bimonthly. **Print Method:** Sheetfed offset. **Trim Size:** 8 3/4 x 10 7/8. **Cols./Page:** 4. **Col. Width:** 1 3/4 inches. **Col. Depth:** 9 3/8 inches. **Key Personnel:** Marni Andrews, Editor, phone (416)596-9464; Jody Bishop, Advertising Mgr.; Stan Davidson. **Subscription Rates:** $24.95 Canada; $29.95 individuals U.S. **Remarks:** Accepts advertising.
     Circ: (Not Reported)

📖 **866 Elm Street**
655 Bay St., Ste. 1100
Toronto, ON, Canada M5G 2K4

Consumer magazine for women in Canada. **Freq:** 8/year. **Trim Size:** 8 x 10 3/4. **Subscription Rates:** $5.95 individuals; $11.65 two years.

📖 **867 Exclaim!**
1059434 Ontario Inc.
7B Pleasant Blvd., Ste. 966   Phone: (416)535-9735
Toronto, ON, Canada M4T 1K2   Fax: (416)535-0566
Publication E-mail: exclaim@exclaim.ca

Consumer magazine covering music, entertainment and youth culture. **Founded:** 1992. **Freq:** Monthly. **Key Personnel:** I. Danzig, Publisher; T.

Ad Rates: GLR = general line rate; BW = one-time black & white page rate; 4C = one-time four color page rate; SAU = standard advertising unit rate; CNU = Canadian newspaper advertising unit rate; PCI = per column inch rate.
Circulation: ★ = ABC; △ = BPA; ◆ = CAC; ● = CCAB; ❏ = VAC; ⊕ = PO Statement; ‡ = Publisher's Report; Boldface figures = sworn; Light figures = estimated.
Entry type: 📖 = Print; ⚲ = Broadcast.

143

Goodwin, Circulation Mgr. **Subscription Rates:** Free; $25 by mail. **URL:** http://exclaim.ca.

Circ: Non-paid •92,680

☐ **868 Infosystems Executive**
Plesman Publications Ltd.
2005 Sheppard Ave. E., 4th Fl.　　Phone: (416)497-9562
Toronto, ON, Canada M2J 5B1　　Fax: (416)497-9427
　　　　　　　　　　　　　　　　Free: (800)387-5012

Publication E-mail: lgreen@plesman.com
Publisher E-mail: lgreen@plesman.com

Professional magazine for corporate users of information technology products, facilities, and services. **Founded:** 1996. **Freq:** Monthly. **Key Personnel:** G. Soltys, Publisher; V. Nisbet-Rumboldt, Circulation Mgr. **URL:** http://www.plesman.com/ise.

Circ: Combined •18,628

☐ **869 Ivey Business Journal**
405 The West Mall, 6th Fl.　　Phone: (416)620-0116
Toronto, ON, Canada M9C 5K7　　Fax: (416)620-1302
　　　　　　　　　　　　　　　　Free: (800)646-8531

Publisher E-mail: ibj@ivey.uwo.ca

Professional journal covering business. **Key Personnel:** Ed Pearce, Editor, epearce@ivey.uwo.ca. **URL:** http://www.ivey.uwo.ca/publications/.

☐ **870 Mission Canada**
Catholic Church Extension Society of Canada
201-1155 Yonge St.　　　　　　Phone: (416)934-3424
Toronto, ON, Canada M4T 1W2　　Fax: (416)934-3425
　　　　　　　　　　　　　　　　Free: (800)361-1128

Magazine of the Catholic Church Extension Society of Canada. **Key Personnel:** Father Roger W. Formosi, President.

☐ **871 Nickel**
Nickel Development Institute
214 King St. W., Ste. 510　　Phone: (416)591-7999
Toronto, ON, Canada M5H 3S6　　Fax: (416)591-7987

Professional journal covering nickel and its applications. **Founded:** 1985. **Freq:** Quarterly. **Key Personnel:** Patrick Whiteway, Editor. **ISSN:** 0829-8351. **Subscription Rates:** Free to qualified subscribers. **Remarks:** Advertising not accepted. **URL:** http://www.nidi.org.

Circ: Non-paid 37,000

☐ **872 Patron Magazine**
ARRT Corp.
260 Richmond St. W., No. 200　　Phone: (416)596-9464
Toronto, ON, Canada M5V 1W5　　Fax: (416)596-9052
Publisher E-mail: dabdat@aol.com

Trade magazine covering items of interest to owners and managers of bars and restaurants. **Subtitle:** Ideas for Business and Lifestyle. **Founded:** Aug. 1987. **Freq:** Bimonthly. **Print Method:** Sheetfed offset. **Trim Size:** 8 3/4 x 10 7/8. **Cols./Page:** 4. **Col. Width:** 1 3/4 inches. **Col. Depth:** 9 3/8 inches. **Key Personnel:** David Barbour, Publisher, phone (416)596-9222; Marni Andrews, Editor; Jody Bishop, Advertising Sales. **Subscription Rates:** $29.95 individuals; $24.95 Canada. **Remarks:** Accepts advertising.

Circ: Controlled 30,000

☐ **873 Pharmacy Post**
Maclean Hunter Healthcare Ltd.
777 Bay St., 5th Fl.　　　　　Phone: (416)596-5000
Toronto, ON, Canada M5W 1A7　　Fax: (416)596-3499
Publication E-mail: pharmacypost@mhpublishing.com

Professional magazine in English and French for retail and hospital pharmacists and others in the pharmaceutical industry. **Subtitle:** The Drugstore News & Merchandising Report. **Founded:** 1994. **Freq:** Monthly. **Key Personnel:** J. Smith, Assoc. Publisher; M. Andrews, Circulation Mgr.

Circ: Combined •19,029

☐ **874 Professionally Speaking/Pour Parler Profession**
Ontario College of Teachers
121 Bloor St. E., 6th Fl.　　Phone: (416)961-8800
Toronto, ON, Canada M4W 3M5　　Fax: (416)961-8822
Publication E-mail: ps@oct.on.ca

Professional journal in English and French for members of the Ontario College of Teachers. **Founded:** 1997. **Freq:** Quarterly. **Key Personnel:** R. Lewko, Publisher; C. Morrison, Circulation Mgr. **URL:** http://www.oct.on.ca.

Circ: Combined •161,093

☐ **875 Prudent Investors**
The Corporate Group
357 Bay St., Ste. 900　　　Phone: (416)362-9949
Toronto, ON, Canada M5H 2T7　　Fax: (416)369-0129

Consumer magazine covering business and finance. **Freq:** Quarterly. **Key Personnel:** Zorana Kydd, Managing Editor; Stacey Monteith, Senior Ed./Advertising Mgr., smonteith@thecorpgroup.com. **Subscription Rates:** $36 individuals; $64 two years.

☐ **876 Retail News**
The Canadian Gift & Tableware Association
265 Yorkland Blvd., Ste. 301　　Phone: (416)497-5771
Toronto, ON, Canada M2J 1S5　　Fax: (416)497-3448

Trade magazine for the gift, tableware, stationery, bed, bath, linen, and home accessory industry in Canada. **Founded:** 1996. **Freq:** Quarterly. **Key Personnel:** D. Daniels, Editor and Publisher, d.daniels@gift.org; G. Atkinson, Asst. Circ. Mgr. **URL:** http://www.cgta.org.

Circ: Combined •15,691

☐ **877 Share**
Arnold A. Auguste Associates Ltd.
658 Vaughan Rd.　　　　　Phone: (416)656-3400
Toronto, ON, Canada M6E 2Y5　　Fax: (416)656-3711

Ethnic community newspaper serving the Black and Caribbean community in Toronto. **Founded:** Apr. 1976. **Subscription Rates:** Free. **Remarks:** Accepts advertising. **URL:** http://www.sharenews.com.
Ad Rates:　GLR: $1.95　　　　　**Circ:** Combined 130,000
　　　　　　　BW: $2,457
　　　　　　　4C: $3,457
　　　　　　　PCI: $27.30

☐ **878 Theatre Research in Canada/Recherches Theatrales Au Canada**
University of Toronto
214 College St.　　　　　　Phone: (416)978-7984
Toronto, ON, Canada M5T 2Z9　　Fax: (416)971-1378
Publication E-mail: trican@chass.utoronto.ca

Scholarly journal covering theatre research in Canada. **Founded:** 1980. **Freq:** Semiannual. **Key Personnel:** Stephen Johnson, Editor; Deborah Cottreau, Editor. **ISSN:** 1196-1198. **Subscription Rates:** $25 individuals; $32 institutions; $22 students. **Remarks:** Advertising not accepted. **Former name:** Theatre History in Canada.

Circ: (Not Reported)

☐ **879 Today's Boating**
Ranmor Publishing Inc.
184 Front St. E., Ste. 401　　Phone: (416)869-9211
Toronto, ON, Canada M5A 4N3　　Fax: (416)869-9181
Publication E-mail: nicolen@passport.ca

Consumer magazine covering power boating. **Subtitle:** The Power Boat Television Show Magazine. **Founded:** 1996. **Freq:** 5/year. **Key Personnel:** R. Morris, Publisher; S. Gregory, Circulation Mgr. **Subscription Rates:** $3 members annual; $11.95 nonmembers.

Circ: Combined •28,791

☐ **880 United Irish Press**
United Irish Societies
70 Pleasant Blvd., Ste. 956
Toronto, ON, Canada M4T 1K2

Newspaper covering local news of interest to the Irish community. **Freq:** Quarterly. **Key Personnel:** Viv D'Arcy, Editor.

WINDSOR

📖 **881 The International Citizen**
76 University Ave. W., Ste. 200   Phone: (519)977-8499
Windsor, ON, Canada N9A 5N7   Fax: (519)977-1777

Community newspaper covering multi-cultural issues. **Freq:** Weekly. **Subscription Rates:** Free.

📖 **882 Room**
Room Communications and Design
PO Box 7183
Windsor, ON, Canada N9C 3Z1
Publication E-mail: room@wincom.net

Local news magazine. **Key Personnel:** Kate Milberry, Editor; Julian Revin, Assoc. Editor; Marc Papineau, Advertising. **URL:** http://www.roomag.com.

📖 **883 View**
University of Windsor
Windsor, ON, Canada N9B 3P4
Publication E-mail: mbeaud@uwindsor.ca

College alumni magazine. **Subtitle:** University of Windsor Alumni Magazine. **Freq:** Quarterly. **Key Personnel:** Dr. Ross Paul, Publisher; Jennifer Barone, Managing Editor; Barbara Barone, Advertising. **ISSN:** 0841-1069. **Subscription Rates:** $20 individuals. **Remarks:** Accepts advertising. **URL:** http://www.uwindsor.ca/alumni.

                                        Circ: (Not Reported)

PRINCE EDWARD ISLAND

CHARLOTTETOWN

884 The Buzz

PO Box 1945
Charlottetown, PE, Canada C1A 7N5

Phone: (902)628-1958
Fax: (902)628-1953

Arts and entertainment newspaper. **Freq:** Monthly. **Key Personnel:** Peter Richards, Managing Editor; Nancy Richards, Asst. Editor. **URL:** http://www.isn.net/buzzon.

885 Island Sport Scene

Sport Prince Edward Island, Inc.
PO Box 302
Charlottetown, PE, Canada C1A 7K7

Phone: (902)368-4110
Fax: (902)368-4548

Periodical covering local athletes, sports-program volunteers, and athletic events for sports associations and others. **Founded:** 1978. **Freq:** Quarterly. **Trim Size:** 8 1/2 x 11. **Key Personnel:** Cy Yard, Editor. **Subscription Rates:** Free to qualified subscribers. **Remarks:** Accepts advertising.

Circ: Non-paid 35,000

Ad Rates: GLR = general line rate; BW = one-time black & white page rate; 4C = one-time four color page rate; SAU = standard advertising unit rate; CNU = Canadian newspaper advertising unit rate; PCI = per column inch rate.
Circulation: ★ = ABC; △ = BPA; ♦ = CAC; ● = CCAB; ❑ = VAC; ⊕ = PO Statement; ‡ = Publisher's Report; Boldface figures = sworn; Light figures = estimated.
Entry type: ◻ = Print; ♦ = Broadcast.

QUEBEC

L'ANNONCIATION

886 Emploi Plus
DGR Publication
1256 Principale N. St., Ste. 203
L'Annonciation, PQ, Canada J0T 1T0   Phone: (819)275-3293

Periodical covering alternative nonfiction in English and French. **Subtitle:** Le Journal Nord-Americain. **Founded:** 1990. **Key Personnel:** D.G. Reid, Editor and Publisher. **ISSN:** 1180-4092.

CHICOUTIMI

887 Saguenayensia
Societe Historique du Saguenay
930 rue Jacques-Cartier Est
CP 456   Phone: (418)549-2805
Chicoutimi, PQ, Canada G7H 5C8   Fax: (418)549-3701

French historical and genealogical journal. **Founded:** 1959. **Freq:** Semiannual. **ISSN:** 0581-295X. **Subscription Rates:** $25 individuals; $35 institutions.

CHOMEDEY

888 The Chomedey News
400 Cure-Labelle, Ste. 340   Phone: (514)978-9999
Chomedey, PQ, Canada H7V 2S7   Fax: (514)687-6330

Community newspaper. **Founded:** 1993. **Freq:** Weekly (Sat.). **Col. Width:** 1.142 inches. **Key Personnel:** George Bakoyannis, General Mgr.; Peter Karahalios, Editor. **Remarks:** Advertising accepted; rates available upon request. **URL:** http://www.chomedeynews.ca.

Circ: (Not Reported)

GATINEAU

889 Info Plein Air Chasse et Peche
178 Greber Blvd., Ste. 9   Phone: (819)568-1234
Gatineau, PQ, Canada J8T 6Z6   Fax: (819)568-4464
Publication E-mail: ipacp@reseau.com

French language consumer magazine covering outdoor sports and recreation in Quebec, especially hunting and fishing. **Founded:** 1993. **Freq:** Monthly. **Key Personnel:** G. Gagnon, Publisher. **Subscription Rates:** Free.

Circ: Non-paid •112,500

MONTREAL

890 L'Actualite Medicale
MacLean Hunter Ltd.
1001 Maisonneuve Blvd. W., Ste. 1000   Phone: (514)843-2542
Montreal, PQ, Canada H3A 3E1   Fax: (514)845-2063

Professional medical magazine for physicians, specialists, interns, residents, students and others. **Founded:** 1980. **Freq:** Weekly. **Key Personnel:** J. Lafontaine, Publisher; G. Consolante, Circulation Mgr.

Circ: Combined •17,157

891 Bulletin de Droit de L'Environnement
Les Editions Yvon Blais Inc.
430, rue St-Pierre   Phone: (514)266-1086
Montreal, PQ, Canada H2Y 2M5   Fax: (514)263-9256
                                            Free: (800)363-3047
Publisher E-mail: commandes@editionsyvonblais.qc.ca

French language professional journal covering law. **ISSN:** 1188-682X. **Remarks:** Advertising not accepted.

Circ: (Not Reported)

892 Maison D'Aujourd'hui
Maison Direct Ltee
3390 Cremazie Est   Phone: (514)729-0000
Montreal, PQ, Canada H2A 1A4   Fax: (514)729-2552

French language consumer magazine covering lifestyle. **Founded:** 1996. **Freq:** Annual. **Key Personnel:** P. Masse, Editor. **Subscription Rates:** $3.95 single issue.

Circ: Combined •14,860

893 The Montreal Gazette
Southam, Inc.
250 St-Antoine St. W.   Phone: (514)987-2350
Montreal, PQ, Canada H2Y 3R7   Fax: (514)987-2323
                                            Free: (800)363-6765

General newspaper. **Freq:** Daily. **Remarks:** Accepts advertising. **URL:** http://www.montrealgazette.com.

Circ: (Not Reported)

894 Nouvelles CEQ
Centrale de l'enseignement du Quebec
9405 Sherbrooke St. E.   Phone: (514)356-8888
Montreal, PQ, Canada H1L 6P3   Fax: (514)356-9999

Consumer magazine for Centrale de l'enseignement du Quebec (CEQ) union members in the Quebec education, health, and social services industries. **Founded:** 1980. **Freq:** 5/year. **Key Personnel:** L. Allaire, Publisher; J. Fleurent, Circulation Mgr. **Subscription Rates:** Free to qualified subscribers.

Circ: Non-paid •95,498

895 Virage
Editador (9012-3993 Quebec inc.)
4545 Pierre-De Coubertin Ave.
C.P. 1000, Succursale M.   Phone: (514)252-3017
Montreal, PQ, Canada H1V 3R2   Fax: (514)252-3154

Consumer magazine for members of The Quebec Federation of Senior Citizens. **Founded:** 1992. **Freq:** 5/year. **Key Personnel:** N. Moir, Publisher; A. Larocque, Circulation Mgr. **Subscription Rates:** $2.50 members; $13.91 nonmembers; $2.95 single issue. **Former name:** Le Magazine Fadoq.

Circ: Combined •198,086

Ad Rates: GLR = general line rate; BW = one-time black & white page rate; 4C = one-time four color page rate; SAU = standard advertising unit rate; CNU = Canadian newspaper advertising unit rate; PCI = per column inch rate.
Circulation: ★ = ABC; △ = BPA; ♦ = CAC; • = CCAB; ❏ = VAC; ⊕ = PO Statement; ‡ = Publisher's Report; Boldface figures = sworn; Light figures = estimated.
Entry type: ❏ = Print; ✦ = Broadcast.

149

QUEBEC

📖 **896 Adorable**

Magazine Adorable Inc.
132, rue St-Pierre 6e etage   Phone: (418)692-5123
Quebec, PQ, Canada G1K 4A7   Fax: (418)692-0942
Publication E-mail: fleonard@globetrotter.qc.ca

Consumer magazine for teenagers. **Founded:** 1996. **Freq:** Monthly. **Subscription Rates:** $26 individuals; $52 two years; $2.95 single issue. **URL:** http://www.adorable.qc.ca.

Circ: Combined •**22,970**

SASKATCHEWAN

MOOSE JAW

📖 **897 The Reviewer**
Laurence H. Pion
710 High St. W.
Moose Jaw, SK, Canada S6H 1T8
Publication E-mail: picapre@sk.sympatico.ca

Community newspaper. **Freq:** Monthly. **Key Personnel:** Laurence H. Pion, Editor and Publisher. **URL:** http://www3.sk.sympatico.ca/picapre.

📖 **898 The Times-Herald**
The Moose Jaw Times-Herald
44 Fairford St. W. **Phone:** (306)692-6441
Moose Jaw, SK, Canada S6H 1V1 **Fax:** (306)692-2101

General newspaper. **Freq:** Daily. **Key Personnel:** Ab Calvert, Pub./Adv. Mgr.; Lesley Sheppard, Managing Editor. **URL:** http://www.mjtimes.sk.ca. **Feature Editors:** Duane Booth, *City*; Rick Moore, *Sports*; John Strauss, *News*.

REGINA

📖 **899 Leader-Post**
1964 Park St. **Phone:** (306)565-8211
Regina, SK, Canada S4P 3G4 **Fax:** (306)565-8350

General newspaper. **Founded:** 1883. **Freq:** Daily. **Key Personnel:** Bob Hughes, Editor, phone (306)565-8242; Marlon Marshall, Managing Editor, phone (306)565-8241; John Swan, Assoc. Editor, phone (306)565-8244. **URL:** http://www.leader-post.sk.ca. **Feature Editors:** Andy Cooper, *City*.

📖 **900 Regina Free Press**
Prairie Free Press Newspapers Ltd.
208-1911 Park St. **Phone:** (306)522-3733
Regina, SK, Canada S4N 2G5 **Fax:** (306)751-4500
Publication E-mail: regina.freepress@sk.sympatico.ca

Community newspaper. **Founded:** 1996. **Freq:** Weekly (Sat.). **Key Personnel:** P. Martin, Publisher. **Subscription Rates:** Free.
Circ: Non-paid ●57,766

SASKATOON

📖 **901 Saskatoon Free Press**
Prairie Free Press Newspapers Ltd.
2270 Northridge Dr. **Phone:** (306)978-3733
Saskatoon, SK, Canada S7L 1B9 **Fax:** (306)477-7373
Publication E-mail: saskatoon.freepress@sk.sympatico.ca

Community newspaper. **Founded:** 1996. **Freq:** Weekly (Fri.). **Key Personnel:** B. Peterson, Publisher; D. Gardner, Circulation Mgr. **Subscription Rates:** Free.
Circ: Combined ●58,177

📖 **902 Saskatoon History Review**
Saskatoon Heritage Society
PO Box 7051
Saskatoon, SK, Canada S7K 4J1 **Phone:** (306)373-8693
Publisher E-mail: aa080@sfn.saskatoon.sk.ca

Journal covering local history. **Key Personnel:** William A. Sarjeant, Editor, william.sarjeant@usask.ca. **ISSN:** 0843-6002. **URL:** http://www.sfn.saskatoon.sk.ca/arts/heritage.
Circ: Combined 350

Master Index

The Master Index is a comprehensive listing of all entries, both print and broadcast, included in this *Directory*. Citations in this index are interfiled alphabetically throughout regardless of media type. Publications are cited according to title and important keywords within titles; broadcast citations are by station call letters or cable company names. Indexed here also are: notices of recent cessations; former call letters or titles; foreign language and other alternate publication titles; other types of citations. Indexing is word-by-word rather than letter-by-letter, so that "New York" files before "News". Listings in the Master Index include geographic locations and entry numbers. An asterisk (*) after a number indicates that the title is mentioned within the text of the cited entry.

A

Abortion Review; The Post- (Springfield, IL) **267**
Academic Physician & Scientist (Philadelphia, PA) **665**
Acarology; International Journal of (West Bloomfield, MI) **410**
Access (Greenwood) (Franklin, IN) **276**
Accident Investigation Quarterly (Waldorf, MD) **343**
Accident Reconstruction Journal (Waldorf, MD) **344**
Acorn Press (Ridgefield, CT) **166**
L'Actualite Medicale (Montreal, PQ, Can.) **890**
Actuarial; North American (Schaumburg, IL) **265**
Adams Addenda II (Onalaska, TX) **735**
Adoption Helper; Post- (Sault Sainte Marie, ON, Can.) **858**
Adorable (Quebec, PQ, Can.) **896**
Africa, and the Middle East; Comparative Studies of South Asia, (Durham, NC) **609**
African-American News & Issues (Houston, TX) **726**
African Languages; Journal of West (Calgary, AB, Can.) **804**
Afro-American Historical and Genealogical Society Journal (Washington, DC) **178**
The Afro News (Aldergrove, BC, Can.) **812**
Aftermarket Today (Elk Grove Village, IL) **250**
The Age Dispatch (Strathroy, ON, Can.) **859**
Agency Sales Magazine (Laguna Hills, CA) **73**
Air Classics (Canoga Park, CA) **51**
Ajax-Pickering News Advertiser (Barrie, ON, Can.) **839**
Alaska Highway News (Fort St. John, BC, Can.) **813**
Aldrichimica Acta (Milwaukee, WI) **785**
Alexandria Gazette Packet (Alexandria, VA) **742**
Alleghenies; Journal of the (Frostburg, MD) **328**
American Chinese Herald (New York, NY) **538**
American Jones Building & Maintenance (Seattle, WA) **766**
The American Journal of Criminal Law (Austin, TX) **702**
American Painting Contractor (Richmond, VA) **757**
The American Psychoanalyst (Mahwah, NJ) **477**
America's Family Support Magazine (Chicago, IL) **236**
Americus Times-Recorder (Americus, GA) **209**
Amicus Times-Recorder (Americus, GA) **209**
Animal Welfare Science; Journal of Applied (Mahwah, NJ) **486**
Annual Review of Earth and Planetary Sciences (Palo Alto, CA) **101**
ANS Bulletin (New York, NY) **539**
Anvil's Ring (Washington, MO) **446**
APLA Bulletin (Halifax, NS, Can.) **832**
Appleseeds (Peterborough, NH) **465**
Applicator (Kansas City, MO) **438**
Applied Developmental Science (Mahwah, NJ) **478**
Applied Neuropsychology (Mahwah, NJ) **479**
Archaeology; Discovering (El Paso, TX) **721**
Archaeology's Dig (New York, NY) **540**
Arizona Pet Guide Magazine (Phoenix, AZ) **22**
Arts; Diablo (Walnut Creek, CA) **148**
Art's Garbage Gazette (Madison, WI) **784**
Arts; Women in the (Washington, DC) **190**
Arts'n Crafts Showguide (Jefferson City, MO) **437**
Artvoice (Buffalo, NY) **521**
Asahi Shimbun (New York, NY) **541**
Ashrae Journal (Atlanta, GA) **210**
Asia, Africa, and the Middle East; Comparative Studies of South (Durham, NC) **609**
Asian Americans Magazine; New (Chicago, IL) **241**
Asian Law; Columbia Journal of (New York, NY) **546**
Aspen Hill Gazette (Gaithersburg, MD) **329**
Atlantic Snowmobile (Fredericton, NB, Can.) **826**
AutoCAD User (Toronto, ON, Can.) **860**
Automation; Manufacturing (Mississauga, ON, Can.) **851**
Automotive Parts & Technology (Etobicoke, ON, Can.) **846**
AWHONN Lifelines (Philadelphia, PA) **666**
AZ Humanities Association Journal **20***

B

The Barnes Family Quarterly (Wauseon, OH) **639**
Bay Area Reporter (San Francisco, CA) **113**
Berkley Mirror; Huntington Woods/ (Royal Oak, MI) **404**
The Best from American Canals (York, PA) **685**
Bethel Beacon (New Milford, CT) **159**
Bethesda Almanac; Potomac/ (Potomac, MD) **340**
Birmingham Mirror (Royal Oak, MI) **402**
Bisbee Daily Review (Sierra Vista, AZ) **25**
The Blitz (Oakland, CA) **100**
The Bloomington Voice (Bloomington, IN) **270**
Boating; Today's (Toronto, ON, Can.) **879**
Booster Advertiser (Bullhead City, AZ) **15**
Borderlines (Silver City, NM) **511**
Boulder Weekly (Boulder, CO) **150**
Boundary 2 (Pittsburgh, PA) **680**
Bradley News Weekly (Cleveland, TN) **695**
Brand Marketing (New York, NY) **542**
Brant Life (St. George, ON, Can.) **857**
Bridge U.S.A. (Torrance, CA) **141**
Bristol Express (Burlington, NJ) **470**
Broadband Systems & Design (Morris Plains, NJ) **502**
Broken Pencil (Toronto, ON, Can.) **861**
Broward-Palm Beach; New Times (Fort Lauderdale, FL) **195**
Budget Watch (Washington, DC) **179**
Budstikken (Minneapolis, MN) **418**
Bulletin de Droit de L'Environnement (Montreal, PQ, Can.) **891**
The Bulletin of Marine Science (Miami, FL) **197**
Burlington Mail (Burlington, NJ) **471**
The Bush Blade (Anchor Point, AK) **13**
Business in Calgary (Calgary, AB, Can.) **803**
Business; CIO Web (Framingham, MA) **367**
Business Computing & Communications; Small (New York, NY) **576**
Business Digest (New Milford, CT) **160**
Business First (Charlotte, NC) **604**
Business Gazette (Gaithersburg, MD) **330**
Business; Global Technology (Mountain View, CA) **98**
Business Journal; Insider (Brighton, MI) **396**
Business Journal; Ivey (Toronto, ON, Can.) **869**
The Business Journal of Phoenix (Phoenix, AZ) **23**
Business Journal; Rochester (Rochester, NY) **598**
Business Journal; The Southern Nevada Small (Las Vegas, NV) **459**
Business Law; Texas Journal of (Austin, TX) **709**
Business News; U.S. Japan (Los Angeles, CA) **93**
Business Report; The Northern Colorado (Fort Collins, CO) **151**
Business Resource Guide; Iowa Small (Des Moines, IA) **288**
Business & Technology; Wireless (Cedar Knolls, NJ) **475**
Buyer's Guide; Cent Saver (Portage, WI) **793**
The Buzz (Charlottetown, PE, Can.) **884**

C

Cactus and Succulent Journal (Azusa, CA) **39**
Calgary; Business in (Calgary, AB, Can.) **803**
California Chronicles (Peterborough, NH) **466**
California Fairways (Arlington Heights, IL) **228**
Canada; Mission (Toronto, ON, Can.) **870**
Canada/Recherches Theatrales Au Canada; Theatre Research in (Toronto, ON, Can.) **878**
Canals; The Best from American (York, PA) **685**
Cancer Case Presentations (Philadelphia, PA) **667**
CAOT National Newsletter **824***
Car Review; Muscle (Los Angeles, CA) **88**
Car Toy Collectibles (Canoga Park, CA) **52**
Carolina Woman (Durham, NC) **608**
CARPNews (Toronto, ON, Can.) **862**
Casco Bay Weekly (Portland, ME) **323**
The Catholic News & Herald (Charlotte, NC) **605**
Catskill Shopper-Eastern Sullivan Edition (Liberty, NY) **535**
CBAT-TV (Fredericton, NB, Can.) **827**
Cedar Hill Today (Duncanville, TX) **717**
Cellular & Mobile International (Overland Park, KS) **308**
Cent Saver Buyer's Guide (Portage, WI) **793**
Cent Saver Extra (Portage, WI) **794**
Cent Saver Reminder (Portage, WI) **795**
Center Grove Gazette (Fishers, IN) **272**
Challenge New York (New York, NY) **543**
The Chariho Times (Wakefield, RI) **687**
The Chemical Bond (Washington, DC) **180**
Chevy Truck (Los Angeles, CA) **78**
Chicago Shimpo (Chicago, IL) **237**
Child and Family Nursing; Journal of (Philadelphia, PA) **671**
Children Magazine; LA (Los Angeles, CA) **85**
Children's Services (Mahwah, NJ) **480**
China Press (New York, NY) **544**
Chinese American Daily News (Monterey Park, CA) **97**
Chinese Free Daily News (El Monte, CA) **65**
Chinese Herald; American (New York, NY) **538**
ChinMusic Magazine (San Francisco, CA) **114**
Chiropractic & Rehabilitation; Sports (Philadelphia, PA) **677**
Chirp (Toronto, ON, Can.) **863**
CHKG-FM - 96.1 (Vancouver, BC, Can.) **822**
The Chomedey News (Chomedey, PQ, Can.) **888**
Chosun Daily (Flushing, NY) **524**
Christian Chronicle; Minnesota (Minneapolis, MN) **421**
Christian Parenting Today (Carol Stream, IL) **232**
Chronicle Weekender (Arnprior, ON, Can.) **837**
CILT-FM - 96.7 (Altona, MB, Can.) **825**
CIO Web Business (Framingham, MA) **367**
Cityview (Des Moines, IA) **284**
Civil Liberties and Civil Rights; Texas Forum on (Austin, TX) **706**
Civil Rights; Texas Forum on Civil Liberties and (Austin, TX) **706**
The Clarion (Palestine, TX) **736**
Clasificado; El (Los Angeles, CA) **80**
Classical Singer Magazine (Maplewood, NJ) **495**
Clawson Mirror (Royal Oak, MI) **403**
Clayton Word; West End- (St. Louis, MO) **441**

Clearwater Tribune (Big Lake, MN) **411**
Clinical Laboratory Reference; CLR/ (Montvale, NJ) **496**
Clinical Research; Multivariate Experimental (Wichita, KS) **310**
CLR/Clinical Laboratory Reference (Montvale, NJ) **496**
The Clubhouse (Nashua, NH) **462**
CNS Focus (Garden City, NY) **527**
Coin Review; Rare (Wolfeboro, NH) **469**
Collectibles; Car Toy (Canoga Park, CA) **52**
College Park Gazette (Gaithersburg, MD) **331**
The Collingwood Connection (Barrie, ON, Can.) **840**
The Colonial (Fort Washington, PA) **657**
The Colony Leader (Lewisville, TX) **732**
Colorado Business Report; The Northern (Fort Collins, CO) **151**
Colorado River Weekender (Bullhead City, AZ) **16**
Columbia Human Rights Law Review (New York, NY) **545**
Columbia Journal of Asian Law (New York, NY) **546**
Columbia Journal of Environmental Law (New York, NY) **547**
Columbus Alive (Columbus, OH) **627**
Columbus Area Choice (Columbus, NE) **449**
Comic Relief (Eureka, CA) **67**
Communication Booknotes Quarterly (Mahwah, NJ) **481**
Communications Industries Report (Fairfax, VA) **750**
Communications; Small Business Computing & (New York, NY) **576**
Comparative Studies of South Asia, Africa, and the Middle East (Durham, NC) **609**
Computer Magazine (Los Alamitos, CA) **75**
Computer Telephony (New York, NY) **548**
Computer Times (Bardstown, KY) **311**
Computers in Human Services **516***
Computing & Communications; Small Business (New York, NY) **576**
Computing and Electronic Commerce; Journal of Organizational (Mahwah, NJ) **488**
Computing; Smart (Lincoln, NE) **451**
Computing Today (Carol Stream, IL) **233**
Confronting Violence in Women's Lives (Toronto, ON, Can.) **864**
Cong Thuong (New York, NY) **549**
Connecticut Ancestry (Stamford, CT) **171**
Connecticut Housing Production and Permit Authorized Construction (Hartford, CT) **157**
Construction; Connecticut Housing Production and Permit Authorized (Hartford, CT) **157**
Consumers Press (Great Falls, MT) **447**
Contemporary Dialysis & Nephrology (New York, NY) **550**
Contractor; American Painting (Richmond, VA) **757**
Cookbooks; Pillsbury Classic (Minneapolis, MN) **423**
Cooking Pleasures (Minnetonka, MN) **425**
Cook's Illustrated (Brookline, MA) **361**
Corvette Fever (Los Angeles, CA) **79**
Cotton (Washington, DC) **181**
Cottonwood Journal Extra (Sedona, AZ) **24**
Counter Culture (Toronto, ON, Can.) **865**
Country Living Gardener (New York, NY) **551**
The Courier (Dardanelle, AR) **30**
The Coventry Courier (Wakefield, RI) **688**
Creemore Echo (Creemore, ON, Can.) **843**
Crestview News Leader (Crestview, FL) **193**
Criminal Law; The American Journal of (Austin, TX) **702**
Critical Sociology (Boston, MA) **349**
Croydon Express (Burlington, NJ) **472**
CT LIFE (New Haven, CT) **158**
CTI (Norwalk, CT) **165**
Cuisine (Des Moines, IA) **285**
Curio (Bronxville, NY) **519**

D

Daily Breeze (Torrance, CA) **142**
Daily Herald-Tribune (Grande Prairie, AB, Can.) **809**
The Daily News Worldwide (Halifax, NS, Can.) **833**
The Daily Press (Victorville, CA) **147**
Daily Sentinel (Le Mars, IA) **298**
The Daily Sun (The Villages, FL) **206**
Dan Chung News (Irvine, CA) **71**
Databased Web Advisor (San Diego, CA) **107**
Decorative Surfaces; Tile & (New York, NY) **581**
Deh Cho Drum (Yellowknife, NT, Can.) **830**
The Democrat (Senatobia, MS) **432**
Des Moines; Metropolitan (Des Moines, IA) **290**
Design Times (Boston, MA) **350**
Desoto Today (Duncanville, TX) **718**
Developmental Science; Applied (Mahwah, NJ) **478**
Dharma Beat (Lowell, MA) **373**
Diablo Arts (Walnut Creek, CA) **148**

Dialysis & Nephrology; Contemporary (New York, NY) **550**
Digital Video (San Mateo, CA) **127**
DirectGuide (Edmonton, AB, Can.) **806**
Dirt Late Model (West Springfield, MA) **384**
Discourse Processes (Mahwah, NJ) **482**
Discovering Archaeology (El Paso, TX) **721**
The Dispatch (Lexington, NC) **617**
Dispute Resolution Times (New York, NY) **552**
Dog; The National Stock (Butler, IN) **271**
Dong-A Daily (Philadelphia, PA) **668**
Dredging Research (Vicksburg, MS) **433**
Duncanville Today (Duncanville, TX) **719**
Dziennik Chicagowski (Chicago, IL) **238**

E

E-business Advisor (San Diego, CA) **108**
Earth and Planetary Sciences; Annual Review of (Palo Alto, CA) **101**
East West Journal (Honolulu, HI) **222**
Eastern Iowa Shopping News (Edgewood, IA) **296**
Eastern Sullivan Edition; Catskill Shopper- (Liberty, NY) **535**
Economic Law; University of Pennsylvania Journal of International (Philadelphia, PA) **679**
EconSouth (Atlanta, GA) **211**
EDI Forum (Oak Park, IL) **262**
Editor's Choice (Jackson Heights, NY) **532**
Education Bulletin; Harvard (Cambridge, MA) **363**
Education for Students Placed at Risk; Journal of (Mahwah, NJ) **487**
Educator Journal; The Rural (Fort Collins, CO) **152**
El Clasificado (Los Angeles, CA) **80**
El Puente (Goshen, IN) **277**
Electrocardiology; Noninvasive (Armonk, NY) **515**
Electronic Commerce; Journal of Organizational Computing and (Mahwah, NJ) **488**
Electronic Retailing (Los Angeles, CA) **81**
Electronic Systems; PCIM Power (Ventura, CA) **144**
Elm Street (Toronto, ON, Can.) **866**
Elmhurst; Suburban Life (Oak Brook, IL) **260**
Elroy Wonewoc Keystone Tribune (Portage, WI) **796**
Emploi Plus (L'Annonciation, PQ, Can.) **886**
Endovascular Surgery; Journal of (Armonk, NY) **514**
Engineering and IT Professionals; Workforce Diversity for (Huntington, NY) **530**
Engineering Network News; Science & (Worcester, MA) **388**
Entertainment Guide; Satellite (Edmonton, AB, Can.) **807**
Entrepreneurs; Publishing for (Traverse City, MI) **407**
Environmental Law; Columbia Journal of (New York, NY) **547**
Environmental Law Journal; Texas (Austin, TX) **705**
Environmental Technology (Solon, OH) **634**
Equipment Echoes (Grand Rapids, OH) **630**
Ergonomics; International Journal of Cognitive (Mahwah, NJ) **485**
Exclaim! (Toronto, ON, Can.) **867**
Executive Intelligence Review (Washington, DC) **182**
Executive Technology (New York, NY) **553**
Exercise Exchange (Boone, NC) **603**
Exercise Science; Measurement in Physical Education and (Mahwah, NJ) **489**
The Expressline (Wilkes Barre, PA) **684**

F

FacilityCare (Libertyville, IL) **254**
Fairfield Minuteman (New Milford, CT) **161**
Fairless Hills Express (Burlington, NJ) **473**
Fairways; California (Arlington Heights, IL) **228**
Families in Michiana (La Porte, IN) **278**
Family Futures (Mahwah, NJ) **483**
Family; Little Rock (Little Rock, AR) **32**
Family Support Magazine; America's (Chicago, IL) **236**
Faribault Area Shopper (Faribault, MN) **412**
Fax Mainichi U.S.A. (Santa Monica, CA) **136**
Fenestration (New York, NY) **554**
Fermata (Victoria, BC, Can.) **823**
Fern Society; Journal of the Los Angeles International (Pasadena, CA) **104**
Ferndale Mirror; Pleasant Ridge/ (Royal Oak, MI) **405**
The Filipino-American Headliner (Santa Clara, CA) **133**
The Filipino Monitor (San Martin, CA) **126**
FirstLine (Montvale, NJ) **497**
Fleet Maintenance Supervisor (Laguna Hills, CA) **74**

Flight Safety Digest (Alexandria, VA) **743**
Flooring Magazine (Richmond, VA) **758**
The Florida News (Miami, FL) **198**
Flying Physician (Orlando, FL) **202**
(FN); Footwear News (New York, NY) **555**
Focus News (Roseville, MN) **428**
Footsteps (Peterborough, NH) **467**
Footwear News (FN) (New York, NY) **555**
Ford; Super (Los Angeles, CA) **92**
Foreign Policy in Focus (Silver City, NM) **512**
Forensic Quarterly (Kansas City, MO) **439**
Fort Pierce News (Stuart, FL) **203**
The Fort Saskatchewan Record (Fort Saskatchewan, AB, Can.) **808**
Foundation Update (Vienna, VA) **762**
Frederick Gazette (Gaithersburg, MD) **332**
Freeport Shopping News (Freeport, IL) **251**
Fresh Trends (Lenexa, KS) **306**
Frontiers (Pullman, WA) **765**

G

Garden Gate (Des Moines, IA) **286**
Garden Guide; Southern Living (Birmingham, AL) **2**
Gardener; Country Living (New York, NY) **551**
Gardening How-To (Minnetonka, MN) **426**
Genealogical Society Journal; Afro-American Historical and (Washington, DC) **178**
Geological Survey, Mineral Industry Surveys- Commodities: Barite; U.S. (Reston, VA) **756**
Gestalt Review (Mahwah, NJ) **484**
Glass Digest (New York, NY) **556**
Glass Industry (New York, NY) **557**
Glen Ridge Voice (Nutley, NJ) **504**
Glenside News (Fort Washington, PA) **658**
Global Technology Business (Mountain View, CA) **98**
GLQ (Durham, NC) **610**
GMC Directions (Troy, MI) **408**
Golf Resort News (Stratford, CT) **173**
Good Morning Advertiser (Whitewater, WI) **802**
Good News (Asheville, NC) **601**
Green Line **602***
(Greenwood); Access (Franklin, IN) **276**

H

The Halifax Herald Ltd. (Halifax, NS, Can.) **834**
The Hamden Journal (Shelton, CT) **168**
Handheld PC Magazine (Fairfield, IA) **297**
Harvard Education Bulletin (Cambridge, MA) **363**
Harvard Journal of Law and Public Policy (Cambridge, MA) **364**
Hawaii Hochi (Honolulu, HI) **223**
Headliner (Sonoma, CA) **137**
Health Care Journal; The Southern Nevada (Las Vegas, NV) **457**
Healthcare Nurse Manager; Home (Philadelphia, PA) **670**
The Heartland Shopping News (Fergus Falls, MN) **415**
The Herald Democrat (Salida, CO) **155**
Herald Values (Miami, FL) **199**
HERMENAUT (Allston, MA) **346**
(HFN); Home Furnishings News (New York, NY) **558**
High Points (High Point, NC) **616**
The Hill Times (Ottawa, ON, Can.) **854**
Hispanic Journal of Law and Policy; Texas (Austin, TX) **707**
Historical Footnotes (Stonington, CT) **172**
Historical and Genealogical Society Journal; Afro-American (Washington, DC) **178**
Historical Journal of Massachusetts (Westfield, MA) **387**
Historical Society Annual; Hubbell Family (Lakewood, OH) **631**
History Review; Saskatoon (Saskatoon, SK, Can.) **902**
Hoa Thinh Don Viet Bao (Lorton, VA) **753**
Holidays; Southern Living Home for the (Birmingham, AL) **3**
Home Care Manager (Philadelphia, PA) **669**
Home Digest (Ajax, ON, Can.) **835**
Home Furnishings News (HFN) (New York, NY) **558**
Home Healthcare Nurse Manager (Philadelphia, PA) **670**
Hopscotch (Amherst, MA) **347**
The Hospice Professional (Arlington, VA) **746**
Housatonic Weekend (New Milford, CT) **162**
Housing Production and Permit Authorized Construction; Connecticut (Hartford, CT) **157**
Houston Newspaper; La Voz De (Houston, TX) **727**
How-To; Gardening (Minnetonka, MN) **426**

Master Index